MODULAR STUDY GUIDE
For
GENERAL CHEMISTRY I
(CHM 1045)

Fourth Edition

Matha E. Goicoechea-Pappas
Anthony J. Pappas

Aglob Publishing

Published by: **Aglob Publishing**
Hallandale Beach, Florida
Tel: 954-456-1476
E-Mail: info@aglobpublishing.com
www.aglobpublishing.com

Library of Congress Control Number: 2003116955
ISBN: 1-59427-009-0

Manufactured in the United States of America

PREFACE

The study of chemistry will provide you, the student, with the opportunity to study certain abstract concepts and to learn new problem-solving techniques necessary in understanding chemical phenomena.

We created this modular study guide with several purposes in mind:

1. To provide our students with a brief summary of those topics that are emphasized both in lecture and examinations. Topics are presented in roughly the same order as that found in the text that is currently being employed. Each topic covered contains illustrative examples showing detailed set-ups.

2. To provide exercises and multiple choice practice exams similar in format to that used in examinations. The exercises and multiple choice practice exams are also intended to provide you, the student, with an opportunity to master the topics that are covered in each module. The exercises also show the variety of ways in which numerical problems may be asked, and the variety of pertinent definitions, notations, and symbolism that should be mastered.

3. To emphasize the importance of problem solving. No matter what your career goals are, learning how to solve problems is very important; with this in mind, many of the problems provided have been designed to stimulate your intellectual curiosity and to encourage analytical thinking.

We would like to acknowledge the contribution of many of our general chemistry students and fellow colleagues who have given us feedback and corrections. We are more than willing to give consideration to any feedback; we thus welcome your comments as to the usefulness of this modular study guide, to any suggestions that you may have, and to any errors or ambiguities that we have inadvertently overlooked.

Marta E. Goicoechea-Pappas
Anthony J. Pappas

LIST OF MODULES & APPENDICES

MODULE 1. *Basic Concepts - Matter, Mathematical Manipulations, Dimensional Analysis, Density, Specific Gravity, Temperature, and Heat Transfer*

I. Basic Ideas

Chemistry - the science that studies the composition, characterization, and transformation of matter.

Scientific Method - A systematic approach to research that involves collecting & analyzing data.

> *Hypothesis* - a tentative explanation for a set of observations that is made after the collection of enough information.

> *Law* - a concise verbal or mathematical statement of a relationship between phenomena that is always the same under the same conditions that is made after the collection of a large amount of information.

> *Theory* - a unifying principle that explains a body of facts and those laws that are based on them.

Matter - anything that has mass and occupies space. The following concept map illustrates the classifications of matter.

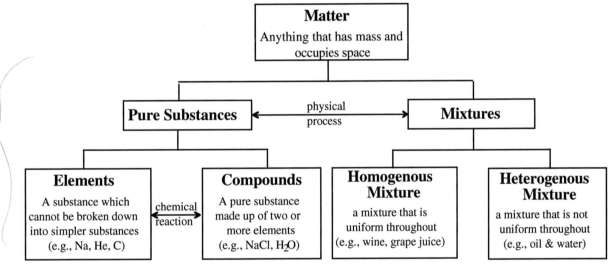

States of Matter - Depending on its temperature, a sample of matter can exist in any one of the following physical states: solid, liquid or gas. The following diagram illustrates how temperature affects the interconversion among states.

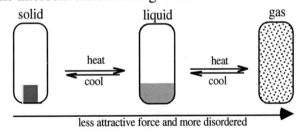

The terminology that is employed during a phase transition is illustrated in the following diagram.

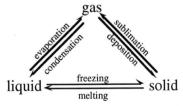

evaporation = boiling   freezing = solidification = crystallization   melting = fusion

Common Elements - Because they are so commonly used, learn the symbol and name for the elements listed below.   Check with your instructor to see if there are other elements besides the ones listed below that should (or should not) be included in this list.

1~2

quest.

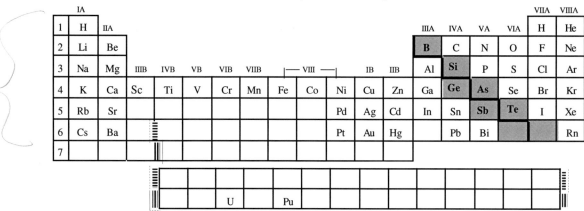

Types of Solutions (i.e., homogeneous mixtures) - Liquid solutions are the most common, but there are also gas and solid solutions. Solutions have two components: a) solute (solution component(s) present in the lesser amount) and b) solvent (solution component present in the greatest amount).

Solute	Solvent	Appearance	Example
Gas	Liquid	Liquid	Carbonated Water
Liquid	Liquid	Liquid	90 Proof Rum
Solid	Liquid	Liquid	Seawater
Gas	Gas	Gas	Air
Solid	Solid	Solid	14-karat gold

Characteristics of Solutions
   a) Uniform distribution.
   b) Components do not separate upon standing.
   c) Components can not be separated by filtration.
   d) Within certain limits its composition can vary.
   f) Almost always transparent (i.e., one can see through it).

Alloy -   Homogenous mixture of metals (e.g., 14-karat gold)

Energy -   the capacity to do work or transfer heat.
   Potential Energy (PE) -   the energy an object possesses because of its position or composition. This is the kind of energy found in chemicals such as natural gas and gasoline.
   Kinetic Energy (KE) -   the energy of motion.

Physical Property -   a property that can be observed in the absence of any change in composition. (e.g., color, odor, taste, melting point, boiling point, freezing point, density, length, specific heat)

Physical Change - changes observed *without* a change in composition. (e.g., cutting wood, melting of solids & boiling of liquids -- water, ice → water, liquid → water, steam)

Chemical Property - a property that matter exhibits as it undergoes changes in composition. (Examples: coal and gasoline burn in air to form carbon dioxide and water; iron reacts with oxygen in the air to form rust; bleach turns hair blonde)

Chemical Change -   changes observed only when a change in composition is occuring. (e.g, reaction of sodium with chlorine, rusting of iron, dying of hair, burning of wood)

Extensive Property - a property that depends on the amount of material present. (e.g., volume & mass)

Intensive Property - a property that does not depend on the amount of material present. (e.g., melting point, boiling point, freezing point, color, density).

Law of Conservation of Mass - There is no observable change in the quantity of matter during an *ordinary* chemical reaction. For example,

$$Ni \quad + \quad C \quad \rightarrow \quad NiC$$
$$58.7 \text{ g} \qquad 12.0 \text{ g} \qquad 70.7 \text{g} \ (58.7 \text{ g Ni} + 12.0 \text{ g C})$$

Law of Conservation of Energy - Energy cannot be created or destroyed; it may only be converted from one form to another.

Law of Definite Proportions - Different samples of any pure compound contain the same element in the same proportion by mass [e.g., water (H_2O) contains 11.1% H and 88.9% O by mass; thus a 25.0 g sample of water would contain 2.78 g of H and 22.2 g of O]

$$25.0 \text{ g water} \left(\frac{11.1 \text{ g H}}{100 \text{ g water}} \right) = 2.78 \text{ g H} \qquad 25.0 \text{ g water} \left(\frac{88.9 \text{ g O}}{100 \text{ g water}} \right) = 22.2 \text{ g O}$$

Accuracy - Tells us how close a measurement is to the true value.

Precision - Tells us how closely two or more measurements agree with one another.

II. Rounding Off Numbers

The following are examples of numbers that have been rounded off to the second decimal place. The answer depends on the identity of the "next" digit (i.e., the digit after the cut-off point).

Previous digit

1 . 2 9 ¦ 4

Next digit

Rules	Example Number	Answer
1. If the next digit is less than 5, then the previous digit remains the same	1.294 0.9946	1.29 0.99
2. If the next digit is greater than 5 or 5 followed by nonzeros, then the previous digit is increased by one.	0.999 1.2951 1.325001	1.00 1.30 1.33
3. If the next digit is 5 or 5 followed by all zeros, then the previous digit remains the same if it is even or increased by one if it is odd (i.e., keep or make the previous digit even).	1.285 1.295 1.22500	1.28 1.30 1.22

III. Scientific Notation

To handle very large and very small numbers, scientists use a system called *scientific notation*. Regardless of a numbers magnitude, all numbers can be expressed in scientific notation, whose general form is as follows:

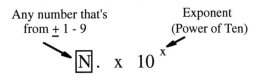

Any number that's from ± 1 - 9

Exponent (Power of Ten)

$$\boxed{N} . \ x \ 10^{x}$$

For example, $\underline{3}.21 \times 10^3$, $-\underline{9}.9 \times 10^{-4}$, and $\underline{1}. \times 10^0$. [Note: $10^0 = 1$]

To convert numbers into scientific notation, use the following guidelines:

a)   As you move the decimal place to the left (i.e., make the number *smaller*), the power of ten (i.e., exponent) must *increase* by the same amount.   For example,

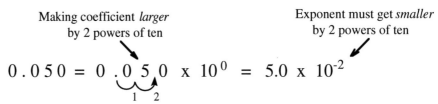

b)   As you move the decimal place to the right (i.e., make the number *larger*), the power of ten (i.e., exponent) must *decrease* by the same amount.   For example,

Making coefficient *larger*
by 2 powers of ten

Exponent must get *smaller*
by 2 powers of ten

$$0.050 = 0.050 \times 10^0 = 5.0 \times 10^{-2}$$

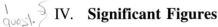

IV.   Significant Figures

Significant figures indicate how accurately measurements have been made. Exact numbers have an infinite number of significant figures (i.e., a decimal point and an infinite number of zeros are not shown for convenience). An example of an exact number is 1 dozen = 12.

To find how many significant figures a number has:

1)   locate the first nonzero digit (start from left -> right)

first non-zero digit

0.02500

2)   then starting with the first nonzero digit - count the number of digits the number has.

0.02500   This number has 4 significant figures
 1 2 3 4

Zeros at the end of a number that has no decimal point may or may not be significant. For example, the number 300 may have 1, 2, or 3 significant figures. It is for this reason that decimal points should be included if zeros are significant.

V.   Manipulating Powers of Ten

a) When multiplying powers of ten, the exponents are added. For example,

$$10^5 \times 10^{-4} = 10^{5+(-4)} = 10^1$$

b) When dividing powers of ten, the exponents are subtracted. For example,

$$\frac{10^4}{10^{-4}} = 10^{4-(-4)} = 10^8$$

c) When rasing powers of ten to an exponent, the exponents are multiplied. For example,

$$(10^4)^3 = 10^{(4 \times 3)} = 10^{12}$$

VI.   Multiplying and Dividing Numbers with Powers of Ten

1)   Place the powers of ten together and the coefficients together. [Note: In the number 2.6×10^3 ---> 2.6 is called the coefficient.]

2) The final answer has the same number of significant figures as the number with the least number of significant figures.
3) You must round off correctly.
4) Preferably report the answer in scientific notation.

Example Problems:

1. $(1.76 \times 10^{200}) \times (2.650 \times 10^{200}) = (1.76 \times 2.650) \times (10^{200+200})$

$$= 4.66 \times 10^{400} \quad \text{(answer with correct number of significant figures)}$$

2. $1.760 \times 10^2 / 2.65 \times 10^{-2} = \dfrac{1.760 \times 10^2}{2.65 \times 10^{-2}} = \dfrac{1.760}{2.65} \times \dfrac{10^2}{10^{-2}} = 0.664 \times (10^{2-(-2)}) = 0.664 \times 10^4$

$$= 6.64 \times 10^3 \quad \left(\begin{array}{l}\text{written in scientific notation \& rounded off}\\ \text{to the correct number of significant figures}\end{array}\right)$$

VII.   Adding and Subtracting Numbers with Powers of Ten

1) All numbers must have the same power of ten before addition or substraction is performed.
2) Once the powers of ten are the same, the coefficients can then be added or subtracted while the power of ten remains the same.
3) After adding or subtracting the coefficients, the answer must have the same number of decimal places as the coefficient with the fewest decimal places at the time of the operation.
4) You must round off correctly.
5) Preferably report the answer in scientific notation.

Example Problems:

1. $4.76 \times 10^{200} + 9.6 \times 10^{201} = ?$

$$0.4\,|\,76 \ \times \ 10^{201}$$
$$+ \ 9.6\,| \qquad \times \ 10^{201}$$
$$\overline{10.0\,|\,76 \ \times \ 10^{201}} \ \longrightarrow \ 1.01 \times 10^{202} \quad \left(\begin{array}{l}\text{written in scientific notation \& rounded off}\\ \text{to the correct number of significant figures}\end{array}\right)$$

2. $2.95 \times 10^{-15} - 1.00 \times 10^{-14} = ?$

$$-1.00\,| \qquad \times \ 10^{-14}$$
$$0.29\,|\,5 \ \times \ 10^{-14}$$
$$\overline{-0.70\,|\,5 \ \times \ 10^{-14}} \ \longrightarrow \ - 7.0 \times 10^{-15} \quad \left(\begin{array}{l}\text{written in scientific notation \& rounded off}\\ \text{to the correct number of significant figures}\end{array}\right)$$

VIII.   Mixing Addition/Subtraction with Multiplication/Division

Example Problem:

$$\frac{7.54 \times 10^{-5}\,(99.\times 10^{200} + 1.25 \times 10^{201})}{(1.75 \times 10^{-3})^3}$$

$$\frac{7.54 \times 10^{-5}\,(9.9 \times 10^{201} + 1.25 \times 10^{201})}{1.75 \times 10^{-3} \times 1.75 \times 10^{-3} \times 1.75 \times 10^{-3}} = \frac{7.54 \times 10^{-5}\,[(9.9 + 1.25) \times 10^{201}]}{1.75 \times 1.75 \times 1.75 \times 10^{-3} \times 10^{-3} \times 10^{-3}} =$$

$$\frac{7.54 \times 10^{-5}\,(11.2 \times 10^{201})}{5.36 \times 10^{-9}} = \frac{7.54 \times 11.2}{5.36} \times \frac{10^{-5} \times 10^{201}}{10^{-9}} = 1.58 \times 10^{206}$$

IX. Units of Measurements

A. English System

volume	mass	length	time
1 pt = 16 fl oz	1 lb = 16 oz	1 ft = 12 in	1 min = 60 sec
1 qt = 2 pt	1 ton = 2000 lb	1 yd = 3 ft	1 hr = 60 min
1 gal = 4 qt		1 mi = 5280 ft	1 day = 24 hr

B. Metric System & International System of Units (SI Units)

Both systems are decimal systems in which the units are related to each other by powers of ten; prefixes are used to indicate fractions and multiples of ten.

1. Basic Units

volume	mass	length	time
liter = L	gram = g	meter = m	second = sec = s

NOTE: $1 \text{ mL} = 1 \text{ cm}^3 = 1 \text{ cc}$

2. Prefixes to know

Prefix	Abbreviation	Meaning
giga	G	10^9 (1,000,000,000)
mega	M	10^6 (1,000,000)
kilo	k	10^3 (1,000)
hecto	h	10^2 (100)
deka	da	10^1 (10)
deci	d	10^{-1} (0.1)
centi	c	10^{-2} (0.01)
milli	m	10^{-3} (0.001)
micro	μ	10^{-6} (0.000001)
nano	n	10^{-9} (0.000000001)
pico	p	10^{-12} (0.000000000001)

The above prefixes are synonymous with their numerical value; thus the following equalities can be written:

1 km = 10^3 m	k = 10^3	1 msec = 10^{-3} sec	m = 10^{-3}
1 dL = 10^{-1} L	d = 10^{-1}	1 μm = 10^{-6} m	μ = 10^{-6}

C. Metric ⇌ English Conversions

volume	mass	length
1 qt = 0.946* L	1 lb = 454.* g	1 in = 2.54 cm

*   0.946 L and 454. g have been rounded off to 3 significant figures, the other conversions and prefixes are exact (i.e., each number has an infinite number of significant figures)

X. Use of Conversion Factors in Calculations

Commonly known relationship (i.e., equality):

1 ft = 12 in

Respective *conversion factors* to above equality:

$$\frac{1 \text{ ft}}{12 \text{ in}} \quad \text{or} \quad \frac{12 \text{ in}}{1 \text{ ft}}$$

The conversion factor that is used in calculations is the one that allows for the cancellation of units. The following is an example of how 24 inches can be converted into feet by the use of one of the above conversion factors:

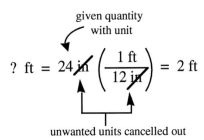

given quantity
with unit

$$? \text{ ft} = 24 \text{ in} \left(\frac{1 \text{ ft}}{12 \text{ in}} \right) = 2 \text{ ft}$$

unwanted units cancelled out

XI. **Dimensional Analysis -- Factor Label Method** (used in performing calculations)

<u>Example Problems</u>:

1. 5.32 mg = ? kg   (Metric-Metric Conversion)

$$? \text{ kg} = 5.32 \text{ mg} \left(\frac{10^{-3} \text{ g}}{1 \text{ mg}} \right) \left(\frac{1 \text{ kg}}{10^3 \text{ g}} \right) = 5.32 \times 10^{-6} \text{ kg}$$

2. 7.33×10^4 cL = ? fl oz   (Metric-English Conversion)

$$? \text{ oz} = 7.33 \times 10^4 \text{ cL} \left(\frac{10^{-2} \text{ L}}{1 \text{ cL}} \right) \left(\frac{1 \text{ qt}}{0.946 \text{ L}} \right) \left(\frac{2 \text{ pt}}{1 \text{ qt}} \right) \left(\frac{16 \text{ fl oz}}{1 \text{ pt}} \right) = 2.48 \times 10^4 \text{ fl oz}$$

3. 6.12×10^5 cm^2 = ? ft^2 (Using square units)

$$? \text{ ft}^2 = = 6.12 \times 10^5 \text{ cm}^2 \left(\frac{1 \text{ in}}{2.54 \text{ cm}} \right)^2 \left(\frac{1 \text{ ft}}{12 \text{ in}} \right)^2 = 6.59 \times 10^2 \text{ ft}^2$$

4. 0.500 km^3 = ? ft^3 (Using cube units)

$$? \text{ ft}^3 = 0.500 \text{ km}^3 \left(\frac{10^3 \text{ m}}{1 \text{ km}} \right)^3 \left(\frac{1 \text{ cm}}{10^{-2} \text{ m}} \right)^3 \left(\frac{1 \text{ in}}{2.54 \text{ cm}} \right)^3 \left(\frac{1 \text{ ft}}{12 \text{ in}} \right)^3 = 1.77 \times 10^{10} \text{ ft}^3$$

5. 55. $\frac{\text{mi}}{\text{hr}}$ = ? $\frac{\text{km}}{\text{min}}$ (Using double units)

$$? \frac{\text{km}}{\text{min}} = 55. \frac{\text{mi}}{\text{hr}} \left(\frac{1 \text{ hr}}{60 \text{ min}} \right) \left(\frac{5280 \text{ ft}}{1 \text{ mi}} \right) \left(\frac{12 \text{ in}}{1 \text{ ft}} \right) \left(\frac{2.54 \text{ cm}}{1 \text{ in}} \right) \left(\frac{10^{-2} \text{ m}}{1 \text{ cm}} \right) \left(\frac{1 \text{ km}}{10^3 \text{ m}} \right) = 1.5 \frac{\text{km}}{\text{min}}$$

6. 3.7 $\frac{\text{m}^3}{\text{hr}}$ = ? $\frac{\text{qt}}{\text{min}}$ (Combination Problem)

$$? \frac{\text{qt}}{\text{min}} = 3.7 \frac{\text{m}^3}{\text{hr}} \left(\frac{1 \text{ hr}}{60 \text{ min}} \right) \left(\frac{1 \text{ cm}}{10^{-2} \text{ m}} \right)^3 \left(\frac{1 \text{ mL}}{1 \text{ cm}^3} \right) \left(\frac{10^{-3} \text{ L}}{1 \text{ mL}} \right) \left(\frac{1 \text{ qt}}{0.946 \text{ L}} \right) = 6.5 \times 10^1 \frac{\text{qt}}{\text{min}}$$

2 5

XII. Density (d) and Specific Gravity (Sp.Gr.)

$$\text{density} = \frac{\text{mass}}{\text{volume}} \quad \text{or} \quad d = \frac{m}{V} \quad \left(\text{common units: liquids \& solids} \rightarrow \frac{g}{mL} \quad \text{gases} \rightarrow \frac{g}{L}\right)$$

$$\text{Sp.Gr.} = \frac{d_{\text{substance}}}{d_{\text{water @ 4°C}}} = \frac{d_{\text{substance}}}{1.00 \text{ g/mL}}$$

Density and specific gravity are numerically equivalent, however, specific gravity is a *unitless* quantity.

Knowledge of a substance's density allows one to make a relationship between mass and volume. For example,

$$d_{\text{ice}} = 0.92 \frac{g}{mL} \quad \text{---> Corresponding equality: } 0.92 \text{ g ice} = 1 \text{ mL ice}$$

To obtain the density of a substance in the laboratory, one needs to measure the substance's mass and volume. The volume of liquids can be measured with a graduated cylinder. The volume of certain solids can be obtained in one of the following ways:

a) Volume of solids by water displacement

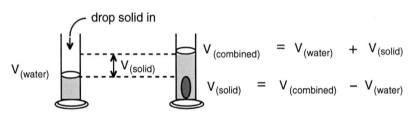

b) Volume of solids through mathematical equations

$$V_{\text{(cubic solid)}} = l \times w \times h \qquad (\text{length} = \text{width} = \text{height})$$

$$V_{\text{(rectangular solid)}} = l \times w \times h$$

$$V_{\text{(sphere)}} = \frac{4}{3}\pi r^3 \qquad \left(r = \text{radius} = \frac{\text{diameter}}{2}\right)$$

NOTE: 1 mL = 1 cc = 1 cm^3

Example Problems:

1. The density of lead is 11.4 g/cm^3. What volume, in ft^3, would be occupied by 10.0 g of lead?

$$? \text{ ft}^3 = 10.0 \text{ g}\left(\frac{1 \text{ cm}^3}{11.4 \text{ g}}\right)\left(\frac{1 \text{ in}}{2.54 \text{ cm}}\right)^3\left(\frac{1 \text{ ft}}{12 \text{ in}}\right)^3 = 3.10 \times 10^{-5} \text{ ft}^3$$

2. If the density of lead is 11.4 g/cm^3, what is its specific gravity?

$$\text{Sp.Gr.} = \frac{d_{\text{substance}}}{1.00 \text{ g/mL}} = \frac{11.4 \text{ g/mL}}{1.00 \text{ g/mL}} = 11.4 \quad \left(\begin{array}{l}\text{density \& Sp. Gr. are numerically equal;}\\ \text{however, Sp.Gr. is unitless}\end{array}\right)$$

3. What is the density (in g/mL) of a rectangular bar of lead that weighs 173 g and has the following the following dimensions: length = 2.00 cm, w = 3.00 cm, h = 1.00 in?

$$V_{\text{(rec. solid)}} = l \times w \times h = (2.00 \text{ cm})(3.00 \text{ cm})\left(1.00 \text{ in} \times \frac{2.54 \text{ cm}}{1 \text{ in}}\right) = 15.2 \text{ cm}^3$$

$$d = \frac{m}{V} = \frac{173 \text{ g}}{15.2 \text{ cm}^3} = 11.4 \frac{g}{cm^3} = 11.4 \frac{g}{mL}$$

4. An irregularly shaped piece of metal with a mass of 0.251 lb was placed into a graduated cylinder containing 50.00 mL of water; this raised the water level to 67.50 mL. i) What is the density (in g/cm^3) of the metal?; ii) Will the metal sink or float on water?

    i) $V_{(displ)}$ = 67.50 mL - 50.00 mL = 17.50 mL

$$d = \frac{m}{V} = \frac{0.251 \text{ lb} \left(\frac{454 \text{ g}}{1 \text{ lb}}\right)}{17.50 \text{ mL}} = 6.51 \frac{g}{mL} = 6.51 \frac{g}{cm^3}$$

    ii) The metal will sink in water because its density is greater than that of water (1.00 g/mL).

XIII. Temperature Conversions

$$°F = (1.8 \times °C) + 32 \qquad\qquad K = °C + 273$$

[NOTE: The temperature scale, Kelvin, does not have a degree sign.]

Comparison of Temperature Scales (not shown to scale)

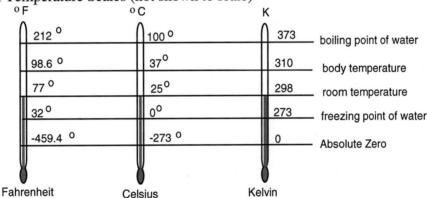

- Note that there is a 100° difference between the freezing point and boiling point of water for both the Celsius and Kelvin scale; whereas, on the Fahrenheit scale, there is a 180° difference .

Example Problems:

1. Normal body temperature is 98.6°F. Convert this to °C.

    $°F = (1.8 \times °C) + 32$ [Note: 1.8 and 32 are exact numbers]

    $98.6 = (1.8 \times °C) + 32$

    $98.6 - 32 = (1.8 \times °C)$ -----> $\frac{98.6 - 32}{1.8} = °C$ -----> 37.0°C

2. 100°C = ? K

    $K = °C + 273$ ----> $K = 100°C + 273$ ----> 373 K

3. 0 K = ? °F

    first convert 0 K ---> °C, then go from °C ---> °F

    $0 K = °C + 273$ ----> $°C = 0 - 273 = -273°C$

    $°F = (1.8 \times (-273)) + 32$ ----> -459°F

XIV. Heat Transfer

Chemical reactions and physical changes occur with either the simultaneous evolution of heat (*exothermic process*) or the absorption of heat (*endothermic process*). The amount of heat transferred in a process is usually expressed in *calories (cal)* or in the SI unit of *joules (J)*.

$$1 \text{ cal} = 4.184 \text{ J}$$

Specific heat is defined as the amount of heat necessary to raise the temperature of 1 g of substance by 1°C. Each substance has a specific heat, which is a physical intensive property, like density and melting point. From a knowledge of a subtance's specific heat, the heat (q) that is absorbed or released in a given process can be calculated by use of the following equation.

q (heat energy) --> cal, kcal, J, or kJ

m (mass) --> g

$$q = m \times s \times \Delta T$$

s (specific heat) --> $\dfrac{cal}{g \cdot °C}$ (kcal, J, or kJ can be used in lieu of cal)

$\Delta T = T_2 - T_1$ (change in temp - make ΔT a positive #) --> °C

Substances with large specific heats require more heat to raise their temperature. Water has one of the highest specific heats, 1.00 cal / g °C. The high specific heat of water (which constitutes ~60% of our body weight) makes our body's task of maintaining a constant body temperature of ~37°C much easier. Thus, our body has the ability to absorb or release considerable amounts of energy with little change in temperature.

subtance	specific heat (cal / g °C)
water	1.00
wood	0.421
gold	0.0306
graphite	0.172

Example Problems:

1. How many joules are required to heat 352. g of water (s = 1.00 cal/g · °C) from 32°C to 95°C?

$$q = m \times s \times \Delta T$$

$$q = (352.\ g) \left(1.00\ \frac{cal}{g \cdot °C} \right) (95°C - 32°C) = 2.2 \times 10^4\ cal$$

$$?\ J = 2.2 \times 10^4\ cal \left(\frac{4.184\ J}{1\ cal} \right) = 9.2 \times 10^4\ J$$

2. If we add 450 cal of heat to 37 g of ethyl alcohol (s = 0.59 cal/ g · °C) at 20°C, what would its final temperature be?

$$q = m \times s \times \Delta T \quad \text{-----}> \quad 450\ cal = 37\ g \times 0.59\ \frac{cal}{g \cdot °C} \times \Delta T$$

$$\Delta T = \frac{450\ cal}{\left(0.59\ \dfrac{cal}{g \cdot °C} \right) \times 37\ g} = 21°C$$

Since heat was added, the final temperature must be greater than the inital temperature.

$$\Delta T = T_2 - T_1 \quad \text{------}> \quad 21°C = T_2 - 20°C \quad \text{-----}> \quad T_2 = 21°C + 20°C = 41°C$$

EXERCISES

Basic Ideas

1. Give the name for each of the following elements.
   a) Pt
   b) Hg
   c) As
   d) Sb
   e) Mn
   f) Ag
   g) Co
   h) Kr

2. Give the symbol for each of the following elements.
   a) gold
   b) magnesium
   c) iodine
   d) zinc
   e) cadmium
   f) iron
   g) strontium
   h) lead

3. Classify each of the following as an element, compound, homogeneous mixture, or heterogeneous mixture.
   a) air
   b) gold
   c) Br_2
   d) CCl_4
   e) a martini on the rocks
   f) alcohol
   g) Cu
   h) sea water
   i) wet cement
   j) the human body

4. In a typical day in Miami, what is the physical state of each of the following.
   a) air
   b) gold
   c) water
   d) sand
   e) alcohol
   f) oxygen

5. Classify the following as possessing mostly kinetic energy or potential energy.
   a) an undetonated nuclear missile
   b) gasoline
   c) a moving car
   d) a rock rolling off a hill

6. Classify the following as a physical property, chemical property, physical change, or chemical change.
   a) water boils at 100°C
   b) shreading paper
   c) separating oil and water
   d) burning wood
   e) water reacts with sodium violently
   f) Tums neutralizes stomach acid
   g) placing sodium into water
   h) chlorine gas is green
   i) bleaching your hair
   j) the freezing of water

7. Classify the following as an intensive or extensive property.
   a) density
   b) color
   c) mass
   d) boiling point
   e) volume
   f) specific heat

8. Consider the following chemical reaction: $Mg + F_2 \rightarrow MgF_2$
   When 24.3 g of Mg react with 38.0 grams of F_2, then: a) how many grams of MgF_2 will be obtained, b) how many grams of Mg are present in the product MgF_2?

9. How many grams of gold will be produced when 157 g of Gd are mixed with 36.5 g of HCl?

10. Methane contains two elements C and H. If there is 75% carbon by weight in methane, then:
    a) What is the %H in methane?   b) How many grams of C and H are there in a 27.0 g sample of methane?

Rounding Off Numbers, Scientific Notation, and Significant Figures

11. How many significant figures do the following numbers have?
- a) 0.002001
- b) 0.11692×10^{-5}
- c) 30.366×10^4
- d) 102.00×10^{-13}
- e) 0.496500
- f) -0.003950

12. Write the following numbers in scientific notation correctly rounded off to 3 significant figures .
- a) 0.002005
- b) 0.99692×10^{-2}
- c) 30.351×10^6
- d) 102.50×10^{-13}
- e) 0.496500
- f) -0.003950×10^5
- g) 136.050
- h) 0.010500×10^{100}

Mathematical Manipulations

13. Perform the following mathematical manipulations. Report the answers to the correct number of significant figures in scientific notation.

a) $6.0 \times 10^{-112} \times 2.0 \times 10^{-115} =$

b) $8.0 \times 10^{-114} \times -4.0 \times 10^{112} =$

c) $-8.0 \times 10^{-114} \times -4.0 \times 10^{112} =$

d) $6.11 \times 10^{-12} \times 7.4 \times 10^{-13} =$

e) $39.2 \times 10^{-14} \times 0.79 \times 10^{15} =$

f) $\dfrac{(270.1 - 273.1)\,(2.191 \times 10^{-5})}{6.712 \times 10^4} =$

g) $\dfrac{(3.11 \times 10^{-8})^3\,(7.121 \times 10^{-6})^3}{(5.29 \times 10^6)^3\,(2.11 \times 10^{-2})^2} =$

h) $\dfrac{7.021 \times 10^{-5}\,(0.277 - 0.273)}{6.89 \times 10^{-2}} =$

i) $5.123 \times 10^{-9} - 6.21 \times 10^{-10} =$

j) $7.88 \times 10^{-117} + 5.211 \times 10^{-116} =$

k) $-7.2 \times 10^{-102} + 6.925 \times 10^{-101} =$

l) $-8.21 \times 10^{-21} - 7.220 \times 10^{-20} =$

m) $39.9 \times 10^{-21} + 4.29 \times 10^{-12} \times 3.1 \times 10^{-9} =$

n) $\dfrac{5.0}{3.62 / 5.0 \times 10^6} =$

Dimensional Analysis

14. Perfom the following conversions

a) 3.36×10^{-5} gal = _____ L

b) 1.60×10^{-5} fl oz = _____ qt

c) 1.34 g = _____ oz

d) 1.27×10^{-4} L = _____ μL

e) 2.96×10^{-7} ton = _____ g

f) 7.65×10^{7} cm = _____ mi

g) 2.59×10^{6} sec = _____ day

h) 1.12×10^{-1} m = _____ yd

i) 1.00 pt = _____ pL

j) 2.51×10^{6} ft = _____ dam

k) 5.00×10^{-1} qt = _____ cL

l) 2.96×10^{-3} lb = _____ dg

m) 5.49×10^{2} cm = _____ ft

n) 2.69×10^{-7} Mg = _____ lb

o) 1.27×10^{5} pg = _____ cg

p) 4.67×10^{-1} in = _____ mi

q) 1.80×10^{2} in^3 = _____ cm^3

r) 1.28×10^{-5} yd^2 = _____ m^2

s) 6.35×10^{4} m^2 = _____ in^2

t) 3.86×10^{-3} yd^3 = _____ mL

u) 4.71×10^{-1} L = _____ ft^3

v) $4.23 \times 10^{-6} \dfrac{L}{day}$ = _____ $\dfrac{mL}{sec}$

w) $1.42 \times 10^{7} \dfrac{mi}{gal}$ = _____ $\dfrac{m}{L}$

x) $9.44 \times 10^{-2} \dfrac{L}{hr}$ = _____ $\dfrac{in^3}{day}$

y) $5.29 \times 10^{-14} \dfrac{gal}{cm^2}$ = _____ $\dfrac{dL}{in^2}$

z) $4.11 \times 10^{-10} \dfrac{ton}{hr}$ = _____ $\dfrac{g}{min}$

Density and Specific Gravity

15. Calculate the volume (in mL) of a sample of CCl_4 having a mass of 80.0 g and whose density is 1.60 g/mL.

16. If 450 mL of carbon dioxide weighs 0.891 g, what is its density (in g/mL)?

17. What is the specific gravity of an unknown sample that weighs 10.0 g and occupies a volume of 22.00 mL?

18. How many grams of mercury (density = 13.6 g/mL) are necessary to to fill a 5.00 mL tube?

19. What is the density of a cube which measures 5.858 cm on its side and has a mass of 1.343 g?

20. What is the mass of a rectangular solid with the following dimensions - l = 10 cm, w = 15 cm, h = 20 cm - and whose density is 1.45×10^{-3} g/mL?

21. What is the radius of a 7.64 g sphere whose density is 0.144 g/cm^3?

22. An unknown metal with a mass of 2.96×10^{-3} lbs was placed into a graduated cylinder containing 21.3 mL of water; this raised the level of the water to 26.7 mL. What is the density (in g/mL) of the unknown metal?

23. An object has a density of 0.417 g/mL and a mass of 5.00 g. After this object is placed into 45.0 mL of water, what should the resulting volume be?

Temperature

24 . Perform the following temperature conversions.

      a) 62.0°C = _____°F   b) 65.3 K = _____°C

      c) -107.1°F = _____°C   d) 373 K = _____°F

      e) 200°C = _____ K   f) 268°F = _____ K

Heat Transfer

25 . How much heat (in cal) is necessary to heat 27.0 mL of octane ($s = 0.526 \frac{cal}{g \, °C}$; d = 0.703 g/mL) from 50.6°C to 67.2°C?

26. How many grams of water (s = 1.00 cal/g · °C) will realease 1367 J of heat when cooled from 45.2°C to 36.2°C?

27. What will the final temperature be, if 82.0 cal of heat are added to 32.0 g of carbon tetrachloride (s = 0.210 cal/g · °C) at 33.0°C?

28. By how many °C will the temperature of 23.67 g of a liquid (s = 0.590 cal/g · °C) at 25.3°C be raised if 1794 J of heat are added to the liquid?

MULTIPLE CHOICE PRACTICE EXAM FOR MODULE 1

1. Which of the following is a systematic approach to research that involves collecting and analyzing data?
   1) Theory   2) Law   3) Hypothesis   4) Scientific Method   5) Chemistry

2. Which of the following is an extensive property?
   a. volume   b. density   c. temperature
   1) only a   2) only b   3) only c   4) only a and c   5) only b and c

3. Which of the following is a homogeneous mixture?
   1) water   2) rum & coke   3) wine
   4) two of the above choices are correct.
   5) All of the above choices are correct.

4. Which of the following is a physical property?
   1) melting of ice   2) burning of paper   3) the density of water is 1.0 g/mL
   4) two of the above choices are correct.
   5) All of the above choices are correct.

5. Consider the following chemical reaction: $Li + HCl \rightarrow LiCl + H_2$. When 5.20 g of Li completely reacted with HCl, 32.6 g of products ($LiCl + H_2$) were produced. If 0.76 g of H_2 were produced, which of the following statements is (are) correct?
   1) 27.4 g of HCl were used in the reaction
   2) 26.6 g of Cl are present in both HCl and LiCl.
   3) 31.8 g of LiCl were produced.
   4) two of the above statements are correct.
   5) all of the above statements are correct..

6. Write the following number in scientific notation and rounded off to four significant figures: 0.060555×10^{103}
   1) 6.055×10^{101} 2) 6.056×10^{101} 3) 6.055×10^{105} 4) 6.056×10^{105} 5) 0.6055×10^{104}

7. What is the answer to the following: $(6.4 \times 10^{-121} - 3.91 \times 10^{-120}) / (2.03 \times 10^{60})^3$
   1) -2.7×10^{-299} 2) -1.4×10^{60} 3) -3.9×10^{-301} 4) -3.91×10^{-301} 5) -1.6×10^{-300}

8. When the following operation is performed, how many significant figures will the final answer have?
$$\frac{2.7512}{(0.0297 - 0.0281)}$$
   1) one   2) two   3) three   4) four   5) five

9. Which of the following units is the smallest?
   1) ML   2) mL   3) daL   4) GL   5) nL

10. How many hm are in 2.7×10^4 km?
   1) 2.7×10^9 2) 2.7×10^5 3) 2.7×10^3 4) 2.7×10^{-1} 5) 2.7×10^8

11. 25.7 L = _____ gal
   1) 2.57×10^4 2) 6.42   3) 6.79   4) 27.2   5) 6.06

12. A car travelling at 30.0 mph is travelling at how many cm/sec?
    1) 6.71×10^{-1}　　2) 2.69×10^9　　3) 1.44　　4) 2.08×10^2　　5) 1.34×10^3

13. How many cm^2 are in 5.02×10^2 in^2?
    1) 3.24×10^3　　2) 7.78×10^{-1}　　3) 7.78×10^1　　4) 1.28×10^3　　5) 8.23×10^4

14. What is the specific gravity of a substance that weighs 52.2 dg and occupies a volume of 2.78 mL?
    1) 14.5 g/mL　　2) 0.533　　3) 18.8　　4) 1.88　　5) 0.533 g/mL

15. What is the volume (in cm^3) of a sphere whose diameter is 0.122 m?
    1) 3.83×10^{-1}　　2) 9.50×10^2　　3) 7.60×10^3　　4) 7.60×10^{-3}　　5) 0.511

16. After an unknown metal whose mass was 0.0220 lb was placed into a graduated cylinder containing 20.00 mL of water, the volume of the liquid level rose to 23.00 mL. What is the density (in g/mL) of the metal?
    1) 3.33　　2) 0.300　　3) 0.500　　4) 0.435　　5) 0.233

17. Which of the following will float on water (d_{water} = 1.00 g/mL). Assume that none of the substances react or dissolve in water.
    a.　a cube having a length of 2.00 cm on one of its sides and a mass of 3.00 g
    b.　a 10.0 g cylinder that occupies a volume of 3.00 cm^3
    c.　a solid whose specific gravity is 0.900
    1) only a　　2) only b　　3) only c　　4) only a and c　　5) a, b, and c

18. If the temperature of a piece of metal was 190°F, what would its temperature in °C be?
    1) 374　　2) 62.4　　3) 87.8　　4) 463　　5) -83

19. A 100. g sample of water absorbs how many Joules of energy as its temperature is changed from 35.0°C to 60.0°C? (s_{water} = 4.184 J/g · °C)
    1) 1.05×10^4　　2) 1.46×10^4　　3) 2.51×10^4　　4) 2.50×10^3　　5) 4.18×10^2

20. If 1.05×10^4 Joules of energy are absorbed 100. g of water (s_{water} = 4.184 J/g · °C) at 35.0°C, then what will its final temperature (in °C) be?
    1) 60.1　　2) 25.1　　3) 9.9　　4) 439.　　5) 474.

21. Ammonia contains N and H. If ammonia contains 82.4% N by weight, then how many grams of H are present in a 22.3 g sample of ammonia?
    1) 18.4　　2) 0.255　　3) 3.92　　4) 0.0543
    5) there is not enough information to answer this question.

22. The phase transition in which $I_{2\,(s)}$ is converted into $I_{2\,(g)}$ is called _____. In order to accomplish this phase transition, the $I_{2\,(s)}$ must be _____.
    1) deposition ; heated　　2) sublimation; cooled　　3) depostion ; cooled
    4) sublimation ; heated　　5) evaporation ; heated

MODULE 1 - ANSWERS

1. a) platinum   b) mercury   c) arsenic   d) antimony   e) manganese   f) silver   g) cobalt
    h) krypton

2. a) Au   b) Mg   c) I   d) Zn   e) Cd   f) Fe   g) Sr
    h) Pb

3. a) homogeneous mixture   b) element   c) element
    d) compound   e) heterogeneous mixture   f) compound
    g) element   h) homogeneous mixture   i) heterogeneous mixture
    j) heterogeneous mixture

4. a) gas   b) solid   c) liquid   d) solid   e) liquid   f) gas

5. a) Potential   b) Potential   c) Kinetic   d) Kinetic

6. a) Physical Property   b) Physical Change   c) Physical Change
    d) Chemical Change   e) Chemical Property   f) Chemical Property
    g) Chemical Change   h) Physical Property   i) Chemical Change
    j) Physical Change

7. a) Intensive   b) Intensive   c) Extensive   d) Intensive   e) Extensive   f) Intensive

8. a) $24.3 + 38.0 = 62.3 \; MgF_2$ b) 24.3 g Mg

9. 0 g (Au can't be made from Gd & HCl)

10. a) 25% H (100% - 75%)   b) 20.3 g C and 6.75 g H

11. a) 4   b) 5   c) 5   d) 5   e) 6   f) 4

12. a) 2.00×10^{-3} b) 9.97×10^{-3} c) 3.04×10^{7} d) 1.02×10^{-11} e) 4.96×10^{-1} f) -3.95×10^{2}
    g) 1.36×10^{2} h) 1.05×10^{98}

13. a) 1.2×10^{-226} b) -3.2×10^{-1} c) 3.2×10^{-1} d) 4.5×10^{-24} e) 3.1×10^{2} f) -9.8×10^{-10}
    g) 1.65×10^{-55} h) $4. \times 10^{-6}$ i) 4.502×10^{-9} j) 5.999×10^{-116} k) 6.20×10^{-101} l) -8.041×10^{-20}
    m) 5.3×10^{-20} n) 6.9×10^{6}

14. a) 1.27×10^{-4} L   b) 5.00×10^{-7} qt   c) 4.72×10^{-2} oz   d) 1.27×10^{2} μL   e) 2.69×10^{-1} g
    f) 4.75×10^{2} mi   g) 3.00×10^{1} day   h) 1.22×10^{-1} yd   i) 4.72×10^{11} pL   j) 7.65×10^{4} dam
    k) 4.72×10^{1} cL   l) 1.34×10^{1} dg   m) 1.80×10^{1} ft   n) 5.93×10^{-4} lb   o) 1.27×10^{-5} cg
    p) 7.37×10^{-6} mi   q) 2.95×10^{3} cm^3 r) 1.07×10^{-5} m^2 s) 9.84×10^{7} in^2 t) 2.95×10^{3} mL
    u) 1.66×10^{-2} ft^3 v) 4.90×10^{-8} mL/sec   w) 6.04×10^{9} m/L   x) 1.38×10^{2} in^3/day   y) 1.29×10^{-11} dL/in^2
    z) 6.22×10^{-6} g/min

15. 50.0 mL
16. 1.98×10^{-3} g/mL
17. 4.55×10^{-1}
18. 68.0 g
19. 6.681×10^{-3} g/mL
20. 4.4 g
21. 2.33 cm
22. 2.5×10^{-1} g/mL
23. 57.0 mL
24. a) 144 °F   b) -208°C   c) -77.28°C   d) 212°F   e) 473°K   f) 404°K
25. 166 cal
26. 36. g
27. 45.2°C
28. 30.7°C

MODULE 2.   *Elements and Compounds*

I. General Ideas about Elements and Compounds

A.   Metals, Non-metals, and Metalloids

Elements to the left of the bold staircase on the periodic table are metals while those to the right are non-metals. Any elements on either side of the staircase are metalloids. *NOTE: Al is considered a metal and not a metalloid and H is considered a non-metal.*

B.   Monatomic, Diatomic, and Polyatomic Elements

Most elements exist as single atoms (the smallest particle of an element which is composed of electrons, protons, and neutrons) -- these are called monatomic elements. Only a few elements are made up of two or more atoms (called molecules). Diatomic elements are made up of two atoms; whereas, polyatomic elements are made up of more than two atoms. The diatomic & polyatomic elements are given in the figure to the right.

C. Physical State of the Elements

All elements are solids at room temperature except:

a)   those that are liquids (Hg and Br_2)

b)   those that are gases (refer to the figure on the right)

D.   Luster, Malleablity, Ductility and Hardness of Elements

Metals have luster, non-metals do not have luster (i.e., they are dull). *Most* metals are malleable (i.e., can be rolled or hammered into shape), ductile (i.e., can be drawn into a wire), and hard. Non-metals are neither malleable, ductile, or hard.

E.   Group, Row, and Section Name of Certain Elements

In the periodic table, horizontal rows are referred to as *periods*; whereas, vertical columns are referred to as *families*. Elements that are in certain groups, rows, and sections have the following specific names:

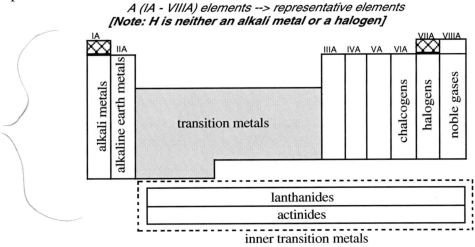

F.   Ions

Elements can gain or lose electrons and become ions. An ion is an atom or a group of atoms that carries an electrical charge.

Cation -   An ion that possess a positive charge. [Examples: Na^+, Mg^{2+}]

Anion -   An ion that posses a negative charge. [Examples: Cl^-, S^{2-}]

Polyatomic Ion - groups of atoms that bear an electrical charge. [Examples: NH_4^+ (cation), SO_4^{2-} (anion)]. [*Common Polyatomic Ions* - NH_4^+, SO_4^{2-}, PO_4^{3-}, OH^-, NO_3^-]

G. Compounds

When different elements combine a compound is formed. There are two types of compounds: Covalent and Ionic.

- **Covalent Compounds**

  If all the elements in a compound are non-metals then the compound is covalent.   As in diatomic and polyatomic elements, the basic repeating unit of a covalent compound is the molecule.

  [Examples: H_2O, PBr_3, $C_6H_{12}O_6$]

- **Ionic Compounds**

  Ionic compounds are composed of ions. For all practical purposes if a compound contains a metal, which is usually written first, then it is ionic. Compounds that contain the polyatomic ion, NH_4^+, are also ionic even though the first element is not a metal. Ionic compounds are made up of ions (a cation and an anion) whose basic repeating unit is the formula unit (FU). The term formula unit can also be used for covalent elements and compounds.

  [Examples: $NaCl$, Fe_2S_3, NH_4OH, Na_2SO_4, $(NH_4)_3PO_4$]

H.   Types & Basic Repeating Unit of Elements and Compounds

- **Atom** - Atoms are the smallest particle of an element that maintains its chemical identity through all physical and chemical changes. Atoms are made up of even smaller particles called subatomic particles: electrons, protons, and neutrons.

- **Formula Unit (FU)** - The smallest repeating unit of a substance. This term applies to both molecular and ionic compounds, as well as, to elements.

  [Examples: FU (oxygen) = O_2, FU (water) = H_2O]

- **Molecule** - The smallest particle of a diatomic/polyatomic element or covalent compound that can have a stable independent existence. It is incorrect to say a molecule of NaCl; instead say a formula unit of NaCl. It is also incorrect to say a molecule of He; instead say an atom of He.

  [Examples: H_2, S_8, H_2O, $C_6H_{12}O_6$]

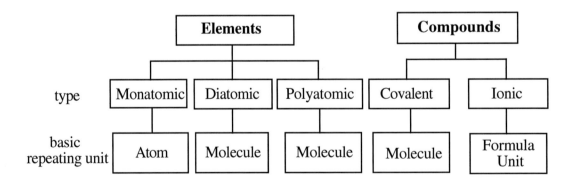

I.   Chemical Formula

A chemical formula gives the elements present for a substance, as well as, the ratio in which they occur. The subscripts represent the number of atoms of the respective element in one formula unit.

[Example: 1 FU of $(NH_4)_2HPO_4$ contains: 2 N atoms, 9 H atoms, 1 P atom, and 4 O atoms]

J.   **Allotropes**

Allotropes are different forms of the same element in the same physical state.

[Examples: C - graphite & diamond; O - O_2 & O_3]

K.   **Hydrates**

A hydrate is a solid compound containing a definite percentage of bound water.

[Example: $CuF_2 \cdot 2H_2O$] The heating of a hydrate results in the loss of bound H_2O -->
$CuF_2 \cdot 2H_2O \overset{\Delta}{\rightarrow} CuF_2 + 2\,H_2O$ ----> This is a chemical change.

II.   **Subatomic Particles**

Atoms are made up of even smaller particles called subatomic particles. These subatomic particles are: electrons, protons, and neutrons. [There are other subatomic particles, but from a chemical perspective, they are rather unimportant.]

Particle	Symbol	Electrical Charge	Approximate Mass
Proton	p^+	+1	1 amu
Neutron	n	0	1 amu
Electron	e^-	-1	0 amu

amu = atomic mass unit   1 amu = 1.66×10^{-24} g

The following diagram depicts the arrangement of subatomic particles.

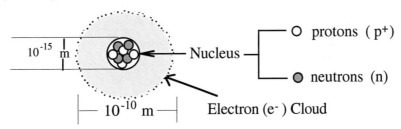

The nucleus, made up of protons and neutrons, is tiny (diameter ~ 10^{-5} Å) yet heavy.

$$1 \text{ Å} = 1 \times 10^{-10} \text{ m} = 1 \times 10^{-8} \text{ cm} \qquad (\text{Å} = \text{Angstrom})$$

Electrons are found outside the nucleus in certain energy levels. In these levels the electrons are dispersed at a relatively great distance from the nucleus. The diameter of an entire atom is in the range of 1 - 5 Å; therefore, the electrons are dispersed at distances that extend up to 10^5 times the diameter of the nucleus.

Since like charges repel each other, that is why electrons are so far away from each other. The nucleus, which contains protons (that have like charges) is very compact however. The neutrons are said to be the glue that hold the protons together.

Like Charges Repel Each Other   Opposite Charges Attract Each Other

III.   **Atomic Number (Z) and Mass Number (M)**

The atomic number, Z, is what determines the atom's identity.

Atomic Number = # of protons in atom

The atomic number (i.e., the number of protons) for each element is found in the periodic table. Depending on the periodic table, the atomic number is either written below or above the element's symbol, for example:

For atoms, # of protons = # of electrons (i.e., atoms are electrically neutral).

For ions, # of protons ≠ # of electrons. Cations with a charge of (c+) have c less electrons (but the same number of protons & neutrons) than its corresponding neutral atom. Anions with a charge of (c-) have c more electrons (but the same number of protons & neutrons) than its corresponding neutral atom.

Being that electrons hardly weigh anything, the number of protons and neutrons that are present in a given atom is what essentially determines the mass of an atom.

$$\text{Mass Number} = \text{\# of protons} + \text{\# of neutrons}$$

Example Problem: What is the mass number, atomic number, and how many protons, electrons, and neutrons do the following species have?

a) $^{40}_{18}Ar$ mass number = 40, atomic number = 18
    # of protons = 18 = # of electrons, # of neutrons = 40 - 18 = 22

b) $^{32}_{16}S^{2-}$ mass number = 32, atomic number = 16
    # of protons = 16, # of electrons = 18, # of neutrons = 32 - 16 = 16

c) $^{1}_{1}H^{+}$ mass number = 1, atomic number = 1
    # of protons = 1, # of electrons = 0, # of neutrons = 1 - 1 = 0

IV. Isotopes

Isotopes are any of two or more forms of an element having the *same atomic number* and same chemical properties but *different mass number* and slightly different physical properties. Isotopes of a given element have the same number of protons but different number of neutrons.

To distinguish between different isotopes of the same element we write an *isotope symbol* that indicates the mass number and the atomic number of the atom. The isotope symbol for one isotope of argon is:

Mass Number (M)
Symbol of Element ⟶ $^{40}_{18}Ar$ where,
Atomic Number (Z)

M = # of p^+ + # of n
Z = # of p^+
$M - Z$ = [(# of p^+ + # of n) - # of p^+] = # of n

The following represents the arrangement of subatomic particles in an atom of Argon-40 (40 stands for the mass number):

$^{40}_{18}Ar$ mass number = 40
of p^+ = 18
of e^- = 18
# of n = 40 - 18 = 22

⟶   18 p^+ 18 e^-
22 n

Examples: $^{35}_{17}X$ & $^{37}_{17}X$ are isotopes of the same element - Chlorine (atomic # = 17)

^1H, ^2H (deuterium = D), & ^3H (tritium = T) are all isotopes

Uranium-238 & Uranium-235 have different atomic masses (due to the different amount of neutrons), but chemically both would behave similarly.

Example Problem: Which of the following -- $^{13}_5X$, $^{12}_6X$, $^{12}_5X$ -- are isotopes of boron-12?

Only $^{13}_5X$ is an isotope. $^{12}_5X$ is boron-12 (i.e., they are identical).

V. Radioactivity

Elements with Z > 83 are unstable (i.e., are radioactive).

Radioactivity - the spontaneous emission of high energy particles and/or radiation.

Radiation - the emission and transmission of energy through space in the form of waves.

Radioactive Substance - a substance that decays, or breaks down, spontaneously. Radioactive substances can decay by emitting one or more of the following: a) alpha particle, b) beta particle, or c) gamma radiation.

Particles and Rays Frequently Encountered in Radiation

Particle or ray	Name of radiation	Symbol	Charge	Biological Effects
Energetic Radiation	Gamma Ray X-ray	γ x-ray	0 0	most penetrating; most damaging; can't be stopped by shielding materials as easily as α and β particles.
Electron	Beta Particle	$^0_{-1}e$ or $^0_{-1}\beta$	-1	less penetrating than γ-rays; not as harmful unless injested or inhaled.
Helium Nucleus	Alpha Particle	^4_2He or $^4_2\alpha$	+2	least penetrating; not as harmful unless ingested or inhaled.

VI. Atomic Mass (Weight) Scale

The atomic mass scale is based on the mass of the carbon-12 isotope. By definition all masses are determined relative to defining the mass of carbon-12 as *exactly* 12 amu.

Atomic masses (weights), found in the periodic table are not whole numbers because the weighted average of the masses of all the naturally occurring isotopes of the particular element is taken into account.

Since the mass of the electron is negligible compared to the mass of the nucleus, the atomic mass of an isotope is approximately equal to its mass number.

$$AW_{(Average)} = (f_1 \times AW_1) + (f_2 \times AW_2) + ...$$

where, f_1 = fraction of isotope #1

AW_1 = atomic weight of isotope #1

f_2 = fraction of isotope #2

AW_2 = atomic weight of isotope #2

Example Problems:

1. Calculate the average atomic mass of copper. Given the following information:

Isotope	% Abundance	Atomic Mass (amu)
^{63}Cu	69.1	62.9
^{65}Cu	30.9	64.9

$$AW_{(Average)} = (f_1 \times AW_1) + (f_2 \times AW_2)$$

where, f_1 = fraction of the isotope ^{63}Cu $= \dfrac{69.1}{100}$ $= 0.691$

AW_1 = atomic weight of ^{63}Cu = 62.9

f_2 = fraction of the isotope ^{65}Cu $= \dfrac{30.9}{100}$ $= 0.309$

AW_2 = atomic weight of ^{65}Cu = 64.9

$$AW_{(Average)} = (0.691 \times 62.9) + (0.309 \times 64.9) = 63.6$$

2. Antimony has two common isotopes. If one of the isotopes is antimony-121 with an atomic mass of 120.9038 amu and an abundance in nature of 57.25%, what is the atomic mass (to 4 significant figures) of the other isotope?

From the periodic table we know that the average atomic mass for Sb is 121.75 amu.

Since there are only two common isotopes, the % abundance of the second isotope is 42.75% (100 % - 57.25%).

$$AW_{(Average)} = (f_1 \times AW_1) + (f_2 \times AW_2)$$

$$121.75 = (0.5725 \times 120.9083) + (0.4275 \times AW_2)$$

$$AW_2 = \dfrac{121.75 - (0.5725 \times 120.9083)}{0.4275} = 122.9 \text{ amu}$$

3. The atomic weight of fictitious element X is 251.7 amu. If element X consists of two isotopes that have mass numbers of 250 and 253, what is the approximate % natural abundance of each isotope?

Since the mass of the electron is negligible compared to the mass of the nucleus, the atomic weight of an isotope is approximately equal to its mass number.

Since there are only two isotopes, if one has an abundance of X the other isotope must have an abundance of 100% - X or in fractions 1 - X.

Let X be "fractional" abundance of ^{250}X and (1 - X) be "fractional" abundance of ^{253}X

$$AW_{(Average)} = (f_1 \times AW_1) + (f_2 \times AW_2)$$

$$251.7 = [X \times 250] + [(1-X) \times 253]$$

$$251.7 = 250X + 253 - 253X$$

$$251.7 = -3X + 253$$

$$\dfrac{251.7 - 253}{-3} = X \text{ -------> } 0.43 \quad (\text{Fraction of } ^{250}X)$$

Approximate abundance of $^{250}X = 43\%$ and approximate abundance of $^{253}X = 57\%$

EXERCISES

General Ideas

1. Write the formula for the following elements and physical state as they exist naturally.

    a) hydrogen   b) copper
    c) helium   d) sulfur
    e) iodine   f) oxygen
    g) fluorine   h) lithium

2. Classify the following as either: A) monatomic element, B) diatomic element, C) polyatomic element, D) molecular compound, E) ionic compound, F) cation, or G) anion.

    a) NH_4Cl b) H_2O
    c) CuI_2 d) H^{1+}
    e) iodine   f) $FeSO_4$
    g) Cl^{1-} h) helium
    i) C_2H_5OH j) NaCl
    k) $C_2H_3O_2^{1-}$ l) P_4

3. Classify each of the following elements into one or more of the following categories:

    A. alkali metal   B. alkaline earth metal   C. chalcogen
    D. chalcogen   E. halogen   F. noble gas
    G. lantanide   H. actinide   I. inner transition metal
    J. representative element   K. transition metal

    a) Cl   b) Al   c) H   d) U   e) Zn   f) Na   g) Ba

Mass Number, Atomic Number, Isotopes, and Average Atomic Mass

4. What is the mass number, atomic number, and how many protons, electrons, & neutrons do the following species have?

    a) ^{31}P b) $^{19}F^{1-}$ c) $^{40}Ca^{2+}$ d) Uranium-235

    M# 31, AM 15, P 15, N 15, E 16   MA 19, A#9, P 9, N 10, E 10   40, 20, 20, 18, 20   235, 92, 92, 92, 143

5. Complete the following table.

Atomic Number	Mass Number	# of protons	# of electrons	# of neutrons	Name	Isotope Symbol
16	32					
						$^{37}_{17}Cl$
	25	12				
			8	10		
						$^{56}_{26}Fe$
	238				uranium	
7				8		
	70			40		
		1		2		

6. Calculate the average atomic mass for a fictitious element, X, given the following information:

Isotope	% Abundance	Atomic Mass (amu)
^{107}X	30.0	106.9
^{110}X	30.9	109.9
^{112}X	39.1	111.9

7. There are three naturally occuring isotopes of silicon -- silicon-28 (92.21%, 27.977 amu), silicon-29 (4.70%, 28.976 amu), and silicon-30 (29.974 amu). What is the average atomic mass of silicon?

8. Chlorine has two common isotopes. If one of the isotopes is chlorine-35 with an atomic mass of 34.969 amu and an abundance in nature of 75.77%, what is the atomic mass (to 4 significant) of the other isotope?

9. The atomic mass of element X is 51.70 amu. If element X consists of two isotopes that have mass numbers of 50 and 52, what is the approximate % natural abundance of each isotope?

10. Element Y has two isotopes. Their isotopic masses are 91.78 amu and 96.46 amu. If the average atomic mass is 94.79 amu, then calculate the % natural abundance of each isotope?

11. The atomic massof element Z is 79.85 amu. If element Z consists of two isotopes that have mass numbers of 79 and 83, what is the approximate % natural abundance of each isotope?

MULTIPLE CHOICE PRACTICE EXAM FOR MODULE 2

1. Which of the following elements is (are) found naturally as diatomic molecules?
   1) chlorine   2) sulfur   3) argon
   4) two of the above choices are correct.
   5) none of the above choices are correct.

2. Which of the following elements are metals?
            a. Hg   b. Se   c. H
   1) only a   2) only b   3) only c   4) only a and c   5) only b and c

3. The following - H_2; NH_4^+; H_2O - could be correctly (and respectively) classified as:
   1) element; polyatomic anion; compound
   2) molecule; cation; covalent compound
   3) element; polyatomic cation; hydrate
   4) atom; ion; compound
   5) diatomic element; ionic compound; covalent compound

4. Which of the following is an ionic compound?
   1) H_2O 2) PBr_3 3) NH_4OH 4) Au   5) CH_3NH_2

5. How many protons, electrons, and neutrons are present in $^{48}Ti^{2+}$?
   1) $p^+ = 22$, $e^- = 22$, $n = 48$ 2) $p^+ = 20$, $e^- = 22$, $n = 26$ 3) $p^+ = 48$, $e^- = 46$, $n = 22$
   4) $p^+ = 22$, $e^- = 20$, $n = 26$ 5) $p^+ = 22$, $e^- = 24$, $n = 26$

6. What is the symbol of the specie having 21 protons and 20 electrons?
   1) Ca^+ 2) Sc   3) Ca^- 4) Sc^+
   5) There is not enough information to answer this question.

7. Fictitious element X (average atomic mass = 254.9 amu) has only two common isotopes. If one isotope has an abundance of 72.00% and a mass of 250.9 amu, what is the average atomic mass of the other isotope?
   1) 265.2   2) 20.80   3) 245.9   4) 250.9
   5) There is not enough information to answer this question.

8. Which of the following elements is a noble gas?
   1) H   2) Xe   3) O   4) F   5) N

9. Which of the following elements is/are representative elements?
            a. V   b. Se   c. H
   1) only a   2) only b   3) only c   4) only a and c   5) only b and c

10. Which of the following elements exist as gases under normal laboratory conditions?
             a. bromine   b. nitrogen   c. oxygen
    1) only a   2) only b   3) only c   4) only a and c   5) only b and c

11. Which of the following fictitious elements are isotopes? [NOTE: All of the choices have been given the symbol X, do not let this mislead you.]
        a. $^{350}_{200}X$ b. $^{350}_{201}X$ c. $^{351}_{200}X$ d. $^{351}_{201}X$ e. $^{351}_{202}X$
    1) only a and b   2) only b and d   3) only c and d
    4) two of the above choices are correct.
    5) none of the above choices are correct.

12. What is the symbol for antimony?

    1) Ac   2) At   3) Sb   4) Am   5) An

13. The atomic mass of fictitious element, Z, is 261.4 amu. Z has only 2 common isotopes that have a mass number of 260 and 264. Given this information, what is the approximate percent abundance of Z-260?

    1) 53   2) 65   3) 35   4) 57   5) 47

14. Given the partially filled table, which table entries would be considered isotopes?

	Atomic No.	Mass No.	# of e⁻	# of p⁺	# of n
a.	95		92		144
b.		239	95	95	
c.			95	95	144
d.		240	95	95	

    1) only a and b   2) only b and c   3) only c and d

    4) not enough information is given to be able to make a decision

    5) none are isotopes

15. The name of the element that has 32 neutrons and an atomic number of 29 is:

    1) germanium   2) lithium   3) cobalt-29   4) copper-61   5) copper-29

MODULE 2 - ANSWERS

1. a) H_2, g   b) Cu, s   c) He, g   d) S_8, s   e) I_2, s   f) O_2, g   g) F_2, g   h) Li, s

2. a) ionic compound   b) molecular compound   c) ionic compound
   d) cation   e) diatomic element   f) ionic compound
   g) anion   h) monatomic element   i) molecular compound
   j) ionic compound   k) anion   l) polyatomic element

3. a) E,J   b) J   c) J   d) H,I   e) K   f) A,J   g) B,J

4. a) mass # = 31, Z = 15, p = 15, e^- = 15, n = 16   b) mass # = 19, Z = 9, p = 9, e^- = 10, n = 10
   c) mass # = 40, Z = 20, p = 20, e^- = 18, n = 20   c) mass # = 235, Z = 92, p = 92, e^- = 92, n = 143

5.

Atomic Number	Mass Number	# of protons	# of electrons	# of neutrons	Name	Isotope Symbol
16	32	16	16	16	sulfur	$^{32}_{16}S$
17	37	17	17	20	chlorine	$^{37}_{17}Cl$
12	25	12	12	13	magnesium	$^{25}_{12}Mg$
8	18	8	8	10	oxygen	$^{18}_{8}O$
26	56	26	26	30	iron	$^{56}_{26}Fe$
92	238	92	92	146	uranium	$^{238}_{92}U$
7	15	7	7	8	nitrogen	$^{15}_{7}N$
30	70	30	30	40	zinc	$^{70}_{30}Zn$
1	3	1	1	2	hydrogen	$^{3}_{1}H$

6. 109.78 amu

7. 28.09 amu

8. 36.97 amu

9. 15% of ^{50}X and 85% of ^{52}X

10. 35.7% (atomic mass = 91.78) and 64.3 (atomic mass = 96.46)

11. 21% of ^{83}Z and 79% of ^{79}Z

MODULE 3. *Chemical Formulas and Composition Stoichiometry*

I. The Mole (mol) and Avogadro's Number

Just like 1 dozen = 12, **1 mol = 6.02 x 10^{23}**   (Avogadro's Number)

Therefore,

1 mol of monatomic element = 6.02 x 10^{23} atoms

1 mol of diatomic/polyatomic element = 6.02 x 10^{23} molecules

1 mol of covalent compound = 6.02 x 10^{23} molecules

1 mol of ionic compound = 6.02 x 10^{23} FU

1 mol of an ion = 6.02 x 10^{23} ions

For Example,

1 mol Na = 6.02 x 10^{23} Na atoms

1 mol H_2 = 6.02 x 10^{23} H_2 molecules

1 mol H_2O = 6.02 x 10^{23} H_2O molecules

1 mol $MgCl_2$ = 6.02 x 10^{23} $MgCl_2$ FU

1 mol NH_4^+ = 6.02 x 10^{23} NH_4^+ ions

II. Atomic Weight (AW), Molecular Weight (MW), & Formula Weight (FW)

A. Monatomic Elements

- An atomic weight (AW) tells us the weight (mass) of an atom. Monatomic elements are made up of atoms. The weight (mass) of each element is found in the periodic table.

- The weight (mass) of <u>one atom</u> of any element found in the periodic table is expressed in *atomic mass unit* (amu).   The atomic weight of one atom of an element is expressed in units of amu/atom.

- The weight (mass) of <u>one mol of atoms</u> (i.e., 6.02 x 10^{23} atoms) of any element found in the periodic table is expressed in *grams* (g). The mass of one mol of a monatomic is called its molar mass or its atomic weight (with units of g/mol).

The following is an example of the atomic weight of C expressed in amu/atom or in g/mol.

1 C atom = 12.0 amu	1 <u>mol</u> C atoms = 6.02 x 10^{23} atoms = 12.0 g
The AW of 1 C atom is 12.0 $\frac{amu}{atom}$	The AW of 1 mol of C atoms is 12.0 $\frac{g}{mol}$

<u>Example Problem:</u>

1. How much does one lithium atom weigh in amu?

    One lithium atom weighs 6.94 amu (i.e., AW of Li = 6.94 amu/atom)

2. What is the molar mass of lithium?

    One mol of Li atoms weigh 6.94 g; therefore, the molar mass of Li is 6.94 g/mol.

3. How much does one lithium atom weigh (in grams)?

    1 <u>mol</u> Li atoms = 6.02 x 10^{23} Li atoms = 6.94 g Li

    $? \text{ g Li} = 1 \text{ Li atom} \left(\dfrac{6.94 \text{ g Li}}{6.02 \times 10^{23} \text{ Li atoms}} \right) = 1.15 \times 10^{-23} \text{ g Li}$

B. Molecular Elements (diatomic/diatomic) and Compounds

- A molecular weight (MW) tells us the weight (mass) of molecular elements or compounds.
- The weight (mass) of <u>one molecule</u> of a molecular element or compound is the sum of all the atomic weights expressed in *atomic mass unit* (amu). The molecular weight of one molecule is expressed in units of amu/molecule.
- The weight (mass) of <u>one mol of molecules</u> (i.e., 6.02×10^{23} molecules) of a molecular element or compound is the sum of the atomic weights expressed in *grams* (g). The mass of one mol of a molecular element or compound is called its molar mass or its molecular weight (with units of g/mol).

The following is an example of the molecular weight of H_2O expressed in amu/molecule or in g/mol.

2 H atoms = 2 x 1.01 amu = 2.02 amu 1 O atom = 1 x 16.00 amu = 16.00 amu 1 H_2O molecule = 18.02 amu	2 mol H atoms = 2 x 1.01 g = 2.02 g 1 mol O atoms = 1 x 16.00 g = 16.00 g 1 mol H_2O molecules = 18.02 g
The MW of 1 H_2O molecule is: $18.02 \dfrac{amu}{molecule}$	The MW of 1 mol (6.02×10^{23} molecules) of H_2O is: $18.02 \dfrac{g}{mol}$

<u>Example Problem</u>:

1. How much does one molecule of Cl_2 weigh (in amu)?

    1 Cl_2 molecule = 2 Cl atoms = 2 x 35.5 amu = 71.0 amu

    One Cl_2 molecule weighs 71.0 amu (i.e., AW of Cl_2 = 71.0 amu/molecule)

2. How much does one molecule of Cl_2 weigh (in grams)?

    1 <u>mol</u> Cl_2 molecules = 2 <u>mol</u> Cl atoms = 2 x 35.5 g = 71.0 g = 6.02×10^{23} Cl_2 molecules

    $$? \text{ g } Cl_2 = 1 \; Cl_2 \text{ molecule} \left(\frac{71.0 \text{ g } Cl_2}{6.02 \times 10^{23} \; Cl_2 \text{ molecules}} \right) = 1.18 \times 10^{-22} \text{ g } Cl_2$$

C. Formula Weight (can be used in lieu of AW or MW)

- A formula Weight (FW) tells us the weight (mass) of a formula unit (FU). The term formula unit can be used to describe the basic repeating unit of elements or compounds.
- The weight (mass) of <u>one formula unit</u> of an element or compound is the sum of all the atomic weights expressed in *atomic mass unit* (amu). The formula weight of one formula unit is expressed in units of amu/FU.
- The weight (mass) of <u>one mol of formula units</u> (i.e., 6.02×10^{23} FU) of an element or compound is the sum of the atomic weights expressed in *grams* (g). The mass of one mol of formula units is called its molar mass or its formula weight (with units of g/mol).

The following is an example of the molecular weight of $Cu(NO_3)_2 \cdot 6 \, H_2O$ expressed in amu/FU or in g/mol.

1 Cu atom = 1 x 63.5 amu = 63.5 amu 2 N atoms = 2 x 14.0 amu = 28.0 amu 12 O atoms = 12 x 16.0 amu = 192.0 amu 12 H atoms = 12 x 1.01 amu = 12.1 amu 1 $Cu(NO_3)_2 \cdot 6 \, H_2O$ FU = 295.6 amu	1 mol Cu atoms = 1 x 63.5 g = 63.5 g 2 mol N atoms = 2 x 14.0 g = 28.0 g 12 mol O atoms = 12 x 16.0 g = 192.0 g 12 mol H atoms = 12 x 1.01 g = 12.1 g 1 mol $Cu(NO_3)_2 \cdot 6 \, H_2O$ FU = 295.6 g
The FW of 1 $Cu(NO_3)_2 \cdot 6 \, H_2O$ FU is: $295.6 \dfrac{amu}{FU}$	The FW of 1 mol $Cu(NO_3)_2 \cdot 6 \, H_2O$ (6.02×10^{23} FU) is: $295.6 \dfrac{g}{mol}$

Example Problems:

1. Answer the following questions about a 0.125 mol sample of nitrogen gas:

    Nitrogen is a diatomic element with the formula N_2.

$$\frac{2 \text{ N atoms}}{1 \text{ N}_2 \text{ molecule}} = \frac{2 \times 14.0 \text{ amu}}{= 28.0 \text{ amu}} = \frac{28.0 \text{ amu}}{28.0 \text{ amu}} \quad \Big| \quad \frac{2 \text{ mol N atoms}}{1 \text{ mol N}_2 \text{ molecule}} = \frac{2 \times 14.0 \text{ g}}{= 28.0 \text{ g}} = \frac{28.0 \text{ g}}{28.0 \text{ g}}$$

   $1 \text{ mol N}_2 = 28.0 \text{ g N}_2 = 6.02 \times 10^{23} \text{ molecules N}_2$

   a) How many grams does it weigh?

$$? \text{ g N}_2 = 0.125 \text{ mol N}_2 \left(\frac{28.0 \text{ g N}_2}{1 \text{ mol N}_2} \right) = 3.50 \text{ g N}_2$$

   b) How many nitrogen molecules are present?

$$? \text{ N}_2 \text{ molecules} = 0.125 \text{ mol N}_2 \left(\frac{6.02 \times 10^{23} \text{ N}_2 \text{ molecules}}{1 \text{ mol N}_2} \right) = 7.52 \times 10^{22} \text{ molecules N}_2$$

   c) How many N atoms are present?

$$? \text{ N atoms} = 0.125 \text{ mol N}_2 \left(\frac{6.02 \times 10^{23} \text{ N}_2 \text{ molecules}}{1 \text{ mol N}_2} \right) \left(\frac{2 \text{ N atoms}}{1 \text{ N}_2 \text{ molecule}} \right) = 1.50 \times 10^{23} \text{ N atoms}$$

2. Answer the following questions about a 0.125 g sample of $Ca(NO_3)_2$:

$$\frac{\begin{array}{l} 1 \text{ Ca atom} = 1 \times 40.1 \text{ amu} = 40.1 \text{ amu} \\ 2 \text{ N atoms} = 2 \times 14.0 \text{ amu} = 28.0 \text{ amu} \\ 6 \text{ O atoms} = 6 \times 16.00 \text{ amu} = 96.0 \text{ amu} \end{array}}{1 \text{ Ca(NO}_3)_2 \text{ FU} = 164.1 \text{ amu}} \quad \Big| \quad \frac{\begin{array}{l} 1 \text{ mol Ca atom} = 1 \times 40.1 \text{ g} = 40.1 \text{ g} \\ 2 \text{ mol N atoms} = 2 \times 14.0 \text{ g} = 28.0 \text{ g} \\ 6 \text{ mol O atoms} = 6 \times 16.00 \text{ g} = 96.0 \text{ g} \end{array}}{1 \text{ Ca(NO}_3)_2 \text{ FU} = 164.1 \text{ g}}$$

   $1 \text{ mol Ca(NO}_3)_2 = 164.1 \text{ g Ca(NO}_3)_2 = 6.02 \times 10^{23} \text{ Ca(NO}_3)_2 \text{ FU}$

   a) How many moles are there?

$$? \text{ mol Ca(NO}_3)_2 = 0.125 \text{ g Ca(NO}_3)_2 \left(\frac{1 \text{ mol Ca(NO}_3)_2}{164.1 \text{ g Ca(NO}_3)_2} \right) = 7.62 \times 10^{-4} \text{ mol Ca(NO}_3)_2$$

   b) How many FU of $Ca(NO_3)_2$ are present?

$$? \text{ FU Ca(NO}_3)_2 = 0.125 \text{ g Ca(NO}_3)_2 \left(\frac{6.02 \times 10^{23} \text{ FU Ca(NO}_3)_2}{164.1 \text{ g Ca(NO}_3)_2} \right) = 4.59 \times 10^{20} \text{ FU Ca(NO}_3)_2$$

   c) How many molecules of $Ca(NO_3)_2$ are present?

   Zero, because $Ca(NO_3)_2$ is an ionic compound; ionic compounds are not made up of molecules.

   d) How many O atoms are present?

$$? \text{ O atoms} = 0.125 \text{ g Ca(NO}_3)_2 \left(\frac{6 \text{ mol O atoms}}{164.1 \text{ g Ca(NO}_3)_2} \right) \left(\frac{6.02 \times 10^{23} \text{ O atoms}}{1 \text{ mol O atoms}} \right) = 2.75 \times 10^{21}$$

   e) How many grams of N are present?

$$? \text{ g N} = 0.125 \text{ g Ca(NO}_3)_2 \left(\frac{28 \text{ g N}}{164.1 \text{ g Ca(NO}_3)_2} \right) = 2.13 \times 10^{-2} \text{ g}$$

3. A 2.0000 g sample of element X reacted with oxygen to form 2.5392 g of the compound XO_2.

   a) What is the Formula Weight of XO_2?

$$FW = \frac{\# \text{ g } XO_2}{\text{mol } XO_2} = \frac{2.5392 \text{ g } XO_2}{? \text{ mol } XO_2}$$

   • We need to find how many mol of XO_2 there are in the 2.5392 g of XO_2

   • From the law of conservation of matter, we know that 2.0000 g of the 2.5392 g of compound is element X; therefore, the number of grams of O in the sample is:

$$\text{g O in sample} = \text{g } XO_2 - \text{g } X = 2.5392 - 2.000 = 0.5392 \text{ g O}$$

From the grams of O we can calculate how many moles of XO_2 there are in 2.5392 g of XO_2.

$$1 \text{ mol } XO_2 = 1 \text{ mol } X = 2 \text{ mol O}$$

$$? \text{ mol } XO_2 = 0.5392 \text{ g O} \left(\frac{1 \text{ mol O}}{16 \text{ g O}} \right) \left(\frac{1 \text{ mol } XO_2}{2 \text{ mol O}} \right) = 0.01685 \text{ mol } XO_2$$

$$FW = \frac{2.5392 \text{ g } XO_2}{0.01685 \text{ mol } XO_2} = 150.7 \text{ g/mol}$$

   b) X is a real element, what is its identity?

$$FW (XO_2) = 1(AW_X) + 2(AW_O) \text{ ----> } 150.7 \text{ g/mol} = 1(AW_X) \text{ g/mol} + 2(16) \text{ g/mol}$$

$$AW_X = 150.7 - 32 = 118.7 \text{ g/mol} \quad \left(\begin{array}{l} \text{Looking at the periodic table -} \\ \text{Sn is the element with an AW} = 118.7 \end{array} \right)$$

III. Percent Composition

If the formula of a compound is known, its chemical composition can be expressed as the mass (weight) percent of each element in the compound. The % composition for a particular element in a compound can be found as follows:

$$\% \text{ Element} = \frac{\text{g of element in sample}}{\text{g of sample}} \times 100$$

Example Problems:

1. The molecular formula for compound $X = C_7H_5N_3O_3$. Calculate the mass percentage of each element in compound X (or calculate the percent composition of compound X by mass).

   In cases such as this where the sample size is not given, assume that you have 1 mol of compound.

   First, calculate the molecular weight (in g/mol).   In 1 mol of sample,

$$
\begin{array}{llll}
\text{C: } 7 \times 12.0 = & 84.0 \text{ g} & \text{-----> } & \text{g of C in sample} \\
\text{H: } 5 \times 1.0 = & 5.0 \text{ g} & \text{-----> } & \text{g of H in sample} \\
\text{N: } 3 \times 14.0 = & 42.0 \text{ g} & \text{-----> } & \text{g of N in sample} \\
\text{O: } 3 \times 16.0 = & \underline{48.0} \text{ g} & \text{-----> } & \text{g of O in sample} \\
& 179.0 \text{ g} & \text{-----> } & \text{g of sample} \\
\end{array}
$$

$$\% \text{ C} = \frac{84.0}{179.0} \times 100 = 46.9\% \qquad \% \text{ H} = \frac{5.0}{179.0} \times 100 = 2.8\%$$

$$\% \text{ N} = \frac{42.0}{179.0} \times 100 = 23.5\% \qquad \% \text{ O} = \frac{48.0}{179.0} \times 100 = 26.8\%$$

2. A compound X_3O_4 contains 72.03% X and 27.97% O by weight. What is the atomic weight of X?

Assuming that we have a 100.00 g sample -----> 72.03 g of X and 27.97 g O

$$AW_X = \frac{\# \, g \, X}{mol \, X} = \frac{72.03 \, g \, X}{? \, mol \, X} \quad ---> \text{ We can find mol X from the g of O in the sample.}$$

$$1 \, mol \, X_3O_4 = 3 \, mol \, X = 4 \, mol \, O$$

$$? \, mol \, X = 27.97 \, g \, O \left(\frac{1 \, mol \, O}{16 \, g \, O}\right)\left(\frac{3 \, mol \, X}{4 \, mol \, O}\right) = 1.311 \, mol \, X$$

$$AW = \frac{72.03 \, g \, X}{1.311 \, mol \, X} = 54.94 \, g/mol$$

3. A 3.72 g sample of an ionic compound containing iodine when reacted with excess silver nitrate yielded 6.06 g of AgI. What is the % composition (or weight %) of iodine in the sample?

$$\% \, I = \frac{g \, of \, I \, in \, sample}{g \, of \, sample} \, x \, 100 = \frac{x}{3.72} \, x \, 100$$

The # of grams of I in the sample will be the same as the number of grams of I present in 6.06 g AgI (Law of conservation of mass).

$$1 \, mol \, AgI = 234.8 \, g \, AgI = 1 \, mol \, I = 126.9 \, g \, I$$

$$? \, g \, I = 6.06 \, g \, AgI \left(\frac{1 \, mol \, AgI}{234.8 \, g \, AgI}\right)\left(\frac{1 \, mol \, I}{1 \, mol \, AgI}\right)\left(\frac{126.9 \, g \, I}{1 \, mol \, I}\right) = 3.28 \, g \, I$$

This means that 3.28 g out of the 6.06 g of AgI is I and 3.28 g out of the 3.72 g of sample is I.

$$\% \, I = \frac{3.28}{3.72} \, x \, 100 = 88.2\%$$

IV. Finding the Mass of One Element Given a Certain Quantity of a Compound

Example Problem:

1. How many grams of sulfur are in 292. g of $Al_2(SO_4)_3$?

In 1 mol of sample, there are:

        Al: 2 x 27.0 =   54.0 g
        S: 3 x 32.1 =   96.3 g
        O: 12 x 16.0 = 192.0 g
                         342.3 g

$$1 \, mol \, Al_2(SO_4)_3 = 342. \, g \, Al_2(SO_4)_3 = 54.0 \, g \, Al = 96.3 \, g \, S = 192.0 \, g \, O$$

$$? \, g \, S = 292. \, g \, Al_2(SO_4)_3 \left(\frac{96.3 \, g \, S}{342.3 \, g \, Al_2(SO_4)_3}\right) = 82.1 \, g \, S$$

V. Empirical (Simplest) Formulas

The empirical or simplest formula for a compound is the smallest whole-number ratio of atoms present.

Molecular Formula	Empirical Formula
H_2O	H_2O
H_2O_2	HO
C_6H_{12}	CH_2

The ratio of moles of atoms of elements in a compound is the same as the ratio of atoms in that compound. [0.2 mol X, 0.4 mol Y --> "$X_{0.2}Y_{0.4}$" this is not the empirical formula because the numbers are not whole numbers.]

Finding the empirical formula -- Approach to solving problems if grams or % of each element in the compound is given:

1) Convert the amount in grams given of each element present in the formula to moles.

    a)   If grams are given divide by AW ---> $\dfrac{\text{g of element}}{\text{AW of element}}$ = mol of element in compound

    b)   If % given, assume sample size of 100 g so that the % = grams; then divide by AW

2) Once moles are obtained, to obtain a simple whole number ratio*,

    a)   divide each number by the smallest number; if whole numbers are not obtained, then

    b)   multiply all of the resulting numbers by the smallest whole number that will eliminate fractions.

Finding the Empirical Formula of a Hydrocarbon via Combustion Analysis

When a hydrocarbon (a compound containing C and H) is burned (in the presence of oxygen), CO_2 and H_2O are obtained.

$$C_xH_y \quad + \quad O_2 \quad \rangle \quad CO_2 \quad + \quad H_2O$$

By performing a combustion analysis, i.e. determining the amount of CO_2 and/or H_2O, the empirical formula of the hydrocarbon can be ascertained.

All the carbon originally present in the hydrocarbon is the same amount of carbon that is now present in the CO_2. Thus from the grams of CO_2, the grams of C in C_xH_y can be obtained as follows:

$$\text{g C in } CO_2 = \text{g C in } C_xH_y \text{ -----> g C} = \text{\# g } CO_2 \left(\frac{12.011 \text{ g C}}{44.011 \text{ g } CO_2}\right)$$

Likewise, all the hydrogen originally present in the hydrocarbon is the same amount of hydrogen that is now present in the H_2O. Thus from the grams of H_2O, the grams of H in C_xH_y can be obtained as follows:

$$\text{g H in } H_2O = \text{g H in } C_xH_y \text{ -----> g H} = \text{\# g } H_2O \left(\frac{2.016 \text{ g H}}{18.016 \text{ g } H_2O}\right)$$

Once the grams of carbon and hydrogen are known, then the empirical formula of the hydrocarbon can be obtained by following the delineated steps mentioned above.

Example Problems:

1. Elemental analysis of a 10.00 g sample of a pure compound indicated that the compound had 2.16 g Na, 3.33 g Cl, and 4.51g O. Calculate the empirical formula for this compound.

    Note that the formula for this compound will be $Na_xCl_yO_z$, where x, y, and z are the mole ratios for sodium, chlorine, and oxygen, respectively.

    Convert g ---> moles. You do this by dividing by the Atomic Weight of the element

$$\underset{23.0}{Na_{2.16}} \underset{35.5}{Cl_{3.33}} \underset{16.0}{O_{4.51}} \text{ ---> } Na_{0.0939}Cl_{0.0938}O_{0.282} \left(\begin{array}{c}\text{since these are not whole numbers}\\ \text{divide each number by the smallest number}\end{array}\right)$$

$$\underset{0.0938}{Na_{0.0939}} \underset{0.0938}{Cl_{0.0938}} \underset{0.0938}{O_{0.282}} \text{ ---> } Na_{1.00}Cl_{1.00}O_{3.01} \left(\begin{array}{c}\text{since 3.01 is within } \pm 0.08 \text{ of}\\ \text{3.00 we can round it off to 3}\end{array}\right)$$

    This gives us the empirical formula $Na_1Cl_1O_3$. Subscripts of 1 are not used in formulas, thus the formula is rewritten as $NaClO_3$.

----

* *don't round off a number to the nearest whole number, unless the number is within ± 0.08 of a whole number.*

2. Elemental analysis of a pure compound indicated that the compound had 65.2% As and 34.8%O. Find empirical formula.

Assume that you have a 100. gram sample which would then contain 65.2 g As and 34.8 g O.

Convert g ---> moles: $As_{\frac{65.2}{74.9}} O_{\frac{34.8}{16.0}} = As_{0.870}O_{2.18}$

The "formula" obtained is $As_{0.870}O_{2.18}$ (not whole #)

Divide by smallest #: $As_{\frac{0.870}{0.870}} O_{\frac{2.18}{0.870}} = As_{1.00}O_{2.51}$ (not whole #)

Multiply by smallest # that will give whole # - in this case, multply by 2 --> $As_{2.00}O_{5.02}$

The empirical formula is thus: As_2O_5

3. A 5.00 g sample of an unknown compound containing C and H when burned produced 14.6 g of CO_2. What is its empirical formula?

The grams of carbon present in the unknown compound is the same as the grams of C present in CO_2. [Remember the law of conservation of mass.]

$$? \text{ g C} = 14.6 \text{ g } CO_2 \left(\frac{12.011 \text{ g C}}{44.011 \text{ g } CO_2}\right) = 3.98 \text{ g C}$$

Since the compound contains only C and H, the grams of H can be obtained as follows:

$g_{sample} = g \text{ C} + g \text{ H}$

$5.00 = 3.98 + g \text{ H}$

$g \text{ H} = 5.00 - 3.98 = 1.02 \text{ g}$

Now that we have the g of C and g of H we can then we can follow the steps delineated previously.

Convert g ---> moles: $C_{\frac{3.98}{12.0}} H_{\frac{1.02}{1.01}} = "C_{0.332}H_{1.01}"$

Divide by smallest number: $C_{\frac{0.332}{0.332}} H_{\frac{1.01}{0.332}} = C_{1.00}H_{3.04}$

The empirical formula is thus: CH_3

VI. Molecular Formulas

To determine the molecular formula for a molecular compound, both its empirical formula and its molecular weight must be known. The following formula shows how the molecular formula can be obtained.

$$\left(\frac{\text{molecular weight}}{\text{empirical formula weight}}\right) \text{ x empirical formula} = \text{molecular formula}$$

Example Problems:

1. What is the molecular formula for Freon-12 (MW = 121.0 g/mol), whose empirical formula is CCl_2F_2?

The empirical formula weight is 121.0 (Take sum of AW)

$$\left(\frac{121.0}{121.0}\right) \text{ x } CCl_2F_2 = 1 (CCl_2F_2) = CCl_2F_2$$

2. Glucose (MW = 180.) contains C, H, and O. Given the %C (40.0%) & %H (6.72%), what is the molecular formula of glucose?

%O = 100% - 40.0% - 6.72% = 53.3%.

Assume 100. g sample, then do the following to find empirical formula:

Converting g ---> moles $C_{\frac{40.0}{12.0}} H_{\frac{6.72}{1.01}} O_{\frac{53.3}{16.0}}$ = $C_{3.33}H_{6.65}O_{3.33}$

The "formula" obtained is "$C_{3.33}H_{6.65}O_{3.33}$" (not whole #)

Divide by smallest #: $C_{\frac{3.33}{3.33}} H_{\frac{6.65}{3.33}} O_{\frac{3.33}{3.33}}$ = $C_1H_2O_1 = CH_2O$

Empirical Formula Weight = 1(C) + 2(H) + 1(O) = 1(12.0) + 2(1.01) + 1(16.0) = 30.0

Molecular Formula ---> $\left(\dfrac{180.}{30.0}\right)$ x CH_2O = 6 (CH_2O) = $C_6H_{12}O_6$

VII. **Percent Purity of Compounds**

When impure compounds are used for precise work, account must be taken of impurities. A sample that is 98.0% by weight pure PBr_3 means that the sample is 2.0% impure. The following unit factors can be used:

$$\dfrac{98.0 \text{ g } PBr_3}{100 \text{ g sample}} \qquad \dfrac{2.0 \text{ g impurites}}{100 \text{ g sample}} \qquad \dfrac{2.0 \text{ g impurites}}{98.0 \text{ g } PBr_3}$$

Example Problems:

1. Calculate the masses of PBr_3 & impurities in 37.3 g of 98.0% pure PBr_3.

? g PBr_3 = 37.3 g sample $\left(\dfrac{98.0 \text{ g } PBr_3}{100 \text{ g sample}}\right)$ = 36.6 g PBr_3

? g impurities = 37.3 g sample - 36.6 g PBr_3 = 0.7 g impurities

2. How many moles of $CuSO_4$ (FW = 159.6) are there in a 36.3 g sample of 67.3% $CuSO_4$.

? mol $CuSO_4$ = 36.3 g sample $\left(\dfrac{67.3 \text{ g } CuSO_4}{100 \text{ g sample}}\right)\left(\dfrac{1 \text{ mol } CuSO_4}{159.6 \text{ g } CuSO_4}\right)$ = 0.153 mol $CuSO_4$

3. A 2.720 g sample of impure $BaCl_2 \cdot 2 H_2O$ (FW = 244.3) after heating yielded 2.360 g of a solid residue.

a) What is the mass of pure $BaCl_2 \cdot 2H_2O$ in the sample?

With heating ------> $BaCl_2 \cdot 2H_2O_{(s)} \xrightarrow{\Delta} BaCl_{2(s)} + 2 H_2O_{(g)}$

The sample weighs less by the amount of water that was driven off as steam upon heating.
g H_2O = 2.720 g - 2.360 g = 0.360 g H_2O

From the g of H_2O we can find out how much $BaCl_2 \cdot 2H_2O$ was in the original sample.
1 mol $BaCl_2 \cdot 2H_2O$ = 1 mol $BaCl_2$ = 2 mol H_2O

? g $BaCl_2 \cdot 2H_2O$ = 0.360 g $H_2O \left(\dfrac{1 \text{ mol } H_2O}{18.0 \text{ g } H_2O}\right)\left(\dfrac{1 \text{ mol } BaCl_2 \cdot 2H_2O}{2 \text{ mol } H_2O}\right)\left(\dfrac{244.3 \text{ g } BaCl_2 \cdot 2H_2O}{1 \text{ mol } BaCl_2 \cdot 2H_2O}\right)$ = 2.44 g

b) What is the %$BaCl_2 \cdot 2H_2O$ in the sample?

%$BaCl_2 \cdot 2 H_2O = \dfrac{\text{g of } BaCl_2 \cdot 2H_2O}{\text{g of sample}}$ x 100 = $\dfrac{2.44 \text{ g}}{2.720 \text{ g}}$ x 100 = 89.7%

EXERCISES

The Mole Concept, Formulas, and Formula Weights

1. Calculate the fomula weight for each of the following:

   a) $Fe(C_2H_3O_2)_2 \cdot 4 H_2O$ b) K_3PO_4

   c) $IrTe_3$ d) $Al(C_6H_5O)_3$

   e) $C_{12}H_9NO_2$ f) $Fe_4[Fe(CN)_6]_3$

2. How many atoms of each kind make up the substances in question #1 above?

3. Fill in the blanks:

   a) 1 mol $Fe(C_2H_3O_2)_2 \cdot 4 H_2O$ = _____ mol $Fe(C_2H_3O_2)_2$ = _____ mol H_2O

   b) 1 mol $Fe(C_2H_3O_2)_2 \cdot 4 H_2O$ = _____ mol C atoms = _____ C atoms

   c) 1 mol $Fe(C_2H_3O_2)_2 \cdot 4 H_2O$ = _____ g $Fe(C_2H_3O_2)_2 \cdot 4 H_2O$ = _____ g O atoms

   d) 1 FU $Al(C_6H_5O)_3$ = ____ H atoms = _____ mol H atoms = ____ molecules $Al(C_6H_5O)_3$

   e) 1 FU K_3PO_4 = _____ amu K_3PO_4 = _____ g K_3PO_4

   f) 1 molecule $C_{12}H_9NO_2$ = _____ amu $C_{12}H_9NO_2$ = _____ C atoms

   g) 1 mol $C_{12}H_9NO_2$ = _____ molecules $C_{12}H_9NO_2$ = _____ g $C_{12}H_9NO_2$

   h) 1 SO_4^{2-} ion = _____ g SO_4^{2-} = _____ amu SO_4^{2-}

   i) 1 Na atom = _____ amu Na = _____ Na FU = _____ molecules Na

4. In 50.2 g of $InBr_2$ (FW = 274.6) how many:
   a) moles of $InBr_2$ are present,
   b) how many grams of Br are present,
   c) how many molecules of $InBr_2$ are present,
   d) how many formula units of $InBr_2$ are present?

5. What contains the greatest mass of chlorine: 5.0 g of Cl_2 or 0.10 mol KCl?

6. How many moles of O are needed to combine with 0.250 mol of C to form a) CO and b) CO_2?

7. 2 moles of cocaine weigh 606.7 g, what is the molecular weight of cocaine?

8. A 1.00 g sample of an element was found to contain 1.50 x 10^{22} atoms.
   a) What is the atomic weight of that element?
   b) What is the identity of the element?

9. Nicotine ($C_{10}H_{14}N_2$) has a molecular weight of 162.2.
   a) How many amu are present in 10 molecules of nicotine?
   b) How many grams do 10 molecules of nicotine weigh?
   c) How many C atoms are present in 10 molecules of nicotine?
   d) How many atoms of nitrogen are there in 10 molecules of nicotine?
   e) How many grams of nitrogen are present in 2 moles of nicotine?
   f) How many moles of hydrogen atoms are present in 57.0 g of nicotine?

10. A 21.08 g sample of an element Z reacted with oxygen to form 25.40 g of the compound Z_2O.
    a) What is the formula weight of Z_2O?
    b) What is the identity of Z?

Percent Composition

11. Morphine has a molecular formula of $C_{17}H_{19}NO_3$ (MW = 285.35). What is the mass percentage of each element present in morphine?

12. Calculate the percent composition for the following compound: $CoF_3 \cdot 7H_2O$ (FW = 241.9).

13. The compound papaverine (MW = 339.40) contains 70.7% C.
    a) How many grams of carbon are there in 1 mol of papaverine?
    b) How many grams of carbon are there in 3.7 mol of papaverine?

14. Provitamin A (MW = 536.90) contains only C and H. If 1 mol of provitamin A contains 480 g of carbon, what is the % H in provitamin A?

15. After prolonged heating, a 49.2 g sample of a binary ionic compound (one containing 2 elements) was broken down to its respective elements. If 30.0 g of fluorine gas were produced, what is the %F in the ionic compound?

16. 0.230 mol of a compound containing only C, H, and N weighs 30.4 g. This 30.4 g sample was found to contain 22.1 grams of C and 6.44 grams of N. Given this information,
    a) How many grams of H are in the sample?
    b) What is the percent composition of this compound?
    c) What is the molecular weight of this compound?

17. When 629. g of the hormone progesterone (containing only C, H, and O) were burned in the presence of oxygen, 1848. g of CO_2 and 540. g of H_2O were produced.
    a) How many grams of C are in the 629. g sample of progesterone?
    b) How many grams of H are in the 629. g sample of progesterone?
    c) How many grams of O are in the 629. g sample of progesterone?
    d) What is the mass percent of C in progesterone?
    e) What is the mass percent of H in progesterone?
    f) What is the mass percent of O in progesterone?

Empirical and Molecular Formulas

18. What is the empirical formula for each of the following compounds?
    a) C_6H_6 b) $Na_2S_2O_4$ c) B_2H_6 d) CH_4

19. Elemental analysis of 388.5 g of a pure compound (MW = 388.5) indicated that the compound contained 324. g of C, 48.5 g H, and 16.0 g of oxygen. (AW -- C = 12.0, H = 1.01, O = 16.0)
    a) What is the empirical formula of the compound?
    b) What is the molecular formula of the compound?

20. What is the empirical formula of a compound containining 50.8% Zn, 16.1% P, and 33.1% O.

21. Elemental analysis of a pure compound indicated that the compound had 72.2% C, 8.50% H, and 19.3% O.
    a) What is the empirical formula of the compound?
    b) If 0.250 mol of the compound weighs 41.55 g, what is the molecular formula of the compound?

22. Elemental analysis of a pure compound (containing C, H, and O) indicated that the compound had 67.3% C and 5.67% H.
    a) What is the empirical formula of the compound?
    b) Given that 1 molecule of the compound contains 6 oxygen atoms, what is the molecular formula of the compound?

23. When a 1.0 g sample of a compound containing only C and H was heated in the presence of a catalyst, it formed 0.25 g of H_2 (the only source of H in the products). What is the empirical formula of the compound?

24. When a 26.3 g sample of a compound containing only C and H was heated in the presence of a catalyst, it formed as its products 23.5 g C_2H_2 and 2.8 g of H_2. What is the empirical formula of the compound?

25. If 1.61 g of AgCl were obtained upon the addition of excess $AgNO_3$ to 0.573 g of a niobium chloride (Nb_xCl_y) compound, then find the empirical formula of the niobium chloride.

Percent Purity

26. Calculate the mass of NaCl in 15.0 g of 96.7% pure NaCl.

27. How many moles of $KClO_3$ (FW = 122.6) are there in a 1.067 g sample of 43.7% $KClO_3$?

28. Which sample contains a greater water content, a 15.0 g sample of 30.0% pure $CuSO_4 \cdot 5H_2O$ (FW = 249.7) or a 24.0 g sample of 35.0% pure $BaCl_2 \cdot 2H_2O$ (FW = 244.3)?

29. 2.754 g of a solid residue were obtained after 3.067 g of impure $CuSO_4 \cdot 5H_2O$ (FW = 249.7) was heated for 25 minutes. Given this information,

    a) What is the mass of pure $CuSO_4 \cdot 5H_2O$ in the sample?

    b) What is the %$CuSO_4 \cdot 5H_2O$ in the sample?

30. What mass of Na and O is contained in 45.2 g of 98.7% pure Na_2O (FW = 62.0)? (Assume that the impurities contain no Na or O).

MULTIPLE CHOICE PRACTICE EXAM FOR MODULE 3

1. What is the formula weight of $NiSO_4 \cdot 7H_2O$ (AW ---> Ni = 58.7, S = 32.1, O = 16.0, H = 1.0)?
    1) 155   2) 177   3) 349   4) 126   5) 281

2. Which of the following equalities is correct about the compound $H_2C_2O_4 \cdot 2H_2O$ (FW = 126.)?
    1) 1 mol $H_2C_2O_4 \cdot 2H_2O$ = 126 amu $H_2C_2O_4 \cdot 2H_2O$ = 2 mol H_2O
    2) 1 FU $H_2C_2O_4 \cdot 2H_2O$ = 126 g $H_2C_2O_4 \cdot 2H_2O$ = 4 O atoms
    3) 1 FU $H_2C_2O_4 \cdot 2H_2O$ = 126 amu $H_2C_2O_4 \cdot 2H_2O$ = 2 mol H_2O
    4) 1 FU $H_2C_2O_4 \cdot 2H_2O$ = 126 amu $H_2C_2O_4 \cdot 2H_2O$ = 2 (6.02 x 10^{23}) molecules H_2O
    5) 1 mol $H_2C_2O_4 \cdot 2H_2O$ = 126 g $H_2C_2O_4 \cdot 2H_2O$ = 2 (6.02 x 10^{23}) molecules H_2O

3. In 1 mol of K_3PO_4 there are:
    a. 3 K atoms   b. 4 mol of O atoms   c. 4(16.0) amu of O   d. 6.02 x 10^{23} K atoms
    e. 6.02 x 10^{23} K_3PO_4 FU   f. 3(39.1) g of K   g. 212 g of K_3PO_4
    1) only a and c   2) only b, e, f, and g   3) only e and g
    4) only b, d, and g   5) only d, f, and g

4. How many molecules of O_2 are in 3.21 g of O_2?
    1) 3.02 x 10^{22} 2) 1.93 x 10^{24} 3) 0.100   4) 6.04 x 10^{22} 5) 6.02 x 10^{23}

5. How many grams does one molecule of CH_4 (FW = 16.0) weigh?
    1) 16.0   2) 1.66 x 10^{-24} 3) 2.66 x 10^{-23} 4) 6.02 x 10^{23} 5) 6.25 x 10^{-2}

6. How many oxygen atoms are there in 0.139 g of K_3PO_4 (FW = 212)?
    1) 3.94 x 10^{20} 2) 1.58 x 10^{21} 3) 9.72 x 10^{20} 4) 2.61 x 10^{21} 5) 6.55 x 10^{-4}

7. How many mol of hydrogen atoms are there in 0.139 g of NH_4OH (FW = 35.0)?
    1) 3.97 x 10^{-3} 2) 1.99 x 10^{-2} 3) 9.71 x 10^{-1} 4) 1.53 x 10^3 5) 0.0348

8. 3.23 x 10^{22} atoms of an element weighs 10.0 g. Given this information, what is the identity of the element?
    1) Au   2) Ag   3) F   4) Re   5) Li

Use the following information to answer questions 9 and 10. *A 2.50 g sample of a ficticious element, T, reacted with oxygen to produce 3.27 g of TO_3.*

9. Calculate the % O in TO_3.
    1) 77.0   2) 76.5   3) 0.770   4) 52.3   5) 23.5

10. What is the FW of TO_3?
    1) 110   2) 178   3) 8.18   4) 67.9   5) 204

11. Calculate the % N in $(NH_4)_2SO_4$ (FW = 132).
    1) 5.30   2) 7.58   3) 10.6   4) 21.2   5) 37.9

12. When a 4.78 g sample of a compound containing chlorine reacted with excess silver nitrate [$AgNO_3$], 7.11 g of AgCl (FW = 143) were produced. Given this information, what is the percent composition of chlorine in the 4.78 g sample?
    1) 37.0   2) 67.2   3) 24.8   4) 47.3   5) 52.4

13. In a 162 g sample of K_2SO_4 (FW = 174), how many grams of potassium are present?
    1) 36.3   2) 72.8   3) 100   4) 78.2   5) 92.3

14. If a compound were found to contain 26.95% sulfur, 13.43% oxygen, and 59.61% chlorine, then calculate its empirical formula? (AW ---> S = 32.06, O = 16.00, Cl = 35.45)

    1) SO_2Cl_2 2) S_2OCl_2 3) S_2O_2Cl 4) SOCl   5) $SOCl_2$

15. If a 1.520 g sample of a compound containing only N and O was found to contain 0.960 g of O, then calculate its empirical formula? (AW ---> N = 14.0, O = 16.0)

    1) NO   2) NO_2 3) N_2O_3 4) N_2O 5) N_3O_2

16. If 0.120 mol of Fe, 0.360 mol of Cl, and 1.44 mol of O are present in a compound containing only these elements, then determine the empirical formula of the compound?

    1) $Fe(ClO_4)_2$ 2) $Fe(ClO_3)_2$ 3) $Fe(ClO_2)_2$ 4) $Fe(ClO_4)_3$ 5) $Fe(ClO_3)_3$

17. If the molecular weight of an unknown compound is 90.0 g/mol, then what is its molecular formula given that its empirical formula is CH_3?

    1) CH_3 2) C_3H_9 3) C_6H_{18} 4) C_7H_{21} 5) C_9H_{27}

18. How many grams of impurities are present in a 21.7 g sample of P_4O_{10} that is 96.4% pure?

    1) 0.0   2) 20.9   3) 0.4   4) 0.8   5) 10.4

Consider the following information to answer questions 19 and 20. *A 3.712 g sample of impure $BaCl_2 \cdot 2H_2O$ (FW = 244) yielded 3.304 g of a solid residue after heating.*

19. What is the mass (in grams) of pure $BaCl_2 \cdot 2H_2O$ in the sample?

    1) 1.35   2) 2.01   3) 3.16   4) 6.07   5) 2.77

20. What is the % $BaCl_2 \cdot 2H_2O$ in the sample?

    1) 36.37   2) 74.62   3) 1.340   4) 89.01   5) 85.76

Consider the following information to answer questions 21 - 23. *5.275 g of H_2O (FW = 18.02) were produced when 3.712 g of a hydrocarbon were completely burned in the presence of oxygen.*

21. How many grams of hydrogen were present in the 3.712 g sample of the hydrocarbon?

    1) 1.008   2) 0.4153   3) 2.016   4) 0.5901   5) 1.563

22. How many grams of carbon were present in the 3.712 g sample of the hydrocarbon?

    1) 12.01   2) 2.153   3) 2.016   4) 3.122   5) 1.563

23. What is the empirical formula of the hydrocarbon?

    1) C_3H_7 2) C_4H_9 3) C_5H_{11} 4) C_6H_{13} 5) C_4H_5

Consider the following information to answer questions 24 - 25. *When a 5.00 g sample of a hydrocarbon was burned completely in the presence of oxygen, 14.6 g of CO_2 (FW = 44.0) were obtained.*

24. What is the empirical formula of the hydrocarbon?

    1) CH_3 2) CH_2 3) CH_6 4) C_5H_6 5) C_3H_4

25. If one molecule of the hydrocarbon contains 12 hydrogen atoms, then what is the molecular formula of the hydrocarbon?

    1) C_4H_{12} 2) C_4H_{12} 3) C_2H_{12} 4) C_6H_{12} 5) $C_{10}H_{12}$

MODULE 3 - ANSWERS

1. a) 245.9   b) 212.3   c) 575.0   d) 306.2   e) 199.1   f) 858.6

2. a) 1(Fe), 4(C), 14(H), 8(O)   b) 3(K), 1(P), 4(O)   c) 1(Ir), 3(Te)
    d) 1(Al), 18(C), 15(H), 3(O)   e) 12(C), 9(H), 1(N), 2(O)   f) 7(Fe), 18(C), 18(N)

3. a) 1; 4   b) 4; $4(6.02 \times 10^{23})$ c) 245.9; 8(16)
    d) 15; $15/6.02 \times 10^{23}$; 0   e) 212.3; $212.3/6.02 \times 10^{23}$ f) 199.1; 12
    g) 6.02×10^{23}; 199.1   h) $96.1/6.02 \times 10^{23}$; 96.1   i) 23.0; 1; 0

4. a) 0.183 mol $InBr_2$ b) 29.2 g Br   c) 0 molecules   d) 1.10×10^{23} FU $InBr_2$

5. Cl_2

6. a) 0.250 mol O   b) 0.500 mol O

7. 303.4 g/mol

8. a) 40.1 g/mol   b) Ca

9. a) 1622 amu   b) 2.69×10^{-21} g   c) 100 C atoms   d) 20 N atoms   e) 56 g N   f) 4.92 mol H

10. a) 94.1 g/mol   b) K

11. 71.5% C, 6.72% H, 4.90% N, 16.8% O

12. 24.3% Co, 23.6%F, 5.84% H, 46.3% O

13. a) 240.0 g C   b) 888. g C

14. 10.6% H

15. 61.0% F

16. a) 1.86 g H   b) 72.7% C, 21.2% N, 6.12% H   c) 132. g/mol

17. a) 504 g C   b) 60.6 g H   c) 64.4 g O   d) 80.1% C   e) 9.63% H   f) 10.3% O

18. a) CH   b) $NaSO_2$ c) BH_3 d) CH_4

19. a) $C_{27}H_{48}O$ b) $C_{27}H_{48}O$

20. $Zn_3P_2O_8$ ---> $Zn_3(PO_4)_2$

21. a) C_5H_7O b) $C_{10}H_{14}O_2$

22. a) $C_{10}H_{10}O_3$ b) $C_{20}H_{20}O_6$

23. CH_4

24. C_2H_5

25. $NbCl_6$

26. 14.5 g NaCl

27. 3.80×10^{-3} mol $KClO_3$

28. 15.0 g of 30.0% pure $CuSO_4 \cdot 5H_2O$

29. a) 0.868 g $CuSO_4 \cdot 5H_2O$ b) 28.3% $CuSO_4 \cdot 5H_2O$

30. 33.1 g Na & 11.5 g O

MODULE 4.   *Chemical Equations and Reaction Stoichiometry*

I.   **Balancing Chemical Equations**

Chemical equations are used to describe a chemical reaction; they show the substances that react, those substances that are formed, and the relative amount of substances involved. For example,

$$\underbrace{CH_4 + 2\,O_2}_{reactants} \longrightarrow \underbrace{CO_2 + 2\,H_2O}_{products}$$

All atoms present at the start (on the left side of the chemical equation) must be there at the end (on the right side of the chemical equation).

Coefficients (other than <u>one</u>) placed in front of the each of the formulas are used to balance the equation. If no coefficient is present in front of one of the formulas of a balanced equation, then it is assumed that the coefficient is <u>one</u>.

In order to balance a chemical equation so that the same number of atoms of each element are on the left and right hand side of a chemical equation, use the following as a guide:

a) if polyatomic ions are present (on both sides of the equation), balance those as a group first,

b) balance those atoms appearing in only one of the formulas (on the same side of the equation) next,

c) save for last those atoms that appear in more than one of the formulas (on the same side of the equation),

d) if fractions need to be used, clear them up by multiplying all coefficients by the lowest common denominator.

A fraction is used if there is an odd number (other than 1) of atoms on one side of the equation and a diatomic molecule (of the same atom) on the other side of the equation (see Example 3).

e) If there are an odd number of atoms (other than 1) on one side of the equation and an even number on the other (and if those atoms appear only once in their respective side of the equation), then the coefficients will be the cross multiplication product of the subscripts (see Example 4).

In balancing chemical equations, **never change a correct chemical formula to balance an equation**.

<u>Example Problems:</u>   Balance the following chemical equations.

1. $Hg_3(PO_4)_2 + 2Al \rightarrow 2\,AlPO_4 + 3Hg$ (unbalanced)

a) Balance polyatomic ion "PO_4" first. There are two PO_4 on the left side and only one PO_4 on the right hand side of the equation; therefore, place a coefficient of 2 in front of $AlPO_4$.

The following shorthand notation will mean the same thing:

PO_4 $(2 \rightarrow 1)$ $\therefore$ $\rightarrow 2\,AlPO_4$ $Hg_3(PO_4)_2 + Al \rightarrow 2\,AlPO_4 + Hg$

b) We can either balance Hg or Al next, since both appear in only one formula on the same side of the equation. Let's pick Hg next.

Hg $(3 \rightarrow 1)$ $\therefore$ $\rightarrow 3\,Hg$ $Hg_3(PO_4)_2 + Al \rightarrow 2\,AlPO_4 + 3\,Hg$

c) Finally balance Al.

Al $(1 \rightarrow 2)$ $\therefore$ $2\,Al \rightarrow$ $Hg_3(PO_4)_2 + 2\,Al \rightarrow 2\,AlPO_4 + 3\,Hg$

2. $C_5H_{12}O_2 + 7O_2 \rightarrow 5CO_2 + 6H_2O$

Save the O for last because it appears in two formulas on the both sides of the equation.

C $(5 \rightarrow 1)$ $\therefore$ $\rightarrow 5\,CO_2$ $C_5H_{12}O_2 + O_2 \rightarrow 5\,CO_2 + H_2O$

H $(12 \rightarrow 2)$ $\therefore$ $\rightarrow 6\,H_2O$ $C_5H_{12}O_2 + O_2 \rightarrow 5\,CO_2 + 6\,H_2O$

O $(2+2 \rightarrow 16)$ $\therefore$ $7\,O_2 \rightarrow$ $C_5H_{12}O_2 + 7\,O_2 \rightarrow 5\,CO_2 + 6\,H_2O$

3. $C_4H_{10} + O_2 \rightarrow CO_2 + H_2O$

Save the O for last because it appears in two formulas on the right hand side of the equation.

C $(4 \rightarrow 1)$ $\therefore \rightarrow 4\,CO_2$ $C_4H_{10} + O_2 \rightarrow 4\,CO_2 + H_2O$

H $(10 \rightarrow 2)$ $\therefore \rightarrow 5\,H_2O$ $C_4H_{10} + O_2 \rightarrow 4\,CO_2 + 5\,H_2O$

O $(2 \rightarrow 13)$ $\therefore \frac{13}{2}\,O_2 \rightarrow$ $C_4H_{10} + \frac{13}{2}\,O_2 \rightarrow 4\,CO_2 + 5\,H_2O$

  mult. by 2 to clear up fraction: $2\,C_4H_{10} + 13\,O_2 \rightarrow 8\,CO_2 + 10\,H_2O$

4. $Pb + AuBr_3 \rightarrow PbBr_2 + Au$

Br $(3 \rightarrow 2)$ $\therefore 2\,AuBr_3 \rightarrow 3\,PbBr_2$ $Pb + 2\,AuBr_3 \rightarrow 3\,PbBr_2 + Au$

Pb $(1 \rightarrow 3)$ $\therefore 3\,Pb \rightarrow$ $3\,Pb + 2\,AuBr_3 \rightarrow 3\,PbBr_2 + Au$

Au $(2 \rightarrow 1)$ $\therefore \rightarrow 2\,Au$ $3\,Pb + 2\,AuBr_3 \rightarrow 3\,PbBr_2 + 2\,Au$

II. Reaction Stoichiometry

Stoichiometry can be defined as the quantitative relationships among elements & compounds as they undergo chemical change.

To solve stoichiometry problems you must have a correctly balanced equation.

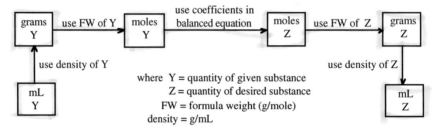

where Y = quantity of given substance
Z = quantity of desired substance
FW = formula weight (g/mole)
density = g/mL

Depending on what is given and/or asked to be solved for, each arrow in the above concept map represents a step (conversion factor) in the solution to the problem.

Example Problems:

1. Given the following balanced equation answer the following:

$$2\,C_6H_6\,(l) + 15\,O_2\,(g) \rightarrow 12\,CO_2\,(g) + 6\,H_2O\,(l)$$

FW   78.0   32.0   44.0   18.0

a) How many moles of O_2 are required to completly react with 6.0 moles of C_6H_6?

$$? \text{ mol } O_2 = 6.0 \text{ mol } C_6H_6 \left(\frac{15 \text{ mol } O_2}{2 \text{ mol } C_6H_6} \right) = 45 \text{ mol } O_2$$

b) _____grams of CO_2 will be formed from 4.0 moles of C_6H_6 reacting with exess O_2.

$$? \text{ g } CO_2 = 4.0 \text{ mol } C_6H_6 \left(\frac{12 \text{ mol } CO_2}{2 \text{ mol } C_6H_6} \right) \left(\frac{44. \text{ g } CO_2}{1 \text{ mol } CO_2} \right) = 1.1 \times 10^3 \text{ g } CO_2$$

c) How many grams of H_2O will be formed from 2.6 g of C_6H_6 reacting with excess O_2?

$$? \text{ g } H_2O = 2.6 \text{ g } C_6H_6 \left(\frac{1 \text{ mol } C_6H_6}{78. \text{ g } C_6H_6} \right) \left(\frac{6 \text{ mol } H_2O}{2 \text{ mol } C_6H_6} \right) \left(\frac{18. \text{ g } H_2O}{1 \text{ mol } H_2O} \right) = 1.8 \text{ g } H_2O$$

d) ___ g of H_2O will be formed from 5.0 mL of C_6H_6 (d = 0.874 g/mL) reacting with excess O_2.

$$? \text{ g } H_2O = 5.0 \text{ mL } C_6H_6 \left(\frac{0.874 \text{ g } C_6H_6}{1.00 \text{ mL } C_6H_6} \right) \left(\frac{1 \text{ mol } C_6H_6}{78. \text{ g } C_6H_6} \right) \left(\frac{6 \text{ mol } H_2O}{2 \text{ mol } C_6H_6} \right) \left(\frac{18. \text{ g } H_2O}{1 \text{ mol } H_2O} \right) = 3.0 \text{ g } H_2O$$

e) If 5.0 mol of O_2 are reacted with excess C_6H_6, how many molecules of CO_2 will be produced?

$$? \text{ molecules } CO_2 = 5.0 \text{ mol } O_2 \left(\frac{12 \text{ mol } CO_2}{15 \text{ mol } O_2} \right) \left(\frac{6.02 \times 10^{23} \text{ molecules } CO_2}{1 \text{ mol } CO_2} \right) = 2.4 \times 10^{24} \text{ molecules } CO_2$$

f) How many grams of C_6H_6 are needed to react with 5.00 g of 96.5% pure O_2?

First we need to find out how many grams of O_2 are in the impure sample that was used.

$$? \text{ g } O_2 = 5.00 \text{ g sample} \left(\frac{96.5 \text{ g}}{100 \text{ g sample}} \right) = 4.82 \text{ g } O_2$$

$$? \text{ g } C_6H_6 = 4.82 \text{ g } O_2 \left(\frac{1 \text{ mol } O_2}{32.0 \text{ g } O_2} \right) \left(\frac{2 \text{ mol } C_6H_6}{15 \text{ mol } O_2} \right) \left(\frac{78.1 \text{ g } C_6H_6}{1 \text{ mol } C_6H_6} \right) = 1.57 \text{ g } C_6H_6$$

III. Limiting Reagent Concept

Excess (or limiting reagent) problems are stoichiometry problems where the amounts of two (or more) reactants are given (instead of only one as seen above). The limiting reagent will be completely used and some of the excess reagent will remain after the reaction has gone to completion. This kind of problem involves doing two stoichiometry problems like those done above. You are to start with each given reagent and see how much of the one of the products is produced. *The excess reagent will always predict too much of the product. The limiting reagent is the one that predicts the smaller amount, which is the correct amount produced.* When the reaction has gone to completion, there will be no limiting reagent left and some excess reagent left unreacted.

Consider the following example:

<big>1 Chassis + 4 tires → 1 Car</big>

If 9 Chassis and 28 tires are available:

a) How many cars can be made?

Set up two stoichiometry problems starting with the initial amount of starting materials (i.e., reactants) given and see how much product (i.e., cars) is produced.

$$? \text{ cars} = 9 \text{ chassis} \left(\frac{1 \text{ car}}{1 \text{ chassis}} \right) = 9 \text{ cars}$$

$$? \text{ cars} = 28 \text{ tires} \left(\frac{1 \text{ car}}{4 \text{ tires}} \right) = 7 \text{ cars}$$

The correct number of cars that can be made is 7 (i.e., the smallest number) and not 9.

b) What is the limiting reagent and the excess reagent?

The limiting reagent is the reagent that predicts the smallest number of product produced; thus the limiting reagent is the tires and the excess reagent are the chassis.

c) How much of the limiting reagent remains unused (i.e., unreacted)?

All of the limiting reagent gets used up in the reaction; thus there are no tires remaining.

d) How much of the excess reagent was only necessary?

Start with the limiting reagent (28 tires) and solve for how much of the excess reagent (chassis) were only necessary.

$$? \text{ chassis} = 28 \text{ tires} \left(\frac{1 \text{ chassis}}{4 \text{ tires}} \right) = 7 \text{ chassis}$$

$\uparrow$

(Note, start with the amount of limiting reagent given)

e) How much of the excess reagent remains unused (i.e., unreacted)?

excess reagent unused = initial amount of excess reagent - amount of excess necessary

$$= 9 - 7$$

$$= 2 \text{ chassis remain unused}$$

The above approach can be used to solve any kind of limiting reagent problem.

Example Problems:

1. If 4.00 mol of C_6H_6 are mixed with 10.0 mol of O_2, then a) what is the limiting reagent; b) what is the excess reagent; c) at the end of the reaction how much of the limiting reagent is left; d) how many grams of H_2O will be obtained; e) how many moles of the excess reagent were actually needed (used) for the reaction; and f) how many moles of the excess reagent were left unreacted?

$$2\ C_6H_6\ _{(l)}\ +\ 15\ O_2\ _{(g)}\ \rightarrow\ 12\ CO_2\ _{(g)}\ +\ 6\ H_2O\ _{(l)}$$

- We do not know which reactant is in excess, C_6H_6 or O_2. Do two stoichiometry problems, one starting with the amount of C_6H_6 given and the other with the amount of O_2 given. The limiting reagent is the reactant that predicts the smaller amount of H_2O (product).

$$? \text{ g } H_2O = \ 4.00 \text{ mol } C_6H_6 \left(\frac{6 \text{ mol } H_2O}{2 \text{ mol } C_6H_6} \right) \left(\frac{18.0 \text{ g } H_2O}{1 \text{ mol } H_2O} \right) = 216 \text{ g } H_2O$$

$$? \text{ g } H_2O = \ 10.0 \text{ mol } O_2 \left(\frac{6 \text{ mol } H_2O}{15 \text{ mol } O_2} \right) \left(\frac{18.0 \text{ g } H_2O}{1 \text{ mol } H_2O} \right) = 72.0 \text{ g } H_2O$$

a) Limiting Reagent --> O_2

b) Excess Reagent ---> C_6H_6

c) 0 g O_2 (0 mol O_2)

d) 72.0 g H_2O

e) $? \text{ mol } C_6H_6 \text{ used} = 10.0 \text{ mol } O_2 \left(\frac{2 \text{ mol } C_6H_6}{15 \text{ mol } O_2} \right) = 1.33 \text{ mol } C_6H_6$ were only needed

↑

(Note, start with the amount of limiting reagent given)

f) mol C_6H_6 left = mol C_6H_6 initial - mol C_6H_6 used = 4.00 mol - 1.33 mol = 2.67 mol C_6H_6

2. If 125. g of copper are mixed with 100. g of selenium, then a) what is the limiting reagent; b) what is the excess reagent; c) at the end of the reaction how much of the limiting reagent is left; d) how many grams of Cu_2Se are obtained; e) how many grams of the excess reagent were actually needed for the reaction; and f) how many grams of the excess reagent were left unreacted?

$$2\ Cu\ _{(s)} +\ Se\ _{(s)} \rightarrow\ Cu_2Se\ _{(s)}$$

- We do not know which reactant is in excess, copper or selenium. Do two stoichiometry problems, one starting with the amount of copper given and the other with the amount of selenium given. The limiting reagent is the reactant that predicts the smaller amount of Cu_2Se (product).

$$? \text{ g } Cu_2Se = 125. \text{ g } Cu \left(\frac{1 \text{ mol } Cu}{63.5 \text{ g } Cu} \right) \left(\frac{1 \text{ mol } Cu_2Se}{2 \text{ mol } Cu} \right) \left(\frac{206 \text{ g } Cu_2Se}{1 \text{ mol } Cu_2Se} \right) = 203 \text{ g } Cu_2Se$$

$$? \text{ g } Cu_2Se = 100. \text{ g } Se \left(\frac{1 \text{ mol } Se}{79.0 \text{ g } Se} \right) \left(\frac{1 \text{ mol } Cu_2Se}{1 \text{ mol } Se} \right) \left(\frac{206 \text{ g } Cu_2Se}{1 \text{ mol } Cu_2Se} \right) = 261 \text{ g } Cu_2Se$$

a) Limiting Reagent --> Cu

b) Excess Reagent ---> Se

c) 0 g Cu (0 mol Cu)

d) 203 g Cu_2Se

e) ? g Se used = 125 g Cu $\left(\dfrac{1 \text{ mol Cu}}{63.5 \text{ g Cu}}\right)\left(\dfrac{1 \text{ mol Se}}{2 \text{ mol Cu}}\right)\left(\dfrac{79.0 \text{ g Se}}{1 \text{ mol Se}}\right)$ = 77.8 g Se

$\uparrow$

(Note, start with the amount of limiting reagent given)

f) g Se left = g Se initial - g Se used = 100. g - 77.8 g = 22. g Se

IV. Percent Yields from Chemical Reactions

For several reasons, the product yield is less than expected. There are several explanations: a) the reaction does not go to completion (i.e., the reactants are not completely converted to products); b) a reaction other than the one desired (side reactions) also occurs; and/or c) the separation of the desired product is so difficult that all of the product formed can't be successfully isolated. Taking all these factors into consideration, the term percent yield is used to indicate how much of the desired product was actually obtained from a reaction.

$$\% \text{ Yield} = \frac{\text{actual yield}}{\text{theoretical yield}} \text{ x } 100$$

actual yield - amount of specified product actually obtained in the reaction.

theoretical yield - the yield that is calculated assuming that the reaction has gone to 100% completion, no side reactions have taken place, and complete product isolation has occurred.

Example Problems:

1. Considier the following balanced chemical equation:

$$2 \text{ } C_6H_6 \text{ } (l) + 15 \text{ } O_2 \text{ } (g) \rightarrow 12 \text{ } CO_2 \text{ } (g) + 6 \text{ } H_2O \text{ } (l)$$

a) If a 2.6 g sample of C_6H_6 reacted with excess O_2 to produce 1.0 g of water, then what is the percent yield of water in this reaction?

theo. yield -> ? g H_2O = 2.6 g C_6H_6 $\left(\dfrac{1 \text{ mol } C_6H_6}{78. \text{ g } C_6H_6}\right)\left(\dfrac{6 \text{ mol } H_2O}{2 \text{ mol } C_6H_6}\right)\left(\dfrac{18. \text{ g } H_2O}{1 \text{ mol } H_2O}\right)$ = 1.8 g H_2O

actual yield --> 1.0 g

$$\% \text{ Yield} = \frac{\text{actual yield}}{\text{theoretical yield}} \text{ x } 100 = \frac{1.0 \text{ g}}{1.8 \text{ g}} \text{ x } 100\% = 56\%$$

b) If the above reaction only went to 75% completion (i.e., the reaction yielded only 75% of the theoretical yield), then how many moles of CO_2 would be produced if 2.0 moles of C_6H_6 were reacted with excess oxygen?

theo. yield ---> ? mol CO_2 = 2.0 mol C_6H_6 $\left(\dfrac{12 \text{ mol } CO_2}{2 \text{ mol } C_6H_6}\right)$ = 12. mol CO_2

$\% \text{ Yield} = \dfrac{\text{actual yield}}{\text{theo. yield}} \text{ x } 100 ---> 75\% = \dfrac{\text{actual yield}}{12.} \text{ x } 100 ---> \text{ actual yield} = \dfrac{75 \text{ x } 12}{100} = 9.0 \text{ mol}$

2. When 3.0 mol of Li were reacted with 2.0 mol of Cl_2, 2.6 mol of LiCl were obtained. What is the percent yield?

$$2 \text{ Li } (s) + Cl_2 \text{ } (g) \rightarrow 2 \text{ LiCl } (s)$$

Since this is also a limiting reagent problem, the theoretical yield of LiCl will be the smallest amount of it that is produced.

$$? \text{ mol LiCl} = 3.0 \text{ mol Li} \left(\frac{2 \text{ mol LiCl}}{2 \text{ mol Li}}\right) = 3.0 \text{ mol LiCl}$$

$$? \text{ mol LiCl} = 2.0 \text{ mol Cl}_2 \left(\frac{2 \text{ mol LiCl}}{1 \text{ mol Cl}_2}\right) = 4.0 \text{ mol LiCl}$$

The theoretical yield of LiCl is 3.0 mol, the one predicted by the limiting reagent, Li.

$$\% \text{ Yield} = \frac{\text{actual yield}}{\text{theoretical yield}} \times 100 = \frac{2.6 \text{ mol}}{3.0 \text{ mol}} \times 100\% = 87\%$$

V. Concentration of Solutions

The concentration of a solution basically tells us how much solute is present in a given amount of solution. The concentration units of molarity (M), percent by weight (wt %), and normality (N) will be discussed in this section.

Solution - A homogeneous mixture which is composed of two or more pure substances; within certain limits, its composition can be varied.

Solvent - The component of a solution in greatest proportion, the substance that does all the dissolving. (Unless otherwise noted, the solvent will be water).

Solute - The component(s) of a solution that is in lesser quantity (i.e., all substances, except the solvent, in a solution). The substance or substances that are dissolved.

Example Problem: A solution contains 5 g of $HC_2H_3O_2$, 10 g of CH_3OH, and 75 g of CH_3CH_2OH. What is the solvent, solute(s)?

Solvent: CH_3CH_2OH Solutes: $HC_2H_3O_2$ and CH_3OH

A. Molarity, M (Molar Concentration)

$$M = \frac{\text{moles of solute (mol)}}{\text{liter of solution (L)}} \qquad \overset{(g/FW)}{-----{>}} \qquad \text{mol}_{(solute)} = M \times L$$

Molarity can be used as a factor that can be used to convert between mol and L or mL. For example, a 2.7 M NaOH solution yields the following equalities:

2.7 mol NaOH = 1 L NaOH solution = 1000 mL NaOH solution

When a solute is enclosed in brackets -- [NaOH] -- this is equivalent to saying concentration (molarity) of NaOH.
Example Problems:

1. How many moles of HCl are there in 75.0 mL of a 1.25 M HCl solution?

$$? \text{ mol HCl} = 75.0 \text{ mL HCl soln} \left(\frac{1.25 \text{ mol HCl}}{1000 \text{ HCl mL soln}}\right) = 0.0938 \text{ mol HCl}$$

2. What is the molarity of a solution prepared with 60.0 g of $CaBr_2$ (FW = 200) in 550 mL solution?

$$M = \frac{\text{mol CaBr}_2}{\text{L soln}} = \frac{60.0 \text{ g of CaBr}_2 \left(\frac{1 \text{ mol CaBr}_2}{200 \text{ g CaBr}_2}\right)}{550 \text{ mL soln} \left(\frac{10^{-3} \text{ L}}{1 \text{ mL}}\right)} = 0.545 \text{ M}$$

3. How many grams of $CaBr_2$ (FW = 200.) are needed to prepare 100 mL of a 2.00 M solution?

$$? \text{ g } CaBr_2 = 100. \text{ mL } CaBr_2 \text{ soln} \left(\frac{2.00 \text{ mol } CaBr_2}{1000 \text{ } CaBr_2 \text{ mL soln}}\right)\left(\frac{200. \text{ g } CaBr_2}{1 \text{ mol } CaBr_2}\right) = 40.0 \text{ g } CaBr_2$$

B. Percent by Mass or Weight Percent (wt %)

$$\text{wt \%} = \frac{\text{solute weight}}{\text{solution weight}} \text{ x 100} \qquad \text{where --> soln wt = wt of solute(s) + wt of solvent}$$

Weight Percent can be used as a factor that can be used to convert between grams solute and grams of solution or grams of solvent. For example, a 20.0 wt % NaOH solution yields the following equalities:

$$20.0 \text{ g NaOH} = 100 \text{ g solution} = 80.0 \text{ g solvent}$$

Example Problems:

1. What is the weight percent of solute in a solution containing 35.0 g NaCl in 150 mL of H_2O? (d_{water} = 1.00 g/mL)

   solute wt. (NaCl) = 35.0 g

   $$\text{soln wt.} = \text{g NaCl} + \text{g } H_2O = 35.0 \text{ g NaCl} + \left(150 \text{ mL } H_2O \text{ x } \frac{1.00 \text{ g}}{1 \text{ mL}}\right) = 185 \text{ g solution}$$

   $$\text{wt \%} = \frac{\text{solute weight}}{\text{solution weight}} \text{ x 100} = \frac{35.0 \text{ g NaCl}}{185 \text{ g solution}} \text{ x 100} = 18.9\% \text{ NaCl}$$

2. Calculate the mass of $NiSO_4$ contained in 250. grams of a 3.50 wt % solution of $NiSO_4$?

   $$? \text{ g } NiSO_4 = 250. \text{ g soln} \left(\frac{3.50 \text{ g } NiSO_4}{100 \text{ g soln}}\right) = 8.75 \text{ g } NiSO_4$$

3. How many grams of LiCl must be added to 20.0 g of water to prepare a 12.0 wt % solution of LiCl?

   $$12.0 \text{ g LiCl} = 100 \text{ g soln} = 88.0 \text{ g of } H_2O$$

   $$? \text{ g LiCl} = 20.0 \text{ g } H_2O \left(\frac{12.0 \text{ g LiCl}}{88.0 \text{ g } H_2O}\right) = 2.73 \text{ g LiCl}$$

4. If a patient is intervaneously given 995. mL of a 5.00 wt % glucose solution, whose density is 1.10 g/mL, then how many grams of glucose has the patient consumed?

   $$? \text{ g glucose} = 995. \text{ mL soln} \left(\frac{1.10 \text{ g soln}}{1 \text{ mL soln}}\right)\left(\frac{5.00 \text{ g glucose}}{100 \text{ g soln}}\right) = 54.7 \text{ glucose}$$
   $$\qquad\qquad\qquad\qquad\qquad\quad \uparrow \qquad\qquad\qquad \uparrow$$
   $$\qquad\qquad\qquad\qquad\quad \text{density} \qquad\qquad \text{wt \%}$$

C. Normality, N (Normal Concentration)

$$N = \frac{\text{equivalent of solute (eq)}}{\text{liter of solution (L)}} \qquad \text{eq = n x mol} \qquad \text{(n and eq are defined below)}$$

where the definition of *eq* and *n* is dependent on whether the substance is an acid, base, or is undergoing a redox reaction. We will only concentrate our attention on acids (substances that have an H in front of their formula, except H_2O and H_2O_2) and bases (**ionic** compounds that have OH at the end of their formula). The following are "working" definitions of *eq* and *n*..

   for acids, n = # of H present

   for example, 1 mol $HC_2H_3O_2$ = 1 eq $HC_2H_3O_2$ \qquad 1 mol H_2SO_4 = 2 eq H_2SO_4

for bases, n = # of OH present

for example, 1 mol NaOH = 1 eq NaOH   1 mol Fe(OH)$_3$ = 3 eq Fe(OH)$_3$

Normality can be used as a factor that can be used to convert between eq of solute and L or mL of solution or mol of solute. For example, a 1.50 N Ba(OH)$_2$ solution yields the following equalities:

$$1.50 \text{ eq Ba(OH)}_2 = 1 \text{ L Ba(OH)}_2 \text{ soln} = 1000 \text{ mL Ba(OH)}_2 \text{ soln} = \frac{1.50}{2} \text{ mol Ba(OH)}_2$$

An equivalent of an acid is the mass [i.e., equivalent weight (EW)] that will exactly react with an equivalent of a base. *Equivalent Weight* (units -- g/eq) is defined as:

$$EW = \frac{FW \text{ (g/mol)}}{n \text{ (eq/mol)}} \qquad \text{units for EW} = \frac{g}{eq}$$

Taking all the above definitions of equivalents into account, we can come up with the following relationships definitions for eq:

$$eq = N \times L = \frac{g}{EW} = n \times mol$$

Example Problems:

1. What is the normality of a solution prepared by dissolving 3.7 mol of H$_2$SO$_4$ in enough water to make 5000. mL of solution?

$$N = \frac{\text{eq H}_2\text{SO}_4}{\text{L soln}} = \frac{3.7 \text{ mol H}_2\text{SO}_4 \left(\dfrac{2 \text{ eq H}_2\text{SO}_4}{1 \text{ mol H}_2\text{SO}_4} \right)}{5000. \text{ mL soln} \left(\dfrac{10^{-3} \text{ L}}{1 \text{ mL}} \right)} = 1.48 \text{ N}$$

2. What is the equivalent weight for each of the following substances?

   a) H$_2$SO$_4$ (FW = 98.1) -- assume that both hydrogens are undergoing a reaction.

$$EW = \frac{FW \text{ (g/mol)}}{n \text{ (eq/mol)}} = \frac{98.1}{2} = 49.0 \text{ g/eq}$$

   b) Fe(OH)$_3$ (FW = 106.8) -- assume that all "OH" are undergoing a reaction.

$$EW = \frac{FW \text{ (g/mol)}}{n \text{ (eq/mol)}} = \frac{106.8}{3} = 35.6 \text{ g/eq}$$

3. What volume, in L, of solution is required to make a 0.120 N Sr(OH)$_2$ (FW = 122.) solution from 20.0 g of pure Sr(OH)$_2$?

$$? \text{ L Sr(OH)}_2 = 20.0 \text{ g Sr(OH)}_2 \left(\frac{1 \text{ mol Sr(OH)}_2}{122. \text{ g Sr(OH)}_2} \right) \left(\frac{2 \text{ eq Sr(OH)}_2}{1 \text{ mol Sr(OH)}_2} \right) \left(\frac{1 \text{ L Sr(OH)}_2 \text{ soln}}{0.120 \text{ eq Sr(OH)}_2} \right) = 2.73 \text{ L}$$

D. Interconversion Between Concentration Units

In order to interconvert between Molarity & wt. % or vice-versa, the density or specific gravity of the solution must be known.

Example Problems:

1. Commerical sulfuric acid is 96.4% H$_2$SO$_4$ (FW = 98.1) by weight, and its specific gravity is 1.84. Calculate the molarity of commerical sulfuric acid?

$$\text{specific gravity is numerically equal to density} \dashrightarrow \frac{1.84 \text{ g soln}}{1 \text{ mL soln}}$$

$$96.4\% \ H_2SO_4 \ = \ \frac{96.4 \text{ g } H_2SO_4}{100 \text{ g soln}} \quad ----> \quad ? \ M \ = \ \frac{\text{mol } H_2SO_4}{\text{L soln}}$$

$$? \frac{\text{mol } H_2SO_4}{\text{L soln}} \ = \ \frac{96.4 \text{ g } H_2SO_4 \left(\dfrac{1 \text{ mol } H_2SO_4}{98.1 \text{ g } H_2SO_4} \right)}{100 \text{ g soln} \left(\dfrac{1 \text{ mL soln}}{1.84 \text{ g soln}} \right) \left(\dfrac{10^{-3} \text{ L soln}}{1 \text{ mL soln}} \right)} \ = \ 18.1 \ M$$

2. What is the weight percent of a solution that is 14.7 M H_3PO_4 (FW = 98.0) and has a specific gravity of 1.70?

specific gravity is numerically equal to density $--->$ $\dfrac{1.70 \text{ g soln}}{1 \text{ mL soln}}$

$$14.7 \ M \ H_3PO_4 = \frac{14.7 \text{ mol } H_3PO_4}{1 \text{ L soln}} = \frac{14.7 \text{ mol } H_3PO_4}{1000 \text{ mL soln}} \quad ---> ? \text{ wt } \% = \frac{\text{g } H_3PO_4}{\text{soln wt}} \text{ x } 100\%$$

$$? \frac{\text{g } H_3PO_4}{\text{soln wt}} \ = \ \frac{14.7 \text{ mol } H_3PO_4 \left(\dfrac{98.0 \text{ g } H_3PO_4}{1 \text{ mol } H_3PO_4} \right)}{1000 \text{ mL soln} \left(\dfrac{1.70 \text{ g soln}}{1 \text{ mL soln}} \right)} \ = \ 0.847$$

wt % = 0.847 x 100 = 84.7%

Interconversion between Molarity and Normality is accomplished by using the following formula:

$$N = n \text{ x } M$$

<u>Example Problem:</u>

1. What is the normality of a solution that is 14.7 M H_3PO_4 (FW = 98.0)?

   N = n x M = 3 (eq/mol) x 14.7 (mol/L) = 44.1 eq/L = 44.1 N

2. What is the molarity of a solution that is 6 N $Mg(OH)_2$ (FW = 58.3)?

   $N = n \text{ x } M ---> 6 \text{ (eq/L)} = 2 \text{ (eq/mol) x } M ----> M = \dfrac{6 \text{ eq/L}}{2 \text{ eq/mol}} = 3 \dfrac{\text{mol}}{\text{L}} = 3 \ M$

VI. Dilution of Solutions

Solutions are often prepared by diluting a more concentrated solution rather than by weighing out the pure solute. The following handy equations can be used for dilution problems:

$$V_1 \text{ x } C_1 \ = \ V_2 \text{ x } C_2$$

where, C = any concentration unit (M, N, %, can be used as long as they are consistent of both sides of the equation)
   V = volume (any unit of volume can be used as long as they are consistent on both sides of the equation)

<u>Example Problems:</u>

1. How would 400. mL of a 3.00 M solution of acetic acid be prepared from a bottle of 1.00 M acetic acid solution?

   A dilute solution (1.00 M) cannot be used to prepare a concentrated solution (3.00 M).

2. How many mL of a 10.0 M acetic acid solution would be required to prepare 400. mL of a 2.5 M acetic acid solution?

   $V_1 \text{ x } C_1 = V_2 \text{ x } C_2 \quad -----> \quad V_1 (10.0 \text{ M}) = (400. \text{ mL}) (2.5 \text{ M})$

$$V_1 = \frac{2.5 \times 400.}{10.0} = 100 \text{ mL of acetic acid}$$

3. How many mL of water must be added to a 6.00 M HCl solution in order to prepare 600. mL of a 2.00 M HCl solution? [Assume that the volumes are additive.]

$$V_1 \cdot C_1 = V_2 \cdot C_2 \longrightarrow (600. \text{ mL}) (2.00 \text{ M}) = V_2 (6.00 \text{ M})$$

$$V_2 = \frac{2.00 \times 600.}{6.00} = 200. \text{ mL of 6.00 M solution}$$

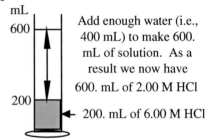

To make this solution, you need to take 200. mL of 6.00 M HCl then add **400 mL water** (i.e., 600 - 200).   As a result you will have 600 mL of a 2.00 M solution.

VII. Quantitative Analysis Involving Solution Stoichiometry

Quantitative Analysis - the analytical procedure that deals with the determination of the amount or concentration of a substance in a sample. There are two types of quantitative analysis that we will be dealing with,

Gravimetric Analysis - an analytical procedure that involves the measurement of mass. One type of gravimetric analysis experiment involves the formation, isolation, and mass determination of a precipitate obtained through a precipitation reaction.

Volumetric Analysis - an analytical procedure involving titration. One type of volumetric analysis involves the reaction of an acid [i.e., a substance that contains an H in front of its formula (except: H_2O and H_2O_2)] with a base [i.e., an ionic substance that contains an OH at the end of its formula] via a titration which involves the gradual addition of an acid of known concentration (called a **standard solution**) to a base of unknown concentration until the chemical reaction is complete (i.e., the **equivalence point**). Note, the converse can be said for a reaction involving a base of known concentration reacting with an acid of unknown concentration. The **equivalence point** (the point in which the acid completely reacts with (i.e., neutralizes) the base) is usually signalled by a sharp color change of an **indicator** (a substance that has distinctly different colors in acidic and basic media) that has been added to the solution.

One of following pathways will be normally used when dealing with problems involving solution stoichiometry using the Mole Method and Molarity.

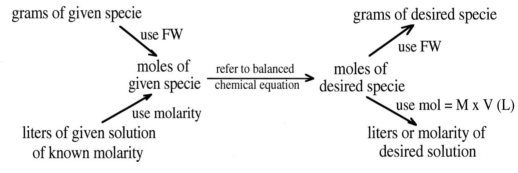

When dealing with problems involving acid-base titrations, the equivalents and normality Method can be used. This method was devised to simplify calculations in chemical analyses so as to retain a one-to-one relationship between the acids and bases. The main utility of this method is when either an unknown acid or base is present; thus, a balanced chemical equation is not available. However, we know that:

$$eq_{acid} = eq_{base}$$

And one of the following expanded equations can be used to solve problems:

$$N_{acid} \times V_{acid} = N_{base} \times V_{base}$$ -->   This equation is used when both reactants are used as aqueous solutions

$$N_{reactant\ 1} \times L_{reactant\ 1} = \frac{g_{reactant\ 2}}{EW_{reactant\ 2}}$$ -->   This equation is used when one reactant is in solution and the other is not in solution (i.e., is weighed out)

Example Problems:

1. How many grams of MgI_2 (FW = 278) are needed to completely react with a 100. mL of a 0.250 M $AgNO_3$ solution?

$$MgI_2 + 2\ AgNO_3 \rightarrow Mg(NO_3)_2 + 2\ AgI$$

$$?\ g\ MgI_2 = 100.\ mL\ AgNO_3 \left(\frac{0.250\ mol\ AgNO_3}{1000.\ mL\ AgNO_3}\right)\left(\frac{1\ mol\ MgI_2}{2\ mol\ AgNO_3}\right)\left(\frac{278\ g\ MgI_2}{1\ mol\ MgI_2}\right) = 3.48\ g$$

2. What is the molarity of a NaOH solution of unknown concentration, if 0.0800 L of it was required to completely react with 0.0400 L of 0.505 M H_2SO_4 according to the following balanced acid-base reaction:

$$H_2SO_4 + 2\ NaOH \rightarrow Na_2SO_4 + 2\ H_2O$$

$$?\ mol\ NaOH = 0.0400\ L\ H_2SO_4 \left(\frac{0.505\ mol\ H_2SO_4}{1\ L\ H_2SO_4}\right)\left(\frac{2\ mol\ NaOH}{1\ mol\ H_2SO_4}\right) = 0.0404$$

$$M = \frac{mol\ NaOH}{L\ soln} = \frac{0.0404\ mol\ NaOH}{0.0800\ L} = 0.505\ M$$

3. Find the volume (in L) of 0.505 M NaOH solution required to react with 40.0 mL of 0.505 M H_2SO_4 according to the reaction:

$$H_2SO_4 + 2\ NaOH \rightarrow Na_2SO_4 + 2\ H_2O$$

$$?\ L\ NaOH = 40.0\ mL\ H_2SO_4\ soln \left(\frac{0.505\ mol\ H_2SO_4}{1000.\ mL\ H_2SO_4\ soln}\right)\left(\frac{2\ mol\ NaOH}{1\ mol\ H_2SO_4}\right)\left(\frac{1\ L\ NaOH\ soln}{0.505\ mol\ NaOH}\right) = 0.0800\ L$$

4. What volume (in mL) of a 2.00 M solution of H_2SO_4 is required to react with 50.0 g $MgCO_3$, according to the following equation: $H_2SO_4 + MgCO_3 \rightarrow MgSO_4 + CO_2 + H_2O$?

$$?\ mL\ H_2SO_4 = 50.0\ g\ MgCO_3 \left(\frac{1\ mol\ MgCO_3}{84.3\ g\ MgCO_3}\right)\left(\frac{1\ mol\ H_2SO_4}{1\ mol\ MgCO_3}\right)\left(\frac{1000\ mL\ H_2SO_4\ soln}{2.00\ mol\ H_2SO_4}\right) = 296.\ mL$$

5. If 0.296 L of a 2.00 M solution of H_2SO_4 is reacted with 60.0 g of $MgCO_3$ (FW = 84.3), then how many grams of $MgSO_4$ (FW = 120.4) are produced?

$$H_2SO_4 + MgCO_3 \rightarrow MgSO_4 + CO_2 + H_2O$$

Since the amount used of both reactants is given, this is a limiting reagent problem. The limiting reagent is the one that predicts the least amount of product ($MgSO_4$) produced.

$$?\ g\ MgSO_4 = 0.296\ L\ H_2SO_4 \left(\frac{2.00\ mol\ H_2SO_4}{1\ L\ H_2SO_4}\right)\left(\frac{1\ mol\ MgSO_4}{1\ mol\ H_2SO_4}\right)\left(\frac{120.4\ g\ MgSO_4}{1\ mol\ MgSO_4}\right) = 71.4\ g$$

$$?\ g\ MgSO_4 = 60.0\ g\ MgCO_3 \left(\frac{1\ mol\ MgCO_3}{84.3\ g\ MgCO_3}\right)\left(\frac{1\ mol\ MgSO_4}{1\ mol\ MgCO_3}\right)\left(\frac{120.4\ g\ MgSO_4}{1\ mol\ MgSO_4}\right) = 85.7\ g\ MgSO_4$$

H_2SO_4 is the limiting reagent, therefore, 71.4 g of $MgSO_4$ are produced.

6. If 100. mL of 1.00 M NaOH are mixed with 120. mL of 1.00 M HCl, then what is the molarity of the resulting solutions?

$$NaOH \; + \; HCl \; \rightarrow \; NaCl \; + \; H_2O$$

Since the amount used of both reactants is given, this is a limiting reagent problem. The limiting reagent is the one that predicts the least amount of product (i.e., NaCl or H_2O) produced.

$$? \text{ mol NaCl} = 100. \text{ mL NaOH soln} \left(\frac{1.00 \text{ mol NaOH}}{1000 \text{ mL NaOH soln}} \right) \left(\frac{1 \text{ mol NaCl}}{1 \text{ mol NaOH}} \right) = 0.100 \text{ mol NaCl}$$

$$? \text{ mol NaCl} = 120. \text{ mL HCl soln} \left(\frac{1.00 \text{ mol HCl}}{1000 \text{ mL HCl soln}} \right) \left(\frac{1 \text{ mol NaCl}}{1 \text{ mol HCl}} \right) = 0.120 \text{ mol NaCl}$$

NaOH is the limiting reagent, therefore, 0.100 mol of NaCl is formed. There are two solutes remaining in solution -- NaCl and excess HCl. To find the number of moles of HCl that reacted (i.e., that were needed), we start with the starting amount of limiting reagent.

$$? \text{ mol HCl needed} = 100. \text{ mL NaOH soln} \left(\frac{1.00 \text{ mol NaOH}}{1000 \text{ mL NaOH soln}} \right) \left(\frac{1 \text{ mol HCl}}{1 \text{ mol NaOH}} \right) = 0.100 \text{ mol}$$

The moles of HCl that are left unreacted: initial moles - needed moles

$$? \text{ mol HCl left} = \left(120. \text{ mL HCl soln} \left(\frac{1.00 \text{ mol HCl}}{1000 \text{ mL HCl soln}} \right) \right) - \; 0.100 \; = \; 0.020 \text{ mol}$$

The molarity of the solutes in the resulting 220 mL of solution (100 mL + 120 mL) is:

$$M_{NaCl} = \frac{0.100 \text{ mol NaCl}}{0.220 \text{ L soln}} = 0.455 \text{ M} \qquad \qquad M_{HCl} = \frac{0.020 \text{ mol NaCl}}{0.220 \text{ L soln}} = 0.091 \text{ M}$$

7. If 39.2 mL of a 0.125 N solution of NaOH is required to titrate 1.00 g of an unknown solid acid, then:

a) What is the equivalent weight of the acid?

We will use the following relationship for the base: eq = N x L since both N & L are given. For the acid we will use the following relationship: eq = g/EW since g was given and we were asked to solve for EW. We thus have the following:

$$\frac{g_{acid}}{EW_{acid}} \; = \; N_{NaOH} \; \text{x} \; L_{NaOH}$$

$$\frac{1.00 \text{ g}}{EW} \; = \; \left(0.125 \; \frac{\text{eq}}{\text{L}} \right) (0.0392 \text{ L}) \; ----> \; EW = \frac{1.00}{0.125 \text{ x } 0.0392} = 204 \; \frac{\text{g}}{\text{eq}}$$

b) If the unknown acid was a diprotic acid, then what is its formula weight?

diprotic acid ---> H_2X thus n = 2

$$EW \; = \; \frac{FW \text{ (g/mol)}}{n \text{ (eq/mol)}} \; ---> \; 204 \; \frac{\text{g}}{\text{eq}} = \frac{FW}{2 \; \frac{\text{eq}}{\text{mol}}} \; ----> \; FW = 204 \text{ x } 2 = 408 \; \frac{\text{g}}{\text{mol}}$$

EXERCISES

Balancing Equations

1. Balance the following chemical equations.

   a) $Pb(NO_3)_2$ + $NaOH$ → $Pb(OH)_2$ + $NaNO_3$

   b) $Na_2S_2O_3$ + I_2 → $Na_2S_4O_6$ + NaI

   c) K + H_2O → KOH + H_2

   d) C_7H_{12} + O_2 → CO_2 + H_2O

   e) $BaCl_2$ + Na_2SO_4 → $NaCl$ + $BaSO_4$

   f) O_2 → O_3

   g) V + S_8 → V_2S_3

   h) $C_3H_6O_2$ + O_2 → CO_2 + H_2O

   i) Fe_2O_3 + C → Fe_3O_4 + CO

   j) P_4 + H_2 → PH_3

   k) C_2H_6 + O_2 → CO_2 + H_2O

   l) MgI_2 + $AgNO_3$ → $Mg(NO_3)_2$ + AgI

2. When the following equations are balanced, what is the sum of all the coefficients.

   a) Al + $MnCl_2$ → Mn + $AlCl_3$

   b) $NaOH$ + HCl → $NaCl$ + H_2O

   c) CO + H_2 → CH_3OH

   d) C_4H_{10} → C_2H_2 + H_2

   e) $Al(OH)_3$ → Al_2O_3 + H_2O

   f) Na_3PO_4 + $FeCl_2$ → $NaCl$ + $Fe_3(PO_4)_2$

Reaction Stoichiometry

3. For each of the following balanced equations, answer the following questions. (Assume that each reaction has gone to 100% completion.)

   A. $2\,Li$ + $MgCl_2$ → $2\,LiCl$ + Mg

   B. $2\,Al$ + $3\,NiCl_2$ → $3\,Ni$ + $2\,AlCl_3$

   C. CH_4 + $4\,Cl_2$ → CCl_4 + $4\,HCl$

   a) If 3.00 mol of the first reactant listed is used, then how many moles of each product will be produced?

   b) If 5.00 g of the second reactant listed is used, then how many moles of each product will be produced?

   c) If 3.00 g of the first reactant listed is used, then how many grams of each product will be produced?

   d) How many mol of the second reactant are needed to completely react with 2.00 mol of the first reactant listed?

4. Given the following unbalanced equation, answer the following questions. (Assume that the reaction has gone to 100% completion.)

$$H_2\,(g) + CO\,(g) → CH_3OH\,(l) \qquad (unbalanced)$$

	H_2	CO	CH_3OH
FW	2.02	28.0	32.0

a) If 1.30 mol of H_2 are reacted with excess CO, then how many mol of CH_3OH are produced?

b) If 4.50 g of CO are reacted with excess H_2, then how many grams of CH_3OH are produced?

c) If 4.50 g of H_2 are reacted with excess CO, then how many mL of CH_3OH (d = 0.791 g/mL) are produced?

d) If 7.50 mol of CO are reacted with excess H_2, then how many molecules of CH_3OH are produced?

e) If 5.00 g of CH_3OH were produced, what quantity (in g) of each reactant must have been originally used?

f) If 5.00 mL of CH_3OH (d = 0.791 g/mL) were produced, what quantity (in g) of each reactant must have been originally used?

g) If a 6.00 g sample of 97.0% pure H_2 was reacted with excess CO, then how many moles of CH_3OH are produced?

h) How many grams of H_2 are needed to completely react with 4.00 mol of CO?

i) How many grams of CO are needed to completely react with 10.0 g of H_2?

5. Given the following unbalanced chemical reaction, answer the following questions. (Assume that the reaction has gone to 100% completion.)

$$KClO_3 \xrightarrow{\Delta} KCl + O_2 \quad \text{(unbalanced)}$$

FW	122.		74.6	32.0

a) How many grams of $KClO_3$ would be required to produce 10.0 g of O_2?

b) If 10.0 g of $KClO_3$ are heated, then how many grams of O_2 are produced?

c) If a 10.0 g sample of 79.0% pure $KClO_3$ are heated, then how many grams of O_2 are produced?

d) If 10.0 g of $KClO_3$ are heated, how many formula units of KCl will be produced?

e) If 5.00 mol of $KClO_3$ are heated, how many O atoms will be produced?

Limiting Reagent Concept

6. For each of the following balanced equations, answer the following questions. (Assume that each reaction has gone to 100% completion.)

   A. $2 Li + MgCl_2 \rightarrow 2 LiCl + Mg$

   B. $2 Al + 3 NiCl_2 \rightarrow 3 Ni + 2 AlCl_3$

   C. $CH_4 + 4 Cl_2 \rightarrow CCl_4 + 4 HCl$

a) If 2.50 mol of each reactant are used in the reaction, which is the limiting reagent?

b) If 2.50 mol of each reactant are used in the reaction, then how many moles of each product are obtained?

c) If 2.50 mol of each reactant are used in the reaction, then how many moles of excess reagent are left unreacted?

d) If 2.00 g of each reactant are used in the reaction, which is the limiting reagent?

e) If 2.00 g of each reactant are used in the reaction, then how many grams of each product are obtained?

f) If 2.00 g of each reactant are used in the reaction, then how many grams of excess reagent are left unreacted?

7. Assuming the following reaction has gone to 100% completion, if 5.00 g of H_2 are reacted with 3.00 g of 96.5% pure CO, then

$$H_2 \, (g) + CO \, (g) \rightarrow CH_3OH \, (l) \quad \text{(unbalanced)}$$

FW	2.02	28.0	32.0

a) Which is the limiting reagent?
b) How many grams of product are obtained?
c) How many mL of CH_3OH (d = 0.791 g/mL) will be obtained?
d) How many grams of the limiting reagent are left unreacted?
e) How many grams of the excess reagent are left unreacted?

Percent Yield

8. Consider the following balanced chemical reaction:

$$C_5H_8 \;+\; 2\,H_2 \;\rightarrow\; C_5H_{12}$$

FW   68.1   2.02   72.1

a) If 3.00 g of C_5H_{12} were obtained in the reaction of 5.00 g of C_5H_8 with excess hydrogen, then what is the percent yield of C_5H_{12}?

b) What is the % yield, if 4.80 mL of C_5H_{12} (d = 0.626 g/mL) were obtained in the reaction of 5.00 g of C_5H_8 with excess hydrogen?

c) What is the % yield, if 4.70 g of C_5H_{12} (d = 0.626 g/mL) were obtained in the reaction of 8.00 g of C_5H_8 with 1.0 g of hydrogen?

9. Consider the following balanced chemical reaction:

$$CH_4 \;+\; 4\,Cl_2 \;\rightarrow\; CCl_4 \;+\; 4\,HCl$$

FW   16.0   71.0   154.   36.5

a) If 10.0 g of HCl were obtained in the reaction of 5.00 g of CH_4 with excess chlorine, then what is the percent yield of HCl?

b) If the above reaction only went to 52.0% completion, then how many grams of CCl_4 would be produced if 10.0 grams of CH_4 was reacted with excess chlorine?

Concentration of Solutions

10. In a solution prepared by mixing the following reagents, which is the solvent and which is/are the solute(s):
    a) 50.0 mL Br_2 + 25.0 g of I_2 + 100.0 mL of CCl_4
    b) 100.0 mL of H_2O + 25.0 g LiCl + 40.0 g of NaCl
    c) 25.0 mL of H_2O + 75.0 mL of CH_3OH

11. How many grams of NaI (FW = 150.) are needed to prepare 250. mL of a 3.50 M solution?

12. A 2.50 L solution prepared by mixing 5.00 mol of LiCl with water has what molarity?

13. What is the molarity of a solution prepared when 5.00 g of SrI_2 (FW = 341.) are mixed with enough water so as to have 1500. mL of solution?

14. How many moles of HCl are there in 1.00 L of a 6.00 M HCl solution?

15. If 10.0 g of a 98.0% pure sample of NaI (FW = 150) are placed in 1.00 L of solution, what is the molarity of the NaI solution?

16. Calculate the volume (in L) of solution that would be required to make a 2.50 M solution containing 7.82 g of $C_{10}H_8$ (FW =128.).

17. What is the wt. % of solute in a solution prepared by mixing 30.0 g of LiOH in 50.0 grams of water?

18. How many mL of water (d = 1.00 g/mL) must be used in the preparation of a 25.0% $MgCl_2$ solution if 25.0 g of $MgCl_2$ are initially used?

19. How many grams of Br_2 are required to prepare 150. grams of a 5.50% Br_2 in CCl_4 solution?

20. How many mL of Br_2 (d = 3.10 g/mL) are required to prepare 150. grams of a 5.50% Br_2 in CCl_4 solution?

21. If 10.0 mL of Br_2 (d = 3.10 g/mL) are mixed with 100.0 mL of CCl_4 (d = 1.59 g/mL), then what is the weight percent of the solution?

22. If a patient consumes 2.50 L of a 5.00% glucose solution (d = 1.10 g/mL) during a 1 day period, how many grams of glucose (FW = 180) has the patient consumed?

23. How many grams of NaBr must be added to 77.5 g of water in order to prepare a 25.0 wt % solution of NaBr?

24. 0.75 mol of $Ca(OH)_2$ contains how many equivalents?

25. What is the equivalent weight of barium hydroxide (FW = 171)?

26. What is the normality of a solution prepared by mixing 9.50 g of barium hydroxide (FW = 171) in enough water to make 2000. mL of solution?

Interconversion Among Concentration Units

27. Calculate the molarity of a 15.0% NH_4OH (FW = 35.0) solution by weight if the density of the solution is 1.14 g/mL.

28. What is the weight percent of a 1.20 M NaOH (FW = 40.0) that has a density of 1.06 g/mL?

29. Concentrated HNO_3 (FW = 63.0) has a concentration of 17.0 M and a specific gravity of 1.42, what is its weight percent?

30. Concentrated HCl (FW = 36.5) is 37.0% HCl by weight; what is its molarity? The density of concentrated HCl is 1.19 g/mL.

31. What is the normality of a solution that is 6.0 M H_2SO_4 (FW = 98.0)?

32. What is the molarity of a solution that is 14.7 N H_3PO_4 (FW = 98.0)?

33. What is the normality of a solution that is 2.0 M $Be(OH)_2$ (FW = 43.0)?

Dilution of Solutions

34. How would 400. mL of 3.00 M NaOH be prepared from a bottle of 6.00 M NaOH?

35. How many liters of a 5.00 M NaCl solution would be required to prepare 1.00 L of a 3.00 M NaCl solution?

36. If you have 500. mL of a 10.0 M NaBr solution, and you want to prepare a 7.50 M solution, how much water would you add? (Assume that the volumes are additive.)

37. How many quarts of a 3.00 M $MgCl_2$ solution would be required to prepare 5.00 gal of a 1.00 M $MgCl_2$ solution? (1 gal = 4 qt)

Quantitative Analysis Involving Solution Stoichiometry

38. Consider the following balanced chemical equation: $HCl + NaOH \rightarrow NaCl + H_2O$

    a) What is the molarity of an HCl solution of unknown concentration, if 100.0 mL of it was required to completely react with 10.0 g of NaOH?

    b) How many mL of 0.100 M NaOH are required to completely react with 5.00 mL of 0.250 M HCl?

    c) How many grams of NaOH are needed to completely react with 2.00 mL of a 10.0 M HCl solution?

    d) If 1.00 mL of 2.00 M HCl is reacted with 1.00 mL of 1.50 M NaOH, then how many grams of NaCl are produced?

    e) How many equivalents of NaOH are required to titrate a 0.100 L sample of 1 M HCl?

39. Consider the following balanced chemical equation: $2\,HCl + Ba(OH)_2 \rightarrow BaCl_2 + 2\,H_2O$

   a) What is the molarity of an HCl solution of unknown concentration, if 100.0 mL of it were required to completely react with 10.0 g of $Ba(OH)_2$?

   b) How many grams of $Ba(OH)_2$ are required to completely react with 10.0 mL of 4.50 M HCl?

   c) How many mL of 0.250 M HCl are required to completely react with 2.50 mL of 3.50 M $Ba(OH)_2$?

   d) What must have been the molarity of both HCl and $Ba(OH)_2$, if 0.100 mol of $BaCl_2$ was produced as a result of 100. mL of HCl completely reacting with 25.0 mL of $Ba(OH)_2$?

   e) How many grams of $Ba(OH)_2$ are required to completely react with 10.0 mL of 4.50 N HCl?

MULTIPLE CHOICE PRACTICE EXAM FOR MODULE 4

1. When the following equation is balanced, the coefficient in front of O_2 is:
$$C_{12}H_{24}O_2 + O_2 \rightarrow CO_2 + H_2O$$
   1) 5   2) 7   3) 8   4) 18   5) 17

2. When the following equation is balanced, the sum of all the coefficients is (remember to add coefficients of 1):
$$Ce(NO_3)_4 + Na_3PO_4 \rightarrow Ce_3(PO_4)_4 + NaNO_3$$
   1) 4   2) 8   3) 16   4) 20   5) 24

3. When the following equation is balanced, the sum of all the coefficients is (remember to add coefficients of 1):
$$Cl_2 + FeBr_3 \rightarrow FeCl_3 + Br_2$$
   1) 4   2) 8   3) 10   4) 12   5) 20

Consider the following balanced reaction: $S_8 + 12\,O_2 \rightarrow 8\,SO_3$ when answering questions 4 - 5

4. How many grams of oxygen are needed to completely react with 2.78 g of sulfur?
   1) 26.8   2) 2.71   3) 2.03   4) 32.4   5) 4.15

5. How many grams of SO_3 would be produced when 0.825 mol of O_2 is reacted with excess S_8?
   1) 99.1   2) 529   3) 44.1   4) 66.1   5) 0.550

Consider the following balanced reaction: $CH_4 + 4\,Cl_2 \rightarrow CCl_4 + 4\,HCl$ and the following information when answering questions 6 - 9. If 0.500 mol of Cl_2 were mixed with 0.150 mol of CH_4, then:

6. How many moles of CCl_4 are produced?
   1) 0.500   2) 0.150   3) 0.125   4) 0.350   5) 0.375

7. How many moles of CH_4 remain unreacted?
   1) 0.000   2) 0.025   3) 0.375   4) 0.112   5) 0.350

8. How many moles of Cl_2 remain unreacted?
   1) 0.000   2) 0.150   3) 0.125   4) 0.350   5) 0.375

9. What is the limiting reagent?
   1) CH_4 2) Cl_2 3) CCl_4 4) HCl
   5) There is no limiting reagent in this particular reaction.

Consider the following balanced equation $2\,Fe + 3\,Br_2 \rightarrow 2\,FeBr_3$ and the following information when answering questions 10 - 13. If 0.326 mol of Fe are mixed with 0.412 mol of Br_2, then:

10. How many mol of $FeBr_3$ will be produced?
   1) 0.326   2) 0.163   3) 0.412   4) 0.275   5) 0.618

11. How many mol of Fe will be left unreacted after the reaction has gone to completion?
   1) 0.00   2) 0.275   3) 0.051   4) 0.137   5) 0.086

12. How many grams of Br_2 will be left unreacted after the reaction has gone to completion?
   1) 0.00   2) 0.275   3) 0.051   4) 0.137   5) 0.086

13. Calculate the % yield if 74.0 g of $FeBr_3$ (FW = 296) were isolated?
   1) 90.9%   2) 79.1%   3) 76.7%   4) 60.1%   5) 126%

14. What is the molarity of a solution prepared by dissolving 74.5 g of K_2SO_4 (FW = 174.) in enough water to prepare 237. mL of solution?
    1) 1.81   2) 0.554   3) 181.   4) 54.7   5) 0.101

15. How many grams of $CaBr_2$ (FW = 200) are needed to prepare 800. mL of a 1.50 M solution of $CaBr_2$?
    1) 375.   2) 240.   3) 2.40×10^5 4) 107.   5) 178.

16. 500. mL of a 1.25 M HCl solution can be prepared by mixing ____ mL of 6.00 M HCl with ___ mL of water?
    1) 396; 104   2) 95; 405   3) 2.40; 498   4) 104; 396   5) 67; 433

17. What is the weight percent of an NaOH solution prepared by mixing 25.0 g of NaOH with 200. g of water?
    1) 12.5   2) 11.1   3) 8.00   4) 26.0   5) 9.00

18. 25.00 g of 5.00 wt % KBr (FW = 119.) can be prepared by mixing ___ g of KBr with ___ g of H_2O.
    1) 1.32; 23.68   2) 5.00; 20.00   3) 1.25; 23.75   4) 5.30; 19.70   5) 4.75; 20.25

19. What is the normality of a solution prepared by dissolving 76.8 g H_3AsO_4 (FW = 142.) in enough water to prepare 800. mL of solution?
    1) 0.676   2) 0.493   3) 0.225   4) 4.44   5) 2.03

20. What is the equivalent weight (in g/eq) of $H_2C_3H_2O_4$ (FW = 104.)?
    1) 416.   2) 104.   3) 208   4) 52.0   5) 26.0

21. What is the weight percent of a 12.0 M HCl solution ($d_{(12.0\ M\ HCl)}$ = 1.18 g/mL)?
    1) 27.9   2) 38.8   3) 49.6   4) 51.7   5) 37.1

22. What is the normality of a 2.0 M H_2SO_4 (FW = 98.0) solution?
    1) 2.0   2) 1.0   3) 4.0   4) 49.0   5) 196.

Consider the following balanced equation 3 NaOH + $H_3PO_4 \rightarrow$ Na_3PO_4 + 3 H_2O when answering questions 23 - 27.

23. How many mL of 0.500 M H_3PO_4 are needed to react with 25.0 mL of 0.200 M NaOH?
    1) 7.50   2) 3.33   3) 20.8   4) 10.0   5) 50.0

24. How many mL of 0.500 N H_3PO_4 are needed to react with 25.0 mL of 0.200 N NaOH?
    1) 7.50   2) 3.33   3) 20.8   4) 10.0   5) 50.0

25. How many mL of 0.500 N H_3PO_4 are needed to react with 4.00 g of NaOH (FW = 40.0)?
    1) 0.200   2) 0.0500   3) 200.   4) 10.0   5) 50.0

26. If 20.0 mL of 4.00 M NaOH are reacted with 7.00 g of H_3PO_4 (FW = 98.0), then how many grams of Na_3PO_4 (FW = 164.) will be produced?
    1) 7.84   2) 11.7   3) 0.0714   4) 31.0   5) 4.37

27. If 20.0 mL of 4.00 M NaOH are reacted with 7.00 g of H_3PO_4 (FW = 98.0), then how many mol of the excess reagent remain unreacted?
    1) 0.080   2) 0.071   3) 0.027   4) 0.044   5) 3.00

28. A 1.00 g sample of phthalic acid (a diprotic acid) is neutralized by a 9.64 mL sample of 1.25 N NaOH solution. The equivalent weight and molecular weight of phthalic acid, respectively, are:
    1) 12.1; 6.03   2) 83.0; 41.5   3) 12.1; 24.1   4) 83.0; 166.   5) 41.5; 83.0

MODULE 4 - ANSWERS

1. a) $Pb(NO_3)_2$ + $2\,NaOH$ $\rightarrow$ $Pb(OH)_2$ + $2\,NaNO_3$

    b) $2\,Na_2S_2O_3$ + I_2 $\rightarrow$ $Na_2S_4O_6$ + $2\,NaI$

    c) $2\,K$ + $2\,H_2O$ $\rightarrow$ $2\,KOH$ + H_2

    d) C_7H_{12} + $10\,O_2$ $\rightarrow$ $7\,CO_2$ + $6\,H_2O$

    e) $BaCl_2$ + Na_2SO_4 $\rightarrow$ $2\,NaCl$ + $BaSO_4$

    f) $3\,O_2$ $\rightarrow$ $2\,O_3$

    g) $16\,V$ + $3\,S_8$ $\rightarrow$ $8\,V_2S_3$

    h) $2\,C_3H_6O_2$ + $7\,O_2$ $\rightarrow$ $6\,CO_2$ + $6\,H_2O$

    i) $3\,Fe_2O_3$ + C $\rightarrow$ $2\,Fe_3O_4$ + CO

    j) $P_4 + 6\,H_2$ $\rightarrow$ $4\,PH_3$

    k) $2\,C_2H_6$ + $7\,O_2$ $\rightarrow$ $4\,CO_2$ + $6\,H_2O$

    l) MgI_2 + $2\,AgNO_3$ $\rightarrow$ $Mg(NO_3)_2$ + $2\,AgI$

2. a) 10   b) 4   c) 4   d) 6   e) 6   f) 12

3. A. a) 3.00 mol LiCl, 1.50 mol Mg   b) 0.105 mol LiCl, 0.0525 mol Mg
        c) 18.4 g LiCl, 5.28 g Mg   d) 1.00 mol $MgCl_2$

    B. a) 4.50 mol Ni, 3.00 mol $AlCl_3$ b) 0.0386 mol Ni, 0.0257 mol $AlCl_3$
        c) 9.78 g Ni,   14.8 g $AlCl_3$ d) 3.00 mol $NiCl_2$

    C. a) 3.00 mol CCl_4, 12.0 mol HCl   b) 0.0176 mol CCl_4, 0.0704 mol HCl
        c) 28.9 g CCl_4, 27.4 g HCl   d) 8.00 mol Cl_2

4. a) 0.650 mol   b) 5.14 g   c) 45.1 mL   d) 4.52×10^{24} molecules
    e) 0.631 g H_2, 4.38 g CO   f) 0.499 g H_2, 3.46 g CO   g) 1.44 mol   h) 16.2 g   i) 69.3 g

5. a) 25.4 g   b) 3.93 g   c) 3.11 g   d) 4.93×10^{22} FU KCl   e) 9.03×10^{24} O atoms

6. A. a) Li   b) 2.50 mol LiCl, 1.25 mol Mg   c) 1.25 mol $MgCl_2$
        d) $MgCl_2$ e) 1.78 g LiCl, 0.510 g Mg   f) 1.71 g Li
    B. a) $NiCl_2$ b) 1.67 mol $AlCl_3$, 2.50 mol Ni   c) 0.83 mol Al
        d) $NiCl_2$ e) 0.905 g Ni, 1.37 g $AlCl_3$ f) 1.72 g Al
    C. a) Cl_2 b) 2.50 mol HCl, 0.625 mol CCl_4 c) 1.88 mol CH_4
        d) Cl_2 e) 1.08 g CCl_4, 1.03 g HCl   f) 1.89 g CH_4

7. a) CO   b) 3.30 g   c) 4.17 mL   d) 0.00 g CO   e) 4.58 g H_2

8. a) 56.7%   b) 56.7%   c) 55.4%

9. a) 21.9%   b) 50.1 g

10. a) solvent-CCl_4, solutes-Br_2 & I_2 b) solvent-H_2O, solutes-LiCl & NaCl   c) solvent-CH_3OH, solute-H_2O

11. 131. g   12. 2.00 M

13. 9.78×10^{-3} M   14. 6.00 mol

15. 6.53×10^{-2} M   16. 2.44×10^{-2} L

17. 37.5%   18. 75.0 mL

19. 8.25 g   20. 2.66 mL

21. 16.3%   22. 138. g

23. 25.8 g   24. 1.50 eq

25. 85.5 g/eq   26. 0.0554 N

27. 4.89 M   28. 4.53%

29. 75.4%   30. 12.1 M

31. 12. N   32. 4.9 M

33. 4.0 N

34. Take 200. mL of 6.00 M NaOH and add enough water until 400. mL of solution are obtained, then mix well.

35. 0.600 L

36. 167 mL

37. 6.67 qt

38. a) 2.50 M   b) 12.5 mL   c) 8.00×10^{-1} g   d) 8.78×10^{-2} g   e) 0.1 eq

39. a) 1.17 M   b) 3.85 g   c) 70.0 mL   d) 2.00 M HCl, 4.00 M $Ba(OH)_2$ e) 3.85 g

MODULE 5. *Predicting Formulas of Ionic Compounds, Oxidation Numbers, and Nomenclature*

I. Predicting the Formula of Ionic Compounds

A. Binary Ionic Compounds

When a binary ionic compound (those composed of a metal & non-metal) is formed, an equal number of electrons must be lost by the metal as are gained by the non-metal. The total charge on the compound must be zero.

For the "A" elements (i.e., representative elements) the following table gives the most common ion* that is formed by the elements. Noble gases are stable and do not form ions and boron does not commonly form binary ionic compounds.

IA	IIA	IIIA	IVA	VA	VIA	VIIA	VIIIA
H^+							-
Li^+	Be^{2+}	-	C^{4-}	N^{3-}	O^{2-}	F^-	-
Na^+	Mg^{2+}	Al^{3+}	Si^{4-}	P^{3-}	S^{2-}	Cl^-	-
K^+	Ca^{2+}	Ga^{3+}	Ge^{4+}	As^{3-}	Se^{2-}	Br^-	-
Rb^+	Sr^{2+}	In^{3+}	Sn^{4+}	Sb^{5+}	Te^{2-}	I^-	-
Cs^+	Ba^{2+}	Tl^{3+}	Pb^{4+}	Bi^{5+}	Po^{6+}	At^-	-
Fr^+	Ra^{2+}						

* less common ions for the following groups can also form, for example:
   Metals in IIIA: +1 charge
   Metals in IVA: +2 charge
   Metals in VA: +3 charge
   Metals in VIA: +4 charge

When the charge on the cation is not equal to the charge on the anion, subscripts must be used to balance the positive and negative charges. Subscripts of <u>one</u> are omitted. One can easily arrive at the formula for ionic compounds that contain anions and cations of unequal charges by "crossing" the charges .

The use of "crossing" charges when the charge on the cation is not equal to the charge on the anion is illustrated below:

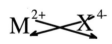

The formula would be MX_2.

Cation charge	= +2
Total anion charge = 2 x (-1)	= -2
Net charge	0

Exception to "crossing" charges:

$$M^{2+} \diagdown X^{4-}$$

Crossing charges would give M_4X_2; however, the formula is M_2X.
In cases such as this, use the simplest whole number ratio.

<u>Example Problem</u>: Write the formulas for the ionic compounds formed between the following elements: a) Na & Cl   b) Mg & Br   c) Al & S

a) Na is in group IA and will form a +1 cation → Na^+

   Cl is in group VIIA and will form a -1 anion → Cl^-

   Since the charge on the cation is equal to the charge on the anion, the formula is: NaCl

b) Mg is in group IIA and will form a +2 cation → Mg^{2+}

   Br is in group VIIA and will form a -1 anion → Br^-

   Since the charge on the cation is not equal to the charge on the anion, subscripts need to be used to balance the positive charges with that of the negative charge so that the net charge is zero. "Crossing" charges gives the following formula: $MgBr_2$.

c) Al is in group IIIA and will form a +3 cation $\rightarrow$ Al^{3+}

S is in group VIA and will form a -2 anion $\rightarrow$ S^{2-}

Since the charge on the cation is not equal to the charge on the anion, subscripts need to be used to balance the positive charges with that of the negative charge so that the net charge is zero. "Crossing" charges gives the following formula: Al_2S_3.

B. Compounds that Contain Polyatomic Ions

Polyatomic ions are charged species composed of several atoms bound together. An example of a polyatomic cation is NH_4^+ and that of a polyatomic anion is OH^-. If subscripts need to be used (because the charge on the anion is not equal to the charge on the cation) the polyatomic ion is enclosed in parenthesis and the subscript is placed outside the parenthesis.

Example Problem: Write the formula for the compound formed by combining the following ions:

a) NH_4^+ & OH^- b) NH_4^+ & O^{2-} c) V^{3+} & SO_4^{2-}

a) NH_4OH (no subscripts or parenthesis are needed because the charge on the cation is equal to the charge on the anion.)

b) $(NH_4)_2O$ (the polyatomic cation needs to be enclosed with parenthesis and then the subscript is placed outside the parenthesis)

c) $V_2(SO_4)_3$ (the polyatomic anion needs to be enclosed with parenthesis and then the subscript is placed outside the parenthesis)

II. Oxidation Numbers

The oxidation number of an atom represents how many electrons the atom has lost (a postive oxidation number), gained (a negative oxidation number), or are being shared unequally (a positive number if atom has electrons drawn closer or negative number if atom has electrons pulled away from itself) when it is chemically combined with another element. In order to predict oxidation numbers, you must remember the following rules for oxidation numbers:

1) F = -1 (always)
2) Cl, Br, I = -1 (except when attached to more a electronegative element -- O or F)
3) O = -2 (except in peroxides, -1, and superoxides, -1/2)
4) Group VIA nonmetals *in binary ionic compounds* = -2
5) Group VA nonmetals *in binary ionic compounds* = -3
6) Group IA metals = +1 (always)
7) Group IIA metals = +2 (always)
8) Al = +3, Zn = +2, Cd = +2, and Ag = +1
9) H = +1 (except when attached to a metal in which case H = -1)

For ions: the sum of all the oxidation numbers = charge on the ion.
For compounds: the sum of all the oxidation numbers = zero.
For elements: the oxidation number = zero.

Example Problem: Predict the oxidation number for the atom that is boldfaced.

a) $K_2Cr_2O_7$ b) PO_4^{3-} c) FeH_2 d) NH_4^+

a) 2(K) + 2 (Cr) + 7(O) = 0   b) 1(P) + 4(O) = -3
    2(+1) + 2(Cr) + 7(-2) = 0   1(P) + 4(-2) = -3
    2 Cr = +12 ---> Cr = +6   P = +5

c) 1(Fe) + 2(H) = 0   d) 1(N) + 4(H) = +1
    1(Fe) + 2(-1) = 0   1(N) + 4(+1) = +1
    Fe = +2   N = -3

III. Nomenclature

A. Binary Compounds (those containing 2 different elements)

a) *Binary Compounds of Two Non-metals - Covalent Compounds*

- The name of the first element is not modified. A prefix is used to denote the number of atoms present in the formula (see Table 1). The prefix mono is never used for naming the first element.
- The name of the second element is modified so that its name ends in ide (see Table 2, which gives the root name of the element with the suffix -ide). A prefix is used to denote number of atoms present in the formula (see Table 1).
- For prefixes that end in *o* or *a*, the *o* or *a* is dropped when the second element is oxygen or arsenic (e.g., tetroxide instead of tetraoxide - denoting 4 oxygens in formula).

Table 1. Prefixes

Prefix	Number
mono-	1
di-	2
tri-	3
tetra-	4
penta-	5
hexa-	6
hepta-	7
octa-	8
nona-	9
deca-	10

Table 2. ide Endings

IVA	VA	VIA	VIIA
			hydride
carbide	nitride	oxide	fluoride
	phosphide	sulfide	chloride
	arsenide	selenide	bromide
		telluride	iodide

Example Problems:

dichloride heptoxide

1. Write the name of the following compounds: a) CO b) Cl_2O_7 c) ICl_3

carbon monoxide iodine trichoride

   a) carbon monoxide
      First element is carbon (prefix *mono* not used).
      Second element is oxygen its name is modified to oxide and the prefix *mon-* (for oxygen the a or o is dropped for those prefixes that end in them) is inserted in front of oxide.
   b) dichlorine heptoxide c) iodine trichloride

2. Write formulas for each of the following compounds:
   a) dichlorine pentoxide b) sulfur hexafluoride c) phosphorous pentachloride
   a) Cl_2O_5 b) SF_6 c) PCl_5

b) *Binary Compounds of a Metal and Non-metal - Ionic Compounds (or Salts)*

Ionic compounds are also called salts. There are two types of binary ionic compounds as far as nomenclature is concerned, those that contain metal ions with a fixed charge (oxidation number) and those that contain metal ions with a variable charge (oxidation number).

1. ***Metal ions with fixed charges (oxidation numbers)***
   - The name of the first element in the formula, the metal, is not modified.
   - The name of the second element in the formula, the non-metal, is modified so that it ends in ide (see Table 2).

   You must learn which metals have a fixed charge (oxidation number); the rest have variable charges. The following metals are the ones that have fixed oxidation numbers:

+1	+2	+3
IA	IIA	Al^{3+}
Ag^{+}	Zn^{2+}	
	Cd^{2+}	

Example, $BaCl_2$ ---> barium chloride
Ba^{2+} --> barium   (in group IIA has fixed charge of +2)
Cl^- --> chloride (in group VIIA has a charge of -1)

Example,   zinc carbide ---> Zn_2C
zinc --> Zn^{2+} (has fixed charge of +2)
carbide --> C^{4-} (in group IVA has a charge of -4)

2. ***Metal ions with variable charges (oxidation numbers)***
   - The name of the first element in the formula, the metal, is not modified; however a Roman numeral corresponding to the charge (oxidation number) is placed in parenthesis after the name of the metal. (This is known as the Stock name of the metal.)
   - The name of the second element in the formula, the non-metal, is modified so that it ends in ide (see Table 2).

Example, $CuCl_2$ ---> copper(II) chloride
Cu^{2+} --> copper(II)   (the charge on Cu is +2)
Cl^- --> chloride   (group VIIA species have a charge of -1)

Example,   nickel(IV) oxide   ---> NiO_2
nickel(IV) --> Ni^{4+} (Roman numeral of IV --> +4 charge)
oxide --> O^{2-} (group VIA species have a charge of -2)

Binary ionic compounds with metals having a variable charge have an alternate (old) nomenclature derived from the Latin name of the metal. Table 3 contains both the new and old nomenclature of those ions having special names (to be memorized).

Table 3. Metals with Special Name

+1 (-ous) +2 (-ic)	+2 (-ous) +3 (-ic)	+2 (-ous) +4 (-ic)
Cu^+ cuprous or copper(I) Cu^{2+} cupric or copper(II)	Co^{2+} cobaltous or cobalt(II) Co^{3+} cobaltic or cobalt(III)	Pb^{2+} plumbous or lead(II) Pb^{4+} plumbic or lead(IV)
Hg_2^{2+} mercurous or mercury(I)* Hg^{2+} mercuric or mercury(II)	Fe^{2+} ferrous or iron(II) Fe^{3+} ferric or iron(III)	Sn^{2+} stannous or tin(II) Sn^{4+} stannic or tin(IV)

Notice from the above table that the metal with the higher charge ends in *ic*, while those with the lower charge end in *ous*.
* The mercury +1 ion exists as the dimer Hg_2^{2+} instead of Hg^+

Example Problems:
1. Name each of the following compounds:
   a) CuO   b) NaBr   c) AlN   d) PbI_4 e) Fe_2O_3 f) Hg_2Cl_2 g) Ga_4C h) ZnO
      a) copper(II) oxide   b) sodium bromide
      c) aluminum nitride   d) lead(IV) iodide
      e) iron(III) oxide   f) mercury(I) chloride
      g) gallium(I) carbide   h) zinc oxide

2. Write the formula for each of the following compounds:
   a) manganese(IV) oxide   b) calcium chloride   c) strontium hydride   d) gold(I) sulfide
      a) MnO_2 b) $CaCl_2$ c) SrH_2 d) Au_2S

3. Name each of the following compounds using the special name for the metal:
   a) CuO   b) PbI_4 c) Fe_2O_3 d) Hg_2Cl_2
      a) cupric oxide   b) plumbic iodide
      c) ferric oxide   d) mercurous chloride

4. Write the formula for each of the following compounds:
   a) ferrous nitride   b) cobaltic fluoride   c) mercuric phosphide   d) plumbous oxide
      a) Fe_3N_2 b) CoF_3 c) Hg_3P_2 d) PbO

B. Binary Acids and Ammonia

Binary acids when present in their natural state (gaseous) are named using nomenclature rules for binary compounds of two non-metals (prefixes are omitted); but when dissolved in water (forming an aqueous solution), then they behave differently and have different names.

Compounds with an H as the first element in their formula [when dissolved in water -- denoted by (aq) aqueous solution] are called **acids.** *H_2O and H_2O_2 are exceptions; they are not acids as defined by Arrhenius. Assume that those compounds in which an H is the first element in the formula are in an aqueous state unless otherwise noted.*

Aqueous binary acids are named **hydro___ic acid,** *where* ___ *stands for the root name (that part of the name in Table 2 without the -ide ending) of the element. [The binary acid derived from H_2S is called hydrosulfuric acid <u>not</u> hydrosulfic acid.]*

	pure gas		aqueous solution
HF (g)	hydrogen fluoride	HF (aq)	hydrofluoric acid
HCl (g)	hydrogen chloride	HCl (aq)	hydrochloric acid
HBr (g)	hydrogen bromide	HBr (aq)	hydrobromic acid
HI (g)	hydrogen iodide	HI (aq)	hydroiodic acid
H_2S (g)	hydrogen sulfide	H_2S (aq)	hydrosulfuric acid
H_2Se (g)	hydrogen selenide	H_2Se (aq)	hydroselenic acid
			(All behave as acids)
NH_3 (g)	ammonia	NH_3 (aq) or NH_4OH	
		NH_4OH	ammonium hydroxide
			(base)

C. Polyatomic Ions and Compounds Containing Polyatomic Ions

In naming and writing the formulas of compounds containing polyatomic ions, follow the same rules as those for naming binary ionic compounds (section - IIIA-b); the name of the polyatomic ion is not modified and used as is. Knowledge of the names and formula of the polyatomic ions given in this section is therefore necessary.

a) *Oxyanions that end in -ate (or "ate" oxyanions)*

Oxyanions are polyatomic anions that contain oxygen and a non-metal. You must memorize (the formula, charge, and name) the following oxyanions that end in -ate (see Table 4).

Table 4*. Oxyanions that end in -ate

IIIA	IVA	VA	VIA	VIIA
BO_3^{3-} <u>bor</u>ate	CO_3^{2-} <u>carbon</u>ate	NO_3^- <u>nitr</u>ate	—	—
	SiO_3^{2-} <u>silic</u>ate	PO_4^{3-} <u>phosph</u>ate	SO_4^{2-} <u>sulf</u>ate	ClO_3^- <u>chlor</u>ate
		AsO_4^{3-} <u>arsen</u>ate	SeO_4^{2-} <u>selen</u>ate	BrO_3^- <u>brom</u>ate
			TeO_4^{2-} <u>tellur</u>ate	IO_3^- <u>iod</u>ate

* that part of the name that has been underlined shows the root name of the central element when naming the oxyanion.

b) **Other Oxyanions**

Having memorized the oxyanions that end in -ate, then those oxyanions having a different number of oxygens than the "ate" oxyanions can be named as shown in Table 5, where the ___ stands for the part of the name in Table 4 that is underlined.   [*NOTE: The charge on the oxyanion does not change upon changing the # of oxygens.*]

Table 5*. Prefixes and Suffixes for Oxyanions

2 oxygens less <u>than</u> "ate" ion	1 oxygen less than "ate" ion	<u>"ate"</u> ion	1 oxygen more than "ate" ion
hypo____ite	____ite	____ate	per____ate

* Only those oxyanions derived from Cl, Br, and I have all the above mentioned oxyanions commonly existing. Boron and carbon just have the "-ate ion" commonly existing and the rest of the elements listed in Table 4 have both the "-ate and -ite ion" commonly existing.

Example of oxyanions derived from Cl:

2 oxygens less than "ate" ion	1 oxygen less than "ate" ion	"ate" ion	1 oxygen more than "ate" ion
ClO^-	ClO_2^-	ClO_3^-	ClO_4^-
hypochlorite ion	chlorite ion	chlorate ion	perchlorate ion

Example Problems:

1. Name the following oxyanions: a) PO_3^{3-} b) NO_2^- c) TeO_2^{2-} d) IO_4^-

     a) phosphite ion   b) nitrite ion   c) hypotellurite ion   d) periodate ion

2. Give the formula for the following oxyanions:
    a) bromite ion   b) sulfite ion   c) silicite ion   d) arsenite ion

    a) BrO_2^- b) SO_3^{2-} c) SiO_2^{2-} d) AsO_3^{3-}

c) **Oxyacids**

Acids derived from oxyanions are called oxyacids. *The acid derived from the "-ate" oxyanion is called ___ic acid.*

The formula for the oxyacid has as many hydrogens (charge of +1) as the magnitiude of the charge on the oxyanion (e.g., the acid derived from the sulfate oxyanion, SO_4^{2-}, is H_2SO_4).
The oxyacids can be named as shown in Table 6, where the _____ stands for the part of the name in Table 4 that is underlined.   NOTE: The root name for the sulfur derived oxyacids is *sulfur* instead of *sulf* and that for phosphorous is *phosphor* instead of *phosph*.

Table 6*. Prefixes and Suffixes for Oxyacids

2 oxygens less <u>than</u> "ic" acid	1 oxygen less <u>than</u> "ic" acid	<u>"ic"</u> acid	1 oxygen more <u>than</u> "ic" acid
hypo___ous acid	___ous acid	___ic acid	per ___ic acid

* Only those oxyacids derived from Cl, Br, and I have all the above mentioned oxyacids commonly existing. Boron and carbon just have the "-ic acid" commonly existing and the rest of the elements listed in Table 4 have both the "-ic and -ous acid" commonly existing.

Example of oxyacids derived from Cl:

2 oxygens less than "ic" acid	1 oxygen less than "ic" acid	"ic" acid	1 oxygen more than "ic" acid
HClO	$HClO_2$	$HClO_3$	$HClO_4$
hypochlorous acid	chlorous acid	chloric acid	perchloric acid

Example Problems:

1. Name the following oxyacids: a) H_3PO_3 b) HNO_2 c) H_2TeO_2 d) HIO_4

    a) phosphorous acid   b) nitrous acid   c) hypotellurous acid   d) periodic acid

2. Give the formula for the following oxyacids:
    a) bromous acid   b) sulfurous acid   c) sulfuric acid   d) hypoiodous acid

    a) $HBrO_2$ b) H_2SO_3 c) H_2SO_4 d) HIO

d) *Other Polyatomic Ions*

There are some polyatomic ions (Table 7) whose names cannot be expanded using suffixes or prefixes. They are used only as given below. You must memorize these also.

Table 7. Other Common Polyatomic Ions

NH_4^+	ammonium	O_2^{2-}	peroxide
OH^-	hydroxide*	$C_2H_3O_2^-$	acetate
CN^-	cyanide	$C_2O_4^{2-}$	oxalate
SCN^-	thiocyanate	CrO_4^{2-}	chromate
MnO_4^-	permanganate	$Cr_2O_7^{2-}$	dichromate

    * *Any compound having the hydroxide ion present in its formula is called a base (e.g., NaOH is a base).*

Three of the above polyatomic ions: cyanide, acetate, and oxalate anions, form the following commonly encountered acids:

> hydrocyanic acid --> HCN (aq)
> [HCN (g) --> hydrogen cyanide]
> acetic acid --> $HC_2H_3O_2$
> oxalic acid --> $H_2C_2O_4$

Any of the anionic polyatomic ions can be combined with any metal ion and the ammonium (NH_4^+) ion.

Example Problems:

1. Name the following: a) Na_3PO_3 b) $Ba_3(AsO_3)_2$ c) NH_4ClO_2 d) $Cu(IO_4)_2$ e) $Fe_2(CO_3)_3$ f) $AuNO_2$ g) $NaSCN$ h) $V(CN)_3$

    a) sodium phosphite   b) barium arsenite
    c) ammonium chlorite   d) copper(II) periodate or cupric periodate
    e) iron(III) carbonate or ferric carbonate   f) gold(I) nitrite
    g) sodium thiocyanate   h) vanadium(III) cyanide

2. Give the formula for the following: a) calcium cyanide   b) ferric acetate   c) lead(IV) phosphite   d) tin(II) hypobromite   e) ammonium carbonate   f) silver oxalate   g) zinc dichromate   h) cobaltous permanganate

    a) $Ca(CN)_2$ b) $Fe(C_2H_3O_2)_3$ c) $Pb_3(PO_3)_4$ d) $Sn(BrO)_2$
    e) $(NH_4)_2CO_3$ f) $Ag_2C_2O_4$ g) $ZnCr_2O_7$ h) $Co(MnO_4)_2$

e) *Acid Anions and Compounds containing Acid Anions (Acid Salts)*

All negative ions having a -2 or -3 charge can form other polyatomic ions by adding one or more hydrogen ions to it; these are called *acid anions.* The acid anions are named using the following rules:

Starting with the anion without any hydrogens:

- addition of <u>one</u> hydrogen decreases the absolute value of the charge on the ion by one. When naming the anion simply put *hydrogen* in front of the name of the polyatomic ion followed by a space.

- addition of <u>two</u> hydrogens (for -3 ions only) decreases the absolute value of the charge of the ion by two. When naming the anion, simply put *dihydrogen* in front of name of the polyatomic ion followed by a space.

Example,

PO_4^{3-} phosphate ion SO_3^{2-} sulfite ion

HPO_4^{2-} hydrogen phosphate ion HSO_3^- hydrogen sulfite ion

$H_2PO_4^-$ dihydrogen phosphate ion

Acid salts are compounds derived from acid anions. When naming the acid salt just name the metal (as previously described) followed by the name of the acid anion.

<u>Example Problems:</u>

1. Give the correct formula for the following: a) cupric dihydrogen phosphate   b) sodium hydrogen arsenate   c) barium dihydrogen phosphite   d) aluminum hydrogen sulfide   e) zinc dihydrogen phosphate

   a) $Cu(H_2PO_4)_2$ b) Na_2HAsO_4 c) $Ba(H_2PO_3)_2$

   d) $Al(HS)_3$ e) $Zn(H_2PO_4)_2$

2. Give the correct name for the following: a) $CuHBO_3$ b) $Pb(HSO_2)_4$ c) $Hg_2(HCO_3)_2$ d) $Al(HCO_3)_3$ e) $MgHAsO_3$

   a) copper(II) hydrogen borate or cupric hydrogen borate
   b) lead(IV) hydrogen hyposulfite or plumbic hydrogen hyposulfite
   c) mercury(I) hydrogen carbonate or mercurous hydrogen carbonate
   d) aluminum hydrogen carbonate
   e) magnesium hydrogen arsenite

D. Hydrates

Compounds that have a specific number of water molecules attached to them are called hydrates. An example of a hydrate is $BaCl_2 \cdot 2H_2O$. Each formula unit of barium chloride has 2 molecules of water associated with it. These water moleucles can be driven off by heating to form the anhydrous compound.

When naming hydrates use the nomenclature rules given in this module followed by a space and the following: _____hydrate. Where _____ is a prefix used to denote the number of water molecules that the compound has. Use the prefixes given in Table 1.

<u>Example Problems:</u>

1. Give the correct formula for the following: a) calcium sulfate dihydrate   b) magnesium hydrogen phosphate heptahydrate   c) sodium carbonate decahydrate

   a) $CaSO_4 \cdot 2H_2O$ b) $MgHPO_4 \cdot 7H_2O$ c) $Na_2CO_3 \cdot 10H_2O$

2. Give the correct name for the following compound: a) $LiCl \cdot H_2O$ b) $CuSO_4 \cdot 5H_2O$ c) $CdBr_2 \cdot 3H_2O$ d) $Mn(C_2H_3O_2)_2 \cdot 4H_2O$

   a) lithium chloride monohydrate   b) copper(II) sulfate pentahydrate
   c) cadmium bromide trihydrate   d) manganese(II) acetate tetrahydrate

EXERCISES

Predicting the Formulas of Ionic Compounds

1. Write the formula for the most common ion formed by each of the following elements:
   a) Rb   b) Ra   c) Ga   d) Si   e) Sn   f) As   g) Bi   h) Te   i) Po   j) I

2. Write formulas for the compounds that are expected to be formed by the following pairs of ions:

	Cl^-	O^{2-}	OH^-	CO_3^{2-}	PO_4^{3-}
NH_4^+					
Na^+					
Ca^{2+}					
Al^{3+}					
Ti^{4+}					
Mn^{7+}					

Oxidation Numbers

3. What oxidation number do the following elements exhibit when chemically combined?
   a) F   b) Ra   c) K   d) Al   e) Zn   f) Cd   g) Ag   h) O

4. Assign oxidation numbers to each of the elements in the following species.
   a) NaF b) Na_3N c) PBr_3 d) $KMnO_4$ e) CuS f) ClO_3^- g) CH_4
   h) IF_7 i) AlN j) $Cd(ClO_4)_2$ k) $V(OH)_3$ l) Fe_2S_3 m) Ag_2CO_3 n) $C_2O_4^{2-}$
   o) SO_4^{2-} p) Cl_2O_5 q) $Ti_3(PO_4)_4$ r) H_2O s) CuH t) Br_2 u) KO_2

Nomenclature

5. Name each of the following compounds:
   a) $PbCl_2$ b) Na_2CrO_4 c) $H_2C_2O_4$ d) $Be(HSO_4)_2$
   e) ICl f) $PbSe$ g) SnS_2 h) BiF_3
   i) $Cd_3(PO_4)_2$ j) SiO_2 k) Cs_2Se l) NiO
   m) VCl_3 n) K_2O o) HIO_2 p) $NaMnO_4$
   q) $NaHS$ r) $Sn(OH)_2$ s) NH_4I t) Hg_2Cl_2
   u) $NaOH$ v) $Fe(H_2PO_3)_2$ w) $KHCO_3$ x) HIO_4
   y) CCl_4 z) IF_7

6. Write formulas for each of the following compounds:
   a) calcium permanganate   b) potassium dichromate   c) mercury(II) nitrate
   d) sulfur tetrafluoride   e) aluminum phosphate   f) lithium nitrite
   g) hypochlorous acid   h) copper(II) oxalate   i) phosphorous acid
   j) sulfuric acid   k) carbon dioxide   l) ammonium hydrogen sulfide
   m) mercury(I) oxide   n) zinc hydroxide   o) lithium carbonate
   p) calcium hydride   q) tin(II) fluoride   r) hydrobromic acid
   s) zinc hydrogen sulfite   t) carbon disulfide   u) nickel(II) iodite
   v) silver sulfite   w) cadmium nitrate   x) beryllium nitride
   y) stannous permanganate   z) silver oxalate

7. Write names of the following compounds:

a) $SrCl_2 \cdot H_2O$ b) $Co(OH)_2$ c) HBr (g)   d) HI (aq)

e) TiO_2 f) $SnSO_4$ g) H_3AsO_3 h) CO_2

i) $Ca(HSe)_2$ j) Cl_2O k) $Ca_3(PO_4)_2$ l) $CuNO_2$

m) Cu_3N n) $HC_2H_3O_2$ o) $H_2C_2O_4$ p) $Mg(NO_3)_2$

q) Fe_2S_3 r) Na_2HAsO_4 s) $Cu(HSO_3)_2$ t) $HBrO$

u) $CsIO_4$ v) $Zn(ClO_2)_2$ w) Ag_3PO_3 x) N_2O

y) $LiCN$ z) $Cd_3(AsO_4)_2$

8. Write formulas for each of the following:

a) iron(III) cyanide   b) hydrogen cyanide   c) carbon monoxide

d) calcium phosphide   e) strontium hydrogen phosphate f) cobalt(III) chloride

g) mercurous fluoride   h) manganese(IV) oxide   i) bromic acid

j) sulfurous acid   k) potassium hypochlorite   l) ferrous nitride

m) barium hydroxide   n) ferric hydrogen sulfate   o) phosphoric acid

p) aluminum oxalate dihydrate q) cobaltic bromate   r) ferric hydroxide

s) tin(IV) nitrite   t) copper(II) dihydrogen phosphate u) beryllium thiocyanate

v) barium dihydrogen phosphite w) aluminum hydrogen arsenite   x) tellurous acid

y) calcium hypobromite   z) sodium hydrogen sulfite

MULTIPLE CHOICE PRACTICE EXAM FOR MODULE 5

1. What is the formula of the ionic compound formed between the following elements: Mg & N?
   1) MgN   2) Mg_2N_3 3) Mg_3N_2 4) MgN_3 5) MgN_2

2. What is the oxidation number of P in P_2O_5? $2(P) + 5(-2) = 0$ $2P + -10 = 0$ $2P = 10$ $P = 5$
   1) -10   2) +10   3) -5   4) +5   5) +2

3. What is the oxidation number of each atom in $Cu(OH)_2$?
   1) Cu = +1, O = -2, H = +1   2) Cu = +2, O = -2, H = +1   3) Cu = +2, O = -2, H = -1
   4) Cu = +2, O = -1, H = +1   5) Cu = +1, O = -2, H = -1

4. What is the oxidation number of each atom in $(NH_4)_2S$?
   1) N = -3, H = +1, S = -2   2) N = -5, H = +1, S = -1   3) N = -2, H = +6, S = -2
   4) N = -5, H = +1, S = -2   5) N = +5, H = +1, S = -2

5. The name for P_4S_7 is:
   1) quadphosphorous septasulfide   2) tetraphosphide heptasulfur
   3) tetraphosphorous heptasulfide   4) phosphorous(IV) sulfide
   5) tetraphosphorous septasulfide

6. The formula for disulfur decafluoride is:
   1) S_2F_{10} 2) S_2F_9 3) $S_{10}F_2$ 4) S_2F_8 5) S_2F_{100}

7. The name for MgF_2 is:
   1) manganese (II) fluoride   2) magnesium difluoride
   3) magnesium fluoride   4) manganese fluoride
   5) magnesium difluorine

8. The formula for barium phosphide is:
   1) BaP   2) Ba_3P_2 3) Ba_2P_3 4) Ba_2P_5 5) Ba_5P_2

9. The name for $CrCl_6$ is:
   1) chromium hexachloride   2) chromium septachloride
   3) chromium chloride   4) chromium(VI) chloride
   5) chromium(VI) hexachloride

10. The formula for titanium(IV) oxide is:
    1) Ti_4O 2) Ti_2O_4 3) Ti_4O_2 4) Ti_4O_2 5) TiO_2

11. The name for PbSe is:
    1) plumbic selenide   2) plumbous monoselenide
    3) plumbous selinium   4) plumbic monoselenium
    5) plumbous selenide

12. The formula for mercurous oxide is :
    1) Hg_2O 2) HgO_2 3) Hg_2O_2 4) HgO   5) Hg_3O_2

13. The name for $H_2S_{(g)}$ is:
    1) hydrosulfuric acid   2) hydrogen sulfide
    3) sulfuric acid   4) sulfide acid
    5) sulfuride acid

14. The name for each of the following polyatomic ions -- AsO_4^{3-} ; BrO_2^- -- is:
    1) perarsenate ; bromite
    2) arsenous ; bromous
    3) arsenate ; hypobromate
    4) arsenate ; bromite
    5) arsenite ; hypobromite

15. The charge for each of the following polyatomic ions -- $C_2O_4^?$; $MnO_4^?$ -- is:
    1) -2 ; +1
    2) -1 ; -1
    3) -2 ; -2
    4) -2 ; -1
    5) -3 ; -2

16. The formula for nickel(IV) sulfate is:
    1) Ni_4SO_4 2) $Ni_2(SO_4)_4$ 3) $Ni(SO_4)_2$ 4) $Ni_2(SO_3)_4$ 5) $Ni_4(SO_4)_2$

17. The formula for carbonous acid is:
    1) H_2CO_3
    2) H_3CO_3
    3) H_3CO_2
    4) HCO_2
    5) H_2CO_2

18. The formula for silver hydrogen arsenite is:
    1) $SiHAsO_3$ 2) Ag_2HAsO_3 3) $Ag(HAsO_3)_2$ 4) $AgHAsO_3$ 5) $AgHAsO_4$

19. The formula for ferrous cyanide is:
    1) $FeCN$ 2) $Fe(CN)_3$ 3) $Fe(CN)_2$ 4) $Fe_2(CN)_3$ 5) $Fe_3(CN)_2$

20. Which formula goes with what name?
    1) $Na_2Cr_2O_7$: sodium chromate
    2) K_2MnO_4 : potassium permanganate
    3) $H_2C_2O_4$: oxalic acid
    4) $HI_{(aq)}$: hydrogen iodic acid
    5) $FePO_4$: ferrous phosphate

21. Which formula goes with what name?
    1) $Hg_2Cr_2O_7$: mercury(I) dichromate
    2) BO_3^{3-} : borite ion
    3) H_2SO_3 : sulfous acid
    4) KS_2 : potassium sulfide
    5) $CdSO_4$: cadmium(II) sulfate

22. Which formula goes with what name?
    1) $HgSO_4$: mercurous sulfate
    2) KH_2BO_3 : potassium dihydrogen borate
    3) $Sn(OH)_3$: stannous hydroxide
    4) ZnH_2S : zinc dihydrogen sulfide
    5) $AlBr$: aluminum bromide

MODULE 5 - ANSWERS

1. a) Rb^+ b) Ra^{2+} c) Ga^{3+} d) Si^{4-} e) Sn^{4+} f) As^{3-} g) Bi^{5+} h) Te^{2-} i) Po^{6+} j) I^-

2.

	Cl^-	O^{2-}	OH^-	CO_3^{2-}	PO_4^{3-}
NH_4^+	NH_4Cl	$(NH_4)_2O$	NH_4OH	$(NH_4)_2CO_3$	$(NH_4)_3PO_4$
Na^+	$NaCl$	Na_2O	$NaOH$	Na_2CO_3	Na_3PO_4
Ca^{2+}	$CaCl_2$	CaO	$Ca(OH)_2$	$CaCO_3$	$Ca_3(PO_4)_2$
Al^{3+}	$AlCl_3$	Al_2O_3	$Al(OH)_3$	$Al_2(CO_3)_3$	$AlPO_4$
Ti^{4+}	$TiCl_4$	TiO_2	$Ti(OH)_4$	$Ti(CO_3)_2$	$Ti_3(PO_4)_4$
Mn^{7+}	$MnCl_7$	Mn_2O_7	$Mn(OH)_7$	$Mn_2(CO_3)_7$	$Mn_3(PO_4)_7$

3. a) -1 b) +2 c) +1 d) +3 e) +2 f) +2 g) +1 h) -2 (usually)

4. a) Na = +1, F = -1 b) Na = +1, N = -3 c) P = +3, Br = -1 d) K = +1, Mn = +7, O = -2
    e) Cu = +2, S = -2 f) Cl = +5, O = -2 g) C = -4, H = +1 h) I = +7, F = -1
    i) Al = +3, N =-3 j) Cd = +2, Cl = +7, O = -2 k) V = +3, O = -2, H = +1 l) Fe = +3, S = -2
    m) Ag =+1, C = +4, O = -2 n) C = +3, O = -2 o) S = +6, O = -2 p) Cl = +5, O = -2
    q) Ti = +4, P = +5, O = -2 r) H = +1, O = -2 s) Cu = +1, H = -1 t) Br = 0 u) K = +1, O = -1/2

5. a) lead(II) chloride
    b) sodium chromate
    c) oxalic acid
    d) beryllium hydrogen sulfate
    e) iodine monochloride
    f) lead(II) selenide
    g) tin(IV) sulfide
    h) bismuth(III) fluoride
    i) cadmium phosphate
    j) silicon dioxide
    k) cesium selenide
    l) nickel(II) oxide
    m) vanadium(III) chloride
    n) potassium oxide
    o) iodous acid
    p) sodium permanganate
    q) sodium hydrogen sulfide
    r) tin(II) hydroxide
    s) ammonium iodide
    t) mercury(I) chloride
    u) sodium hydroxide
    v) iron(II) dihydrogen phosphite
    w) potassium hydrogen carbonate
    x) periodic acid
    y) carbon tetrachloride
    z) iodine heptafluoride

6. a) $Ca(MnO_4)_2$
    b) $K_2Cr_2O_7$
    c) $Hg(NO_3)_2$
    d) SF_4
    e) $AlPO_4$
    f) $LiNO_2$
    g) $HClO$
    h) CuC_2O_4
    i) H_3PO_3
    j) H_2SO_4
    k) CO_2
    l) NH_4HS
    m) Hg_2O
    n) $Zn(OH)_2$
    o) Li_2CO_3
    p) CaH_2
    q) SnF_2
    r) HBr
    s) $Zn(HSO_3)_2$
    t) CS_2
    u) $Ni(IO_2)_2$
    v) Ag_2SO_3
    w) $Cd(NO_3)_2$
    x) Be_3N_2
    y) $Sn(MnO_4)_2$
    z) $Ag_2C_2O_4$

7. a) strontium chloride monohydrate
    b) cobalt(II) hydroxide
    c) hydrogen bromide
    d) hydroiodic acid
    e) titanium(IV) oxide
    f) tin(II) sulfate
    g) arsenous acid
    h) carbon dioxide
    i) calcium hydrogen selenide
    j) dichlorine monoxide
    k) calcium phosphate
    l) copper(I) nitrite
    m) copper(I) nitride
    n) acetic acid
    o) oxalic acid
    p) magnesium nitrate
    q) iron(III) sulfide
    r) sodium hydrogen arsenate
    s) copper(II) hydrogen sulfite
    t) hypobromous acid
    u) cesium periodate
    v) zinc chlorite
    w) silver phosphite
    x) dinitrogen monoxide
    y) lithium cyanide
    z) cadmium arsenate

8. a) $Fe(CN)_3$
    b) HCN
    c) CO
    d) Ca_3P_2
    e) $SrHPO_4$
    f) $CoCl_3$
    g) Hg_2F_2
    h) MnO_2
    i) $HBrO_3$
    j) H_2SO_3
    k) $KClO$
    l) Fe_3N_2
    m) $Ba(OH)_2$
    n) $Fe(HSO_4)_3$
    o) H_3PO_4
    p) $Al_2(C_2O_4)_3 \cdot 2H_2O$
    q) $Co(BrO_3)_3$
    r) $Fe(OH)_3$
    s) $Sn(NO_2)_4$
    t) $Cu(H_2PO_4)_2$
    u) $Be(SCN)_2$
    v) $Ba(H_2PO_3)_2$
    w) $Al_2(HAsO_3)_3$
    x) H_2TeO_3
    y) $Ca(BrO)_2$
    z) $NaHSO_3$

MODULE 6. *Chemical Reactions*

I. **Chemical Reactions**

There are several reaction types that you will be expected to recognize and in some cases be able to predict the final products. These reaction types will be either redox (oxidation-reduction) or non-redox reactions. Redox reactions are reactions in which individual elements (within reactants and products) undergo a change in oxidation number.

A. Types of Non-Redox Reactions

    a) Dissociation/Ionization Reactions

    b) Double Replacement (Metathesis) Reactions

        1. Precipitation Reactions - Reactions in which a water insoluble solid is formed.

        2. Neutralization (Acid-Base) Reactions - Reactions in which acids react with bases to form the weak electrolyte, water.

        3. Slightly Ionized Product Formation Reactions - Reactions in which a slightly ionized (i.e., weak electrolyte) product, such as a weak acid or base, is formed.

        4. Gas Formation Reactions - Reactions in which a gas forms.

B. Types of Redox Reactions

    a) Combination Reactions (not all are redox)

    b) Decomposition Reactions (not all are redox)

    c) Disproportionation Reactions

    d) Combustion Reactions

    e) Single Replacement (Displacement) Reactions

    f) Miscellaneous Redox Reactions (Reactions which are not specifically any of the above redox reactions)

Examples of each will be shown below. For many of the reactions shown, the physical state of the reactants and products are denoted by the use of the following symbols:

(g) ---> gas   (*l*) ---> pure liquid   (s) ---> solid   (aq) ---> aqueous

II. **Non-Redox Reactions**

A. **Dissociation/Ionization Reactions**

Dissociation refers to the process in which a solid *ionic compound*, such as NaCl, separates into its ions in solution. **Ionization** refers to the process in which *acids & bases*, such as HBr or NaOH, separate to form ions in solution.

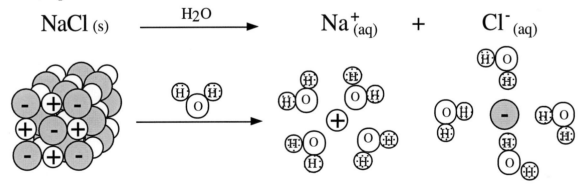

Ions have been separated and surrounded by water. These ions
are hydrated or solvated by water.

Solutes that are water-soluble can be classified as either electrolytes (weak or strong) or nonelectrolytes. **Electrolytes** are substances whose aqueous solutions conduct electrical current.

Electrical current is carried through aqueous solutions by the movement of ions. The strength of the electrolyte depends upon the number of ions in solution, as well as, the charges of these ions.

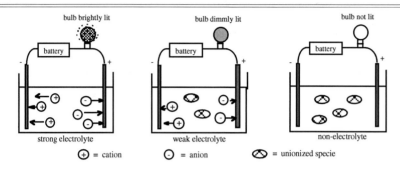

strong electrolyte   weak electrolyte   non-electrolyte

⊕ = cation   ⊖ = anion   ⊗ = unionized specie

Strong electrolytes are substances that completely ionize in water (i.e., substances that conduct electricity well in dilute solutions). A general example of the dissociation/ionization process for strong electrolytes is,

$$A_xB_y \xrightarrow{H_2O} x\,A^{y+} + y\,B^{x-}$$

Soluble = strong.

The following are considered strong electrolytes.

a) **Soluble Salts** (compounds other than acids or base). [*NOTE: Solubility Rule 7, talks about bases. Even though NH₄OH is soluble in water (according to this rule), it is a weak electrolyte.*] *To predict whether an ionic compound is soluble in water, use the solubility rules given below.*

SOLUBILITY RULES

1. All salts of alkali metals (IA) are *soluble*.

2. All NH_4^+ salts are *soluble*.

3. All salts containing the anions: NO_3^-, ClO_3^-, ClO_4^-, $C_2H_3O_2^-$ are *soluble*.

4. All Cl^-, Br^-, and I^- are *soluble* except for Ag^+, Pb^{2+}, and Hg_2^{2+} salts.

5. All SO_4^{2-} are *soluble* except for Pb^{2+}, Sr^{2+}, and Ba^{2+} salts.

6. All O^{2-} are *insoluble* except for IA metals, Ca^{2+}, Sr^{2+}, and Ba^{2+}. [Soluble metal oxides, form hydroxides; for example: $CaO \xrightarrow{H_2O} Ca^{2+} + 2\,OH^-$]

7. All OH^- are *insoluble* except for IA metals, NH_4^+, Ba^{2+} and Sr^{2+}. [Though NH₄OH is soluble in water it is a weak electrolyte and weak base (see below).]

8. All salts containing the anions: CO_3^{2-}, PO_4^{3-}, AsO_4^{3-}, S^{2-} and SO_3^{2-} are *insoluble* except for IA metals and NH_4^+ salts.

9. For salts containing anions not mentioned above (e.g., $Cr_2O_7^{2-}$, P^{3-}, CrO_4^{2-}, $C_2O_4^{2-}$, etc.) assume that they are *insoluble* except for IA metals and NH_4^+ salts, unless otherwise informed.

---

b) **Strong Acids**   All acids are soluble in water

HCl, HBr, HI	
HClO₄, HBrO₄, HIO₄,	Strong acids and strong electrolytes.
HNO₃, H₂SO₄,	

c) **Strong Bases**   All Strong. bases ar Sol. All weak on insol. except $NH_4OH(aq)$.

IA hydroxides	Strong bases and strong electrolytes.
IIA hydroxides except $Be(OH)_2$ and $Mg(OH)_2$	

[NOTE: For all practical purposes, "all" acids are soluble in water. However, only those acids that are strong acids are strong electrolytes. Likewise, only those bases that are strong bases are strong electrolytes.]

If an ionic compound is said to be in an aqueous solution, that means that it has dissolved (dissociated/ionized) in water (i.e., $LiCl_{(aq)} \rightarrow Li^+_{(aq)} + Cl^-_{(aq)}$). [NOTE: For dissociated/ionized substances, the physical state (aq) of the ions will be omitted, i.e., $Li^+ + Cl^-$.]

Weak electrolytes are substances that partially ionize in water (i.e., substances that conduct electricity poorly in dilute aqueous solutions). A general example of the dissociation/ionization process for weak electrolytes is,

$$A_xB_y \xrightleftharpoons{H_2O} x\,A^{y+} + y\,B^{x-}$$

The double arrow means that the reaction is *reversible* (i.e., the reaction can occur in both directions). With weak electrolytes, the unionized specie, A_xB_y is still present in solution.

The following are considered weak electrolytes (in aqueous solutions):
    a) *insoluble salts* - any salt that is not soluble in water according to solubility rules
    b) *weak acids* - any acid that is not one of the strong acids mentioned above
    c) *weak bases* - any base that is not one of the strong bases mentioned above
    d) *water*
    e) *certain gases* (e.g., CO_2, SO_2)

Non-electrolytes do not ionize in water at all (i.e., substances that do not conduct electricity in dilute solutions). A general example of the dissociation/ionization process for non-electrolytes is,

C_2H_5OH – Also insol. in H_2O

$$C_xH_yO_x \xrightarrow{H_2O} \text{N.R.} \quad \text{(no reaction -- no dissociation/ionization)}$$

The following are considered non-electrolytes:

    a) organic compounds containing oxygen [e.g., such as alcohols (general formula: C_xH_yOH) and sugars (general formula: $C_xH_{2x}O_x$)] that dissolve in water, but do not ionize/dissociate.

Example Problems:

1. Complete and balance the following reactions. If the compound does not dissociate/ionize in water "completely" (i.e., is a weak or non-electrolyte) write N.R. (no reaction).

    a) $V(NO_3)_3 \xrightarrow{H_2O}$
        $V(NO_3)_3 \xrightarrow{H_2O} V^{3+} + 3\,NO_3^- \qquad$ (Solubility Rule 3)

    b) $(NH_4)_2SO_4 \xrightarrow{H_2O}$
        $(NH_4)_2SO_4 \xrightarrow{H_2O} 2\,NH_4^+ + SO_4^{2-} \qquad$ (Solubility Rule 2 & 5)

    c) $Al(C_2H_3O_2)_3 \xrightarrow{H_2O}$
        $Al(C_2H_3O_2)_3 \xrightarrow{H_2O} Al^{3+} + 3\,C_2H_3O_2^- \qquad$ (Solubility Rule 3)

d) $AgBr \xrightarrow{H_2O}$

$ AgBr \xrightarrow{H_2O}$ N.R.   (Solubility Rule 4)

e) $CuCO_3 \xrightarrow{H_2O}$

$ CuCO_3 \xrightarrow{H_2O}$ N.R.   (Solubility Rule 8)

f) $NH_4OH \xrightarrow{H_2O}$

$ NH_4OH \xrightarrow{H_2O}$ N.R.   (Weak Base)

g) $H_3PO_4 \xrightarrow{H_2O}$

$ H_3PO_4 \xrightarrow{H_2O}$ N.R.   (Weak Acid)

h) $C_3H_6O_3 \xrightarrow{H_2O}$

$ C_3H_6O_3 \xrightarrow{H_2O}$ N.R.   (Organic compound containing oxygen)

2. Which of the substance in the previous question are: a) strong electrolytes, b) weak electrolytes, c) non-electrolyte.

      a) a, b, c   b) d, e, f, g   c) h

B. Double Replacement (Metathesis) Reactions

These types of reactions are characterized by the cation of one compound exchanging with the cation of another compound. In other words, both compounds trade partners. A general example is:

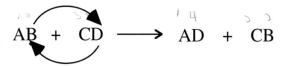

$$AB + CD \longrightarrow AD + CB$$

where A and C are cations and B and D are anions

The driving force that causes a double replacement reaction to occur is the formation of a weak electrolyte. The following are considered weak electrolytes:

- Insoluble salts (Use Solubility Rules -- soluble salts are strong electrolytes)
- Water (formed by an acid-base reaction)
- Weak acids or weak bases
    Weak Acids - any acid other than those strong acids listed previously
    Weak Bases - any base other than those strong bases listed previously
- Certain Gases (e.g., CO_2, SO_2)

One or both of the products of a double replacement reaction must be a weak electrolyte. If both products of a double replacement reaction are strong electrolytes, then no reaction occurs.

The following are examples of double replacement reactions that yield weak electrolytes.

a) *Precipitation Reactions (Formation of a water insoluble solid)*

$$AB_{(aq)} + CD_{(aq)} \rightarrow \underline{AD}_{(s)} + CB_{(aq)}$$

where AD is an insoluble or slightly insoluble salt --> weak electrolyte

To recognize if a precipitate (abbreviated -- ppt) forms, you must learn how to interpret the solubility rules. Also, you must know how to write the formulas of the compounds that form and consequently balance the chemical equation (review the module on writing formulas).

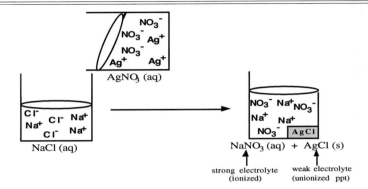

Example Problem : Complete and balance the following reactions:

1. $(NH_4)_3PO_4$ (aq) + $MgSO_4$ (aq) →

Step 1: Exchange Partners. Except for the subscripts on polyatomic ions, don't worry about subscripts.

$(NH_4)_3PO_4$ (aq) + $MgSO_4$ (aq) → $MgPO_4$ + NH_4SO_4

Step 2: Using the solubility rules, predict if at least one of the products is going to be insoluble in water.

$(NH_4)_3PO_4$ (aq) + $MgSO_4$ (aq) → $MgPO_4$ + NH_4SO_4

According to solubility rule 8, $MgPO_4$ (not written correctly yet) is not soluble in water; therefore, the reaction takes place. According to solubility rule 2 & 5, NH_4SO_4 (not written correctly yet) is soluble in water.

Step 3: Using rules that were previously learned, write the charge for each individual ion. Upon changing partners, the charges on the individual ions don't change.

$(NH_4^+)_3PO_4^{3-}$ (aq) + $Mg^{2+}SO_4^{2-}$ (aq) → $Mg^{2+}PO_4^{3-}$ + $NH_4^+SO_4^{2-}$

Step 4: If the charge on the cation is not equal to the charge on the anion, use subscripts in order for the charge on the compound to equal zero.

$(NH_4^+)_3PO_4^{3-}$ (aq) + $Mg^{2+}SO_4^{2-}$ (aq) → $(Mg^{2+})_3(PO_4^{3-})_2$ + $(NH_4^+)_2SO_4^{2-}$

Step 5: Write the correct chemical formula (remove charges and unnecessary parentheses) and denote the physical state of each product.

$(NH_4)_3PO_4$ (aq) + $MgSO_4$ (aq) → $Mg_3(PO_4)_2$ (s) + $(NH_4)_2SO_4$ (aq)

Step 6: Balance the chemical equation.

2 $(NH_4)_3PO_4$ (aq) + 3 $MgSO_4$ (aq) → $Mg_3(PO_4)_2$ (s) + 3 $(NH_4)_2SO_4$ (aq)

2. $FeBr_3$ (aq) + Na_2SO_3 (aq) →

Step 1: $FeBr_3$ (aq) + Na_2SO_3 (aq) → $NaBr$ + $FeSO_3$

Step 2: According to solubility rule 8, one of the products, $FeSO_3$ (not written correctly yet) is insoluble in water; therefore, a reaction takes place. According to solubility rule 1, NaBr is soluble in water.

Step 3: $Fe^{3+}(Br^-)_3$ (aq) + $(Na^+)_2SO_3^{2-}$ (aq) → Na^+Br^- + $Fe^{3+}SO_3^{2-}$

Step 4: $Fe^{3+}(Br^-)_3$ (aq) + $(Na^+)_2SO_3^{2-}$ (aq) → Na^+Br^- + $(Fe^{3+})_2(SO_3^{2-})_3$

Step 5: $FeBr_3$ (aq) + Na_2SO_3 (aq) → $NaBr$ (aq) + $Fe_2(SO_3)_3$ (s)

Step 6: 2 $FeBr_3$ (aq) + 3 Na_2SO_3 (aq) → 6 $NaBr$(aq) + $Fe_2(SO_3)_3$ (s)

3. $NaCl_{(aq)} + AgNO_{3(aq)} \rightarrow$

   Step 1: $NaCl_{(aq)} + AgNO_{3(aq)} \rightarrow AgCl + NaNO_3$

   Step 2: According to solubility rule 4, one of the products, AgCl, is insoluble in water; therefore, a reaction takes place. According to solubility rule 1 & 3, $NaNO_3$ is soluble in water.

   $NaCl_{(aq)} + AgNO_{3(aq)} \rightarrow AgCl_{(s)} + NaNO_{3(aq)}$ (balanced)

4. $CuNO_{3(aq)} + NaC_2H_3O_{2(aq)} \rightarrow$

   Step 1: $CuNO_{3(aq)} + NaC_2H_3O_{2(aq)} \rightarrow NaNO_3 + CuC_2H_3O_2$

   Step 2: According to solubility rule 1 & 3, $NaNO_3$ is soluble in water. According to solubility rule 3, $CuC_2H_3O_2$ is also soluble in water; therefore, no reaction takes place.

   $CuNO_{3(aq)} + NaC_2H_3O_{2(aq)} \rightarrow NR$

b) ***Neutralization (Acid-Base) Reactions***

$$\begin{array}{ccccccc} HA & + & BOH & \rightarrow & BX & + & H_2O \\ \text{acid} & & \text{base} & & \text{salt} & & \text{weak electrolyte} \end{array}$$

To recognize a neutralization reaction you must know what are acids and bases. There are several definitions of what constitutes an acid and a base. The definition of an acid and base that we will be working with, for now, is that supplied by Arrhenius:

> *Acids - Substances that ionize in water to produce H^+*
>
> *Bases - Substances that ionize in water to produce OH^-*

[NOTE: Neutralization reactions are easier to balance if H_2O is written as HOH. Then balance "OH" as a group.]

Example Problem: Complete and balance the following reaction:

1. $HNO_{3(aq)} + NaOH_{(aq)} \rightarrow$

   $HNO_{3(aq)} + NaOH_{(aq)} \rightarrow NaNO_{3(aq)} + H_2O_{(l)}$

   The acid (HNO_3) reacts with the base (NaOH) to form the weak electrolyte water; therefore, the chemical reaction takes place. The equation as written is already balanced.

2. $HClO_{3(aq)} + Mg(OH)_{2(s)} \rightarrow$

   $2 HClO_{3(aq)} + Mg(OH)_{2(s)} \rightarrow Mg(ClO_3)_{2(aq)} + 2 H_2O_{(l)}$

   The acid ($HClO_3$) reacts with the base ($Mg(OH)_2$) to form the weak electrolyte water; therefore, the chemical reaction takes place.

c) ***Slightly Ionized Product Formation Reactions (Reactions yielding a weak acid or weak base)***

$$\begin{array}{ccccccc} AB & + & HX & \rightarrow & \underline{HB} & + & AX \\ \text{salt} & & \text{acid} & & \text{weak acid} & & \end{array}$$

$$\begin{array}{ccccccc} AX & + & BOH & \rightarrow & \underline{AOH} & + & BX \\ \text{salt} & & \text{base} & & \text{weak base} & & \end{array}$$

To recognize if a slightly ionized acid or base forms, you must know (memorize) which are weak acids and bases.

Example Problems: Complete and balance the following reactions:

1. $AgClO_{2(aq)} + HNO_{3(aq)} \rightarrow$

   $AgClO_{2(aq)} + HNO_{3(aq)} \rightarrow AgNO_{3(aq)} + HClO_{2(aq)}$

   $HClO_2$ is a weak acid; therefore, the chemical reaction takes place. The equation as written is already balanced.

2. NH_4NO_3 (aq) + $NaOH$ (aq) $\rightarrow$

   NH_4NO_3 (aq) + $NaOH$ (aq) $\rightarrow$ NH_4OH (aq) + $NaNO_3$ (aq)

   NH_4OH is a weak base; therefore, the chemical reaction takes place. The equation as written is already balanced.

d) **Reactions with Gas Formation**

Many of the weak acids and bases that form as a result of double replacement reactions decompose to form a gas and water. The most common examples are H_2CO_3 and H_2SO_3, both are weak acids that decompose into a gas and water.

$$CaCO_3 \text{ (s)} + 2\,HCl \text{ (aq)} \rightarrow [H_2CO_3] + CaCl_2 \text{ (aq)} \rightarrow CaCl_2 \text{ (aq)} + H_2O \text{ (l)} + CO_2 \text{ (g)}$$

$$MgSO_3 \text{ (s)} + 2\,HCl \text{ (aq)} \rightarrow MgCl_2 \text{ (aq)} + [H_2SO_3] \rightarrow MgCl_2 \text{ (aq)} + H_2O \text{ (l)} + SO_2 \text{ (g)}$$

Example Problem: Complete and balance the following reaction:
  1. Na_2CO_3 (aq) + HNO_3 (aq) $\rightarrow$

     Na_2CO_3 (aq) + $2\,HNO_3$ (aq) $\rightarrow$ $2\,NaNO_3$ (aq) + H_2O (l) + CO_2 (g)

III. Writing Double Replacement Reactions in Total Ionic and Net Ionic Form

In the examples of the double replacement reactions shown above, the reactions were written in *molecular form* -- all formulas were written as if all substances existed as molecules, i.e., only complete formulas were used. [$2\,FeBr_3$ (aq) + $3\,Na_2SO_3$ (aq) $\rightarrow$ $6\,NaBr$ (aq) + $Fe_2(SO_3)_3$ (s)].

When placed in water, strong electrolytes break up into their respective ions. For example, $NaCl$ (s) when placed in water becomes $NaCl$ (aq); however, $NaCl$ (aq) really exists as Na^+ (aq) + Cl^- (aq).

When writing double replacement reactions in *total ionic* form, those substances that are strong electrolytes [i.e., those substances written as (aq), except for weak acids and bases] must be written as their corresponding free ions.

When writing double replacement reactions in *net ionic form*, spectator ions are cancelled from both sides of the chemical reactions. *Spectator ions* - those ions in solution that do not participate in the chemical reaction (those ions appearing on both sides of the chemical equation).

Example Problems: Write balanced molecular, total ionic, and net ionic equations for the following:
  1. HNO_3 (aq) + $NaOH$ (aq) $\rightarrow$

     HNO_3 (aq) + $NaOH$ (aq) $\rightarrow$ $NaNO_3$ (aq) + H_2O (l)   molecular

     $H^+ + NO_3^- + Na^+ + OH^- \rightarrow Na^+ + NO_3^- + H_2O$ (l)   total ionic

     $H^+ + OH^- \rightarrow H_2O$ (l)   net ionic

                          Spectator Ions - Na^+ & NO_3^-

  2. $MnCl_3$ (aq) + Na_2S (aq) $\rightarrow$

     $2\,MnCl_3$ (aq) + $3\,Na_2S$ (aq) $\rightarrow$ Mn_2S_3 (s) + $6\,NaCl$ (aq)   molecular

     $2\,Mn^{3+} + 6\,Cl^- + 6\,Na^+ + 3\,S^{2-} \rightarrow Mn_2S_3$ (s) $+ 6\,Na^+ + 6\,Cl^-$ total ionic

     $2\,Mn^{3+} + 3\,S^{2-} \rightarrow Mn_2S_3$ (s)   net ionic

                          Spectator Ions - Na^+ & Cl^-

  3. $Co(C_2H_3O_2)_2$ (aq) + H_3PO_4 (aq) $\rightarrow$

     $3\,Co(C_2H_3O_2)_2$ (aq) + $2\,H_3PO_4$ (aq) $\rightarrow$ $Co_3(PO_4)_2$ (s) + $6\,HC_2H_3O_2$ (aq)   molecular
                          weak acid   weak acid

$$3 \, Co^{2+} + \, 6 \, C_2H_3O_2^- + \, 2 \, H_3PO_4 \, _{(aq)} \rightarrow \, Co_3(PO_4)_2 \, _{(s)} + \, 6 \, HC_2H_3O_2 \, _{(aq)} \qquad \text{total ionic}$$

$$3 \, Co^{2+} + \, 6 \, C_2H_3O_2^- + \, 2 \, H_3PO_4 \, _{(aq)} \rightarrow \, Co_3(PO_4)_2 \, _{(s)} + \, 6 \, HC_2H_3O_2 \, _{(aq)} \qquad \text{net ionic}$$

Spectator Ions - None

4. $NH_4C_2H_3O_2 \, _{(aq)} + \, Ba(OH)_2 \, _{(aq)} \rightarrow$

$$2 \, NH_4C_2H_3O_2 \, _{(aq)} + \, Ba(OH)_2 \, _{(aq)} \rightarrow \, 2 \, NH_4OH \, _{(aq)} + \, Ba(C_2H_3O_2)_2 \, _{(aq)} \qquad \text{molecular}$$
weak base

$$2 \, NH_4^+ + \, 2 \, C_2H_3O_2^- + \, Ba^{2+} + \, 2 \, OH^- \, _{(aq)} \rightarrow 2 \, NH_4OH \, _{(aq)} + Ba^{2+} + \, 2 \, C_2H_3O_2^- \quad \text{total ionic}$$

$$2 \, NH_4^+ + \quad 2 \, OH^- \, _{(aq)} \rightarrow \, 2 \, NH_4OH \, _{(aq)} \qquad \text{net ionic}$$

Spectator Ions - Ba^{2+} & $C_2H_3O_2^-$

IV. Reduction and Oxidation

Reduction is defined as the gain of electrons.   For example, $Li^+ + \, e^- \rightarrow Li$.

Oxidation is defined as the loss of electrons. For example, $Mg \rightarrow Mg^{2+} + \, 2e^-$

There can be no oxidation without an accompanying reduction or vice-versa. In order to determine which specie in a redox reaction has been oxidized and which has been reduced, one must first determine the oxidation number for each element. For example,

$$\overset{0}{S} \, _{(s)} + \, \overset{0}{O_2} \, _{(g)} \rightarrow \overset{+4 \, -2}{S O_2} \, _{(g)}$$

Sulfur has been oxidized (oxidation number has increased from 0 to +4, i.e., it has lost e^-)

Oxygen has been reduced (oxidation number has decreased from 0 to -2, i.e., it has gained e^-)

Reducing Agent (Reductant) is the reagent that donates the electron(s). Reducing agents are always oxidized.

Oxidizing Agent (Oxidant) is the reagent that accepts the electron(s). Oxidizing agents are always reduced.

In the above reaction: O_2 is the oxidizing agent because it accepted electrons from S and S is the reducing agent because it donated its electrons to oxygen.

<u>Example Problems</u>: The following are redox reactions, which specie has been oxidized and which specie has been reduced. Also give which specie is the oxidant and which is the reductant.

1. $2 \, H_2 \, _{(g)} + \, O_2 \, _{(g)} \rightarrow \, 2 \, H_2O \, _{(g)}$

$$2 \, \overset{0}{H_2} \, _{(s)} + \, \overset{0}{O_2} \, _{(g)} \rightarrow \, 2 \, \overset{+1 \, -2}{H_2O} \, _{(g)}$$

H_2 has been oxidized (oxidation number has increased from 0 to +1)
O_2 has been reduced (oxidation number has decreased from 0 to -2)

H_2 is the reductant (it has donated its electrons to O_2)
O_2 is the oxidant (it has accepted electrons from H_2)

2. $Zn \, _{(s)} + \, CuSO_4 \, _{(aq)} \rightarrow \, ZnSO_4 \, _{(aq)} + \, Cu \, _{(s)}$

$$\overset{0}{Zn} \, _{(s)} + \, \overset{+2}{CuSO_4} \, _{(aq)} \rightarrow \, \overset{+2}{ZnSO_4} \, _{(aq)} + \, \overset{0}{Cu} \, _{(s)}$$

NOTE: Neither S(+6) or O(-2) undergo a change in oxidation number. The sulfate ion is thus a spectator ion.

Zn has been oxidized (oxidation number has increased from 0 to +2)
Cu, in $CuSO_4$, has been reduced (oxidation number has decreased from +2 to 0)

Zn is the reductant (it has donated its electrons to Cu^{2+} in the specie $CuSO_4$)
$CuSO_4$ is the oxidant (it has accepted electrons from Zn)

3. $2 ZnO_{(s)} + C_{(s)} \rightarrow 2 Zn_{(s)} + CO_{2(g)}$

$$\overset{+2}{2 ZnO_{(s)}} + \overset{0}{C_{(s)}} \rightarrow \overset{0}{2 Zn_{(s)}} + \overset{+4}{CO_{2(g)}}$$

NOTE: O(-2) is not undergoing a change in oxidation number

C has been oxidized (oxidation number has increased from 0 to +4)
Zn, in ZnO, has been reduced (oxidation number has decreased from +2 to 0)

C is the reductant (it has donated its electrons to Zn^{2+} in the specie ZnO)
ZnO is the oxidant (it has accepted electrons from C)

V. Redox (Oxidation-Reduction) Reactions

The following are examples of Redox Reactions. The only redox reactions in which you must be able to predict the products are: a) combustion reactions and b) single replacement (displacement) reactions. The other redox reactions you need only be able to recognize the reaction type.

A. Combination Reactions

This type of reaction is characterized by the formation of one compound from simpler materials. Not all combination reactions are redox reactions, those that involve one or more free elements, however, are redox reactions. A general example is:

$$A + B \rightarrow AB \qquad \text{where A and B can be elements or compounds}$$

Specific examples of combination reactions are shown below:

$2 K_{(s)} + F_{2(g)} \rightarrow 2 KF_{(s)}$ redox reaction

$Cl_{2(g)} + PCl_{3(l)} \rightarrow PCl_{5(s)}$ redox reaction

$P_4O_{6(s)} + 6 H_2O_{(l)} \rightarrow 4 H_3PO_{3(aq)}$ not a redox reaction

B. Decomposition Reactions

This type of reaction is characterized by a compound being broken down into simpler compounds or all the way down to the component elements. Not all decompostion reactions are redox reactions, those that involve one or more free elements, however, are redox reactions. A general example is:

$$AB \rightarrow A + B \qquad \text{where A and B can be elements or compounds}$$

Specific examples of decompostion reactions are shown below:

$Ba(ClO_3)_{2(s)} \rightarrow BaCl_{2(s)} + 3 O_{2(g)}$ redox reaction

$2 K_2O_{(s)} \rightarrow 4 K_{(s)} + O_{2(g)}$ redox reaction

$2 KOH_{(s)} \rightarrow K_2O_{(s)} + H_2O_{(g)}$ not a redox reaction

C. Disproportionation Reactions

This type of reaction, is characterized by the same element in a specie undergoing both oxidation and reduction. One of the elements in a compound involved in a disproportionation reaction has at least three oxidation states. The reactant element itself is in one of these states, and there are both a higher and lower possible oxidation states for the same element. The following elements are most likely to undergo disproportionation: N, P, O, S, Cl, Br, I, Mn, Cu, Au, and Hg.

Specific examples of disproportionation reactions are shown below. [NOTE: oxidation numbers are shown only for that element which is undergoing a change in oxidation number.]

$$\overset{-1}{2\,H_2O_2}\,_{(aq)} \rightarrow \overset{-2}{2\,H_2O}\,_{(l)} + \overset{0}{O_2}\,_{(g)}$$

$$\overset{+1}{3\,AuCl}\,_{(s)} \rightarrow \overset{0}{2\,Au}\,_{(s)} + \overset{+3}{AuCl_3}\,_{(aq)}$$

$$\overset{0}{Cl_2}\,_{(g)} + 2\,NaOH\,_{(aq)} \rightarrow \overset{+1}{NaClO}\,_{(aq)} + \overset{-1}{NaCl}\,_{(aq)} + 2\,H_2O\,_{(l)}$$

At first glance the first two reactions appear to be decompositions, however, in disproportionations the same element is undergoing a change in oxidation number; whereas, in decompositions, two (or possibly more) elements are undergoing a change in oxidation number.

D. **Combustion Reactions**

Compounds containing C & H in their formula, when burned in the presence of O_2, form CO_2 $_{(g)}$ and H_2O $_{(l)}$. A general example is:

$$C_xH_y + O_2\,_{(g)} \rightarrow CO_2\,_{(g)} + H_2O\,_{(l)}$$

Example Problems: Complete and balance the following equations:

1. CH_4 $_{(g)}$ + O_2 $_{(g)}$ $\rightarrow$

$$CH_4\,_{(g)} + 2\,O_2\,_{(g)} \rightarrow CO_2\,_{(g)} + 2\,H_2O\,_{(l)}$$

2. C_4H_{10} $_{(g)}$ + O_2 $_{(g)}$ $\rightarrow$

$$2\,C_4H_{10}\,_{(g)} + 13\,O_2\,_{(g)} \rightarrow 8\,CO_2\,_{(g)} + 10\,H_2O\,_{(l)}$$

E. **Single Replacement (Displacement) Reactions**

Reactions in which one element displaces another from a compound are called replacement (or displacement) reactions. Active metals displace less active metals or hydrogen from their compounds in solution.   Also, halogens can displace less active halogens from their compounds in solution.
It has been possible to arrange elements (metals and "H" in one list and halogens in another list) in a series called the electromotive (activity) series, so that each element in the series will displace any of those following it from an aqueous solution of its salt.

Electromotive (Activity) Series*

for metals

Li>K>Ba>Sr>Ca>Na> *Mg>Al>Zn>Cr>Fe>* Cd>Co>Ni>Sn>Pb>(H)>Sb>Bi>Cu>Hg>Ag>Pd>Pt>Au

for halogens

F>Cl>Br>I

---

* with metals having variable oxidation numbers, one of its lower oxidation states is often formed:
Cr^{3+}, Fe^{2+}, Co^{2+}, Ni^{2+}, Sn^{2+}, Pb^{2+}, Sb^{3+}, Cu^+, Hg_2^{2+}, Pd^{3+}, Pt^{3+}

* Bold Print: Reacts with H_2O (l) ; Bold-Italics Print: Reacts with steam (i.e., H_2O (g))

There are basically three types of single replacement reactions:

a. *A free and chemically active metal displacing a less active metal from a compound*

In general this type of single replacement reaction can be illustrated as follows:

$$A + \underline{B}C\,_{(aq)} \rightarrow AC + \underline{B}$$

where A (a metal) displaces B from an aqueous solution containing BC

Example Problems: Complete and balance the following reactions.

1. Mg $_{(s)}$ + $AuBr_3$ $_{(aq)}$ $\rightarrow$

Mg is more active than Au; therefore, it displaces Au. The compound that forms is $MgBr_2$ (Mg^{2+} - group IIA & Br^- - group VIIA).

$$3 \, Mg_{(s)} + 2 \, AuBr_3 \, _{(aq)} \rightarrow 3 \, MgBr_2 \, _{(aq)} + 2 \, Au_{(s)}$$

2. $Ag_{(s)} + Hg(NO_3)_2 \, _{(aq)} \rightarrow$

Ag is less active than Hg; therefore, it does not displace Hg.

$$Ag_{(s)} + Hg(NO_3)_2 \, _{(aq)} \rightarrow \text{No Reaction}$$

3. $Pb_{(s)} + Au(ClO_4)_3 \, _{(aq)} \rightarrow$

Pb is more active than Au; therefore, it displaces Au. Even though Pb has a variable oxidation number; as stated above, the lower +2 oxidation state is often formed. The compound that forms is $Pb(ClO_4)_2$ (Pb^{2+} and ClO_4^-).

$$3 \, Pb_{(s)} + 2 \, Au(ClO_4)_3 \, _{(aq)} \rightarrow 3 \, Pb(ClO_4)_2 \, _{(aq)} + 2 \, Au_{(s)}$$

b. ***A free and chemically active metal displacing hydrogen from acids or water***
In general this type of single replacement reaction can be illustrated as follows:

$$M + \underline{H}X_{(aq)} \rightarrow MX + \underline{H}_2 \, _{(g)}$$

$$^*M + \underline{H}_2O_{(l)} \rightarrow MOH + \underline{H}_2 \, _{(g)}$$

where M (a metal) displaces H from an aqueous solution containing HX or H_2O

Example Problems: Complete and balance the following reactions.

1. $K_{(s)} + H_2O_{(l)} \rightarrow$

K is more active than H; therefore, it displaces H. The compound that forms is KOH (K^+, group IA & OH^-).

$$2 \, K_{(s)} + 2 \, H_2O_{(l)} \rightarrow 2 \, KOH_{(aq)} + H_2 \, _{(g)}$$

2. $Ni_{(s)} + HNO_3 \, _{(aq)} \rightarrow$

Ni is more active than H; therefore, it displaces H. The compound that forms is $Ni(NO_3)_2$ (Ni^{2+}, +2 oxidation state is often formed, and NO_3^-).

$$Ni_{(s)} + 2 \, HNO_3 \, _{(aq)} \rightarrow Ni(NO_3)_2 \, _{(aq)} + H_2 \, _{(g)}$$

c. ***An active halogen (VIIA non-metal) in the uncombined state displacing a less active halogen***
In general this type of single replacement reaction can be illustrated as follows:

$$X_2 + M\underline{Y}_{(aq)} \rightarrow MX + Y_2$$

where X_2 (a halogen) displaces Y (a less active halogen)
the metal does not change oxidation states

Since all halogens form an ion that has a -1 charge, the formula of the salt that forms basically remains the same except for the replacement of Y (in MY) with X.

Example Problems: Complete and balance the following reactions.

1. $Cl_2 \, _{(g)} + FeBr_3 \, _{(aq)} \rightarrow$

Cl is more active than Br; thus, it displaces Br. The compound that forms is $FeCl_3$ (Fe^{3+} & Cl^-)

$3 Cl_{2 (g)} + 2 FeBr_{3 (aq)} \rightarrow 2 FeCl_{3 (aq)} + 3 Br_{2 (l)}$

2. $I_{2 (s)} + NaF_{(aq)} \rightarrow$

I is less active than F; thus, it does not replace F.

$I_{2 (s)} + NaF_{(aq)} \rightarrow$ N.R.

EXERCISES

Reactions

1. Identify the following equations as either one of the following reaction types:
   1) combination   2) decomposition   3) combustion   4) dissociation/ionization
   5) single replacement 6) double replacement 7) disproportionation

   a) $2\ KClO_3\ (s)\ \rightarrow\ 2\ KCl\ (s)\ +\ 3\ O_2\ (g)$

   b) $Cl_2O_3\ (g)\ +\ H_2O\ (l)\ \rightarrow\ 2\ HClO_2\ (aq)$

   c) $2\ Al(NO_3)_3\ (aq)\ +\ 3\ K_2S\ (aq)\ \rightarrow\ Al_2S_3\ (s)\ +\ 6\ KNO_3\ (aq)$

   d) $Ca(OH)_2\ (s)\ \rightarrow\ CaO\ (s)\ +\ H_2O\ (l)$

   e) $Fe_2O_3\ (s)\ +\ 3\ CO_2\ (g)\ \rightarrow\ Fe_2(CO_3)_3\ (s)$

   f) $Mg\ (s)\ +\ 2\ AgNO_3\ (aq)\ \rightarrow\ Mg(NO_3)_2\ (aq)\ +\ 2\ Ag\ (s)$

   g) $H_2SO_4\ (aq)\ +\ Ba(OH)_2\ (aq)\ \rightarrow\ BaSO_4\ (s)\ +\ 2\ H_2O\ (l)$

   h) $2\ C_6H_6\ (l)\ +\ 15\ O_2\ (g)\ \rightarrow\ 12\ CO_2\ (g)\ +\ 6\ H_2O\ (l)$

   i) $Cu_2SO_4\ (aq)\ \xrightarrow{H_2O}\ 2\ Cu^+\ +\ SO_4^{2-}$

   j) $4\ CuNO_3\ (aq)\ \rightarrow\ 2\ Cu\ (s)\ +\ 2\ Cu(NO_3)_2\ (aq)$

   k) $2\ HgO\ (s)\ \rightarrow\ 2\ Hg\ (l)\ +\ O_2\ (g)$

2. Which of the reactions in question 1 are redox reactions?

3. For those reactions in question 1 that are redox reactions, what is the atom that is being oxidized and which is being reduced?

4. For those reactions in question 1 that are redox reactions, what is the oxidizing agent and what is the reducing agent?

5. Classify each of the following as a strong electrolyte, weak electrolyte, or non-electrolyte.
   a) H_2O b) HNO_3 c) H_2SO_3 d) HgO e) NH_4OH f) $NaOH$
   g) $Zn(OH)_2$ h) $Ba(NO_3)_2$ i) $K_2C_2O_4$ j) $C_4H_8O_4$ k) CH_3OH

6. Complete and balance the following dissociation/ionization reactions, if the reactant does not ionize completely in water, write NR.

   a) $FeCl_3\ \xrightarrow{H_2O}$

   b) $K_2C_2O_4\ \xrightarrow{H_2O}$

   c) $Fe_2(SO_4)_3\ \xrightarrow{H_2O}$

   d) $HgCl_2\ \xrightarrow{H_2O}$

   e) $PbCl_4\ \xrightarrow{H_2O}$

   f) $Hg_2Cl_2\ \xrightarrow{H_2O}$

   g) $Cu_2O\ \xrightarrow{H_2O}$

7. Complete and balance the following double replacement reactions, if no reaction occurs write NR. Also write the balanced equation in total ionic and net ionic form.

   a) Na_3PO_4 (aq) + $BaCl_2$ (aq) →

   b) $Fe(C_2H_3O_2)_3$ (aq) + $(NH_4)_3PO_4$ (aq) →

   c) Na_2SO_4 (aq) + $Sr(ClO_3)_2$ (aq) →

   d) Na_2SO_4 (aq) + Li_2CO_3 (aq) →

   e) K_2SO_3 (aq) + HCl (aq) →

   f) $KClO_2$ (aq) + H_2SO_4 (aq) →

   g) $(NH_4)_2S$ (aq) + NaOH (aq) →

   h) $Pb(NO_3)_2$ (aq) + H_2SO_4 (aq) →

   i) $Zn(OH)_2$ (s) + HNO_3 (aq) →

   j) $Ba(OH)_2$ (aq) + H_2SO_4 (aq) →

   k) H_3PO_4 (aq) + $Sr(OH)_2$ (aq) →

   l) $HC_2H_3O_2$ (aq) + NaOH (aq) →

   m) $HClO_3$ (aq) + $Ni(OH)_4$ (s) →

8. Complete and balance the following combustion reactions.

   a) C_3H_6 (g) + O_2 (g) →

   b) C_5H_{12} (l) + O_2 (g) →

   c) C_7H_{12} (l) + O_2 (g) →

9. Complete and balance the following single replacement reactions, if no reaction occurs write NR.

   a) K (s) + $Ba(NO_3)_2$ (aq) →

   b) Mg (s) + $Sn(C_2H_3O_2)_4$ (aq) →

   c) Fe (s) + $PbCl_4$ (aq) →

   d) Cu (s) + $MgSO_4$ (aq) →

   e) Ag (s) + $Au(ClO_3)_4$ (aq) →

   f) Cu (s) + H_2O (l) →

   g) Cd (s) + HCl (aq) →

   h) Ni (s) + H_2SO_4 (aq) →

   i) Al (s) + H_2O (g) →

   j) Pb (s) + H_2O (l) →

   k) Ni (s) + H_2SO_4 (aq) →

   l) I_2 (s) + $FeCl_3$ (aq) →

   m) F_2 (g) + NaCl (aq) →

   n) Cl_2 (g) + CoI_4 (aq) →

   o) Br_2 (l) + NaCl (aq) →

MULTIPLE CHOICE PRACTICE EXAM FOR MODULE 6

1. The following reaction can be classified as:
$$P_4O_{10} + 6\ Na_2O \rightarrow 4\ Na_3PO_4$$

    1) combination reaction   2) decomposition reaction   3) combustion reaction
    4) single replacement reaction   5) double replacement reaction

2. The following reaction can be classified as:
$$2\ PbO + O_2 \rightarrow 2\ PbO_2$$

    1) combination reaction   2) decomposition reaction   3) disproportionation reaction
    4) single replacement reaction   5) double replacement reaction

3. When the following reaction is completed and balanced, the products (including coefficients and physical state) are:
$$C_6H_8\ (l) + O_2\ (g) \rightarrow$$

    1) $6\ CO_2\ (g) + 8\ H_2O\ (l)$ 2) $6\ CO_2\ (g) + 4\ H_2\ (g)$ 3) $6\ CO_2\ (g) + 4\ H_2O\ (l)$
    4) $6\ CO_2\ (l) + 4\ H_2\ (s)$ 5) $C_6H_8O_2\ (l)$

4. When the following reaction is completed and balanced, the products (including coefficients and physical state) are:
$$Zn\ (s) + Fe_2(SO_4)_3\ (aq) \rightarrow$$

    1) $Zn(SO_4)_3\ (aq) + 2\ Fe\ (s)$ 2) $3\ ZnSO_4\ (aq) + 2\ Fe\ (s)$ 3) $Zn_2(SO_4)_3\ (aq) + 2\ Fe\ (s)$
    4) $3\ Zn(SO_4)_2\ (aq) + 2\ Fe\ (s)$ 5) no reaction takes place

5. When the following reaction is completed and balanced, the products (including coefficients and physical state) are:
$$Al\ (s) + HC_2H_3O_2\ (aq) \rightarrow$$

    1) $AlC_2H_3O_2\ (aq) + H\ (g)$ 2) $Al(C_2H_3O_2)_3\ (aq) + 3\ H\ (g)$ 3) $2\ AlC_2H_3O_2\ (aq) + H_2\ (g)$
    4) $2\ Al(C_2H_3O_2)_3\ (aq) + 3\ H_2\ (g)$ 5) no reaction takes place

6. When the following reaction is completed and balanced, the products (including coefficients and physical state) are:
$$Br_2\ (l) + CoI_3\ (aq) \rightarrow$$

    1) $3\ I_2\ (s) + 2\ CoBr_3\ (aq)$ 2) $CoBr_2\ (aq) + I_3\ (s)$ 3) $2\ CoBr_2\ (aq) + 3\ I_2\ (s)$
    4) $2\ Co\ (s) + 6\ BrI\ (s)$ 5) no reaction takes place

7. When the following reaction is completed and balanced, the products (including coefficients and physical state) are:
$$H_2CO_3\ (aq) + Ni(OH)_4\ (s) \rightarrow$$

    1) $NiCO_3\ (aq) + 4\ H_2O\ (l)$ 2) $Ni_2(CO_3)_4\ (s) + 8\ H_2O\ (l)$ 3) $Ni(CO_3)_2\ (s) + 4\ H_2O\ (l)$
    4) $Ni(CO_3)_4\ (s) + 4\ H_2O\ (l)$ 5) no reaction takes place

8. When the following reaction is completed and balanced, the products (including coefficients and physical state) are:
$$Na_2O\ (aq) + Fe_2S_3\ (s) \rightarrow$$

    1) $3\ Na_2S\ (aq) + Fe_2O_3\ (s)$ 2) $Na_2S_3\ (aq) + Fe_2O_3\ (s)$ 3) $3\ Na_2S\ (aq) + Fe_2O_3\ (aq)$
    4) $Na_2Fe\ (aq) + S_3O\ (s)$ 5) no reaction takes place

9. When the following reaction is completed and balanced, the products (including coefficients and physical state) are:
$$Na_2CO_3 \text{ (aq)} + H_3PO_4 \text{ (aq)} \rightarrow$$

1) Na_2PO_4 (aq) $+ H_3CO_3$ (aq)   2) $2 Na_3PO_4$ (aq) $+ 3 H_2O$ (l) $+ 3 CO_2$ (g)

3) $2 Na_3PO_4$ (aq) $+ 2 H_2CO_3$ (aq)   4) $2 Na_2PO_4$ (aq) $+ 3 H_2CO_3$ (g)   5) no reaction takes place

10. The net ionic equation for the following reaction is:
$$Na_2CO_3 \text{ (aq)} + H_3PO_4 \text{ (aq)} \rightarrow$$

1) $2 Na^+ + CO_3^{2-} + 3 H^+ + PO_4^{3-} \rightarrow 2 Na^+ + PO_4^{3-} + 3 H^+ + CO_3^{2-}$

2) $3 CO_3^{2-} + 6 H^+ \rightarrow 3 H_2CO_3$ (aq)

3) $6 Na^+ + 3 CO_3^{2-} + 2 H_3PO_4$ (aq) $\rightarrow 2 Na_3PO_4$ (s) $+ 3 H_2CO_3$ (aq)

4) $3 CO_3^{2-} + 2 H_3PO_4$ (aq) $\rightarrow 2 PO_4^{3-} + 3 H_2O$ (l) $+ 3 CO_2$ (g)

5) $3 Na_2CO_3$ (aq) $+ 2 H_3PO_4$ (aq) $\rightarrow 2 Na_3PO_4$ (aq) $+ 3 H_2CO_3$ (aq)

11. The spectator ion(s) in the following reaction is (are):
$$Na_2CO_3 \text{ (aq)} + H_3PO_4 \text{ (aq)} \rightarrow$$

1) Na^+ and PO_4^{3-} 2) Na^+ 3) Na^+ and CO_3^{3-}

4) $Na^+, PO_4^{3-}, H^+, CO_3^{2-}$ 5) there are no spectator ions

12. Which of the following is a strong base?

       a. $Ba(OH)_2$ b. $NaOH$ c. $Ni(OH)_2$

1) only a   2) only b   3) only a and b

4) only b and c   5) a, b, and c

13. Which of the following is a weak electrolyte?

       a. $Ba(OH)_2$ b. $NaOH$ c. $Ni(OH)_2$

1) only a   2) only c   3) only a and b

4) only a and c   5) a, b, and c

14. Which of the following is a strong acid?

       a. H_3PO_4 b. HI c. HIO_4

1) only b   2) only a and b   3) only a and b

4) only b and c   5) a, b, and c

15. Which of the following is a strong electrolyte?

       a. $PbSO_4$ b. $HgCl_2$ c. $(NH_4)_2S$

1) only a   2) only b and c   3) only a and b

4) only c   5) a, b, and c

16. Which of the following are insoluble in water?

       a. K_2SO_4 b. HgI_2 c. $(NH_4)_2CO_3$

1) only b   2) only b and c   3) only a and b

4) only c   5) none are insoluble water soluble

To answer questions 17 - 25, first complete and balance the following chemical reactions.

    a. C_2H_4 $_{(g)}$ + O_2 $_{(g)}$ $\rightarrow$

    b. $Pb_{(s)}$ + HBr $_{(aq)}$ $\rightarrow$

    c. $NaOH$ $_{(aq)}$ + $PbBr_2$ $_{(s)}$ $\rightarrow$

    d. $Pb(OH)_4$ $_{(s)}$ + HBr $_{(aq)}$ $\rightarrow$

    e. $SnBr_4$ $_{(aq)}$ + Zn $_{(s)}$ $\rightarrow$

17. When equation a is completed and balanced, what is the coefficient in front of O_2?
    1) 1   2) 2   3) 3   4) 4   5) 6

18. What is the weak electrolyte product formed in equation d?
    1) $PbBr_2$ 2) $PbBr_4$ 3) $BrOH$ 4) H_2O 5) PbH_4

19. When equation e is completed, what solid forms?
    1) $ZnBr_2$ 2) $ZnBr_4$ 3) Sn & $ZnBr_4$ 4) Sn
    5) none of the above

20. When equation c is completed and balanced, what is the sum of all the coefficients (remember to add coefficients of 1)?
    1) 12   2) 8   3) 6   4) 5   5) 4

21. In which of the above reactions is water a product?
    1) only a   2) only b & c   3) only c   4) only a & d   5) only a, b, c, & d

22. In which of the above reactions is a water soluble bromide salt a product?
    1) only c   2) only c, d & e   3) only c   4) only b, c, & e   5) only b, c, d, & e

23. In which of the above reactions is one of the products a base?
    1) only c   2) only c & d   3) only a, c, & d   4) only a & d
    5) no reaction yields a base as one of the products

24. In which of the above reactions is one of the products an element?
    1) only a   2) only b   3) only a & d   4) only b & e   5) only e

25. In which of the above reactions is the sum of all the coefficients greater than 7?
    1) only a & c   2) only b & c   3) only a & d   4) only c, d, & e
    5) the sum of all the coefficients is greater than 7 in all reactions

MODULE 6 - ANSWERS

1. a) 2   b) 1   c) 6   d) 2   e) 1   f) 5   g) 6   h) 3   i) 4   j) 7   k) 2

2. a, f, h, j, k

3. a) ox: O, red: Cl   f) ox: Mg, red: Ag   h) ox: C, red: O   j) ox: Cu, red: Cu   k) ox: O, red: Hg

4. a) oxidant: Cl in $KClO_3$, reductant: O in $KClO_3$ f) oxidant: Ag^+ in $AgNO_3$, reductant: Mg
   h) oxidant: O_2, reductant: C in C_6H_6 k) oxidant: Cu^+ in $CuNO_3$, reductant: Cu^+ in $CuNO_3$
   k) oxidant: Hg^{2+} in HgO, reductant: O^{2-} in HgO

5. strong: b, f, h, i   weak: a, c, d, e, g   non: j, k

6. a) $FeCl_3 \xrightarrow{H_2O} Fe^{3+} + 3\ Cl^-$

   b) $K_2C_2O_4 \xrightarrow{H_2O} 2\ K^+ + C_2O_4^{2-}$

   c) $Fe_2(SO_4)_3 \xrightarrow{H_2O} 2\ Fe^{3+} + 3\ SO_4^{2-}$

   d) $HgCl_2 \xrightarrow{H_2O} Hg^{2+} + 2\ Cl^-$

   e) $PbCl_4 \xrightarrow{H_2O} Pb^{4+} + 4\ Cl^-$

   f) $Hg_2Cl_2 \xrightarrow{H_2O}$ N.R.

   g) $Cu_2O \xrightarrow{H_2O}$ N.R.

7. a) $2\ Na_3PO_{4\ (aq)} + 3\ BaCl_{2\ (aq)} \rightarrow 6\ NaCl_{\ (aq)} + Ba_3(PO_4)_{2\ (s)}$ molecular

   $6\ Na^+ + 2\ PO_4^{3-} + 3\ Ba^{2+} + 6\ Cl^- \rightarrow 6\ Na^+ + 6\ Cl^- + Ba_3(PO_4)_{2\ (s)}$ total ionic

   $2\ PO_4^{3-} + 3\ Ba^{2+} \rightarrow Ba_3(PO_4)_{2\ (s)}$ net ionic

   b) $Fe(C_2H_3O_2)_{3\ (aq)} + (NH_4)_3PO_{4\ (aq)} \rightarrow FePO_{4\ (s)} + 3\ NH_4C_2H_3O_{2\ (aq)}$ molecular

   $Fe^{3+} + 3\ C_2H_3O_2^- + 3\ NH_4^+ + PO_4^{3-} \rightarrow FePO_{4\ (s)} + 3\ NH_4^+ + 3\ C_2H_3O_2^-$ total ionic

   $Fe^{3+} + PO_4^{3-} \rightarrow FePO_{4\ (s)}$ net ionic

   c) $Na_2SO_{4\ (aq)} + Sr(ClO_3)_{2\ (aq)} \rightarrow 2\ NaClO_{3\ (aq)} + SrSO_{4\ (s)}$ molecular

   $2\ Na^+ + SO_4^{2-} + Sr^{2+} + 2\ ClO_3^- \rightarrow 2\ Na^+ + 2\ ClO_3^- + SrSO_{4\ (s)}$ total ionic

   $SO_4^{2-} + Sr^{2+} \rightarrow SrSO_{4\ (s)}$ net ionic

   d) $Na_2SO_{4\ (aq)} + Li_2CO_{3\ (aq)} \rightarrow$ N.R.

   e) $K_2SO_{3\ (aq)} + 2\ HCl_{(aq)} \rightarrow 2\ KCl_{\ (aq)} + H_2O_{\ (l)} + SO_{2\ (g)}$ molecular

   $2\ K^+ + SO_3^{2-} + 2\ H^+ + 2\ Cl^- \rightarrow 2\ K^+ + 2\ Cl^- + H_2O_{\ (l)} + SO_{2\ (g)}$ total ionic

   $SO_3^{2-} + 2\ H^+ \rightarrow H_2O_{\ (l)} + SO_{2\ (g)}$ net ionic

   f) $2\ KClO_{2\ (aq)} + H_2SO_{4\ (aq)} \rightarrow K_2SO_{4\ (aq)} + 2\ HClO_{2\ (aq)}$ molecular

   $2\ K^+ + 2\ ClO_2^- + 2\ H^+ + SO_4^{2-} \rightarrow 2\ K^+ + SO_4^{2-} + 2\ HClO_{2\ (aq)}$ total ionic

   $2\ ClO_2^- + 2\ H^+ \rightarrow 2\ HClO_{2\ (aq)}$ net ionic

   g) $(NH_4)_2S_{\ (aq)} + 2\ NaOH_{\ (aq)} \rightarrow 2\ NH_4OH_{\ (aq)} + Na_2S_{\ (aq)}$ molecular

   $2\ NH_4^+ + S^{2-} + 2\ Na^+ + 2\ OH^- \rightarrow 2\ NH_4OH_{\ (aq)} + 2\ Na^+ + S^{2-}$ total ionic

   $2\ NH_4^+ + 2\ OH^- \rightarrow 2\ NH_4OH$ net ionic

h) $Pb(NO_3)_2$ (aq) $+ H_2SO_4$ (aq) $\rightarrow$ $PbSO_4$ (s) $+ 2\,HNO_3$ (aq)   molecular

$Pb^{2+} + 2\,NO_3^- + 2\,H^+ + SO_4^{2-} \rightarrow PbSO_4$ (s) $+ 2\,H^+ + 2\,NO_3^-$ total ionic

$Pb^{2+} + SO_4^{2-} \rightarrow PbSO_4$ (s)   net ionic

i) $Zn(OH)_2$ (s) $+ 2\,HNO_3$ (aq) $\rightarrow$ $Zn(NO_3)_2$ (aq) $+ 2\,H_2O$ (l)   molecular

$Zn(OH)_2$ (s) $+ 2\,H^+ + 2\,NO_3^- \rightarrow Zn^{2+} + 2\,NO_3^- + 2\,H_2O$ (l)   total ionic

$Zn(OH)_2$ (s) $+ 2\,H^+ \rightarrow Zn^{2+} + 2\,H_2O$ (l)   net ionic

j) $Ba(OH)_2$ (aq) $+ H_2SO_4$ (aq) $\rightarrow$ $BaSO_4$ (s) $+ 2\,H_2O$ (l)   molecular

$Ba^{2+} + 2\,OH^- + 2\,H^+ + SO_4^{2-} \rightarrow BaSO_4$ (s) $+ 2\,H_2O$ (l)   total ionic

$Ba^{2+} + 2\,OH^- + 2\,H^+ + SO_4^{2-} \rightarrow BaSO_4$ (s) $+ 2\,H_2O$ (l)   net ionic

k) $2\,H_3PO_4$ (aq) $+ 3\,Sr(OH)_2$ (aq) $\rightarrow$ $6\,H_2O$ (l) $+ Sr_3(PO_4)_2$ (s)   molecular

$2\,H_3PO_4$ (aq) $+ 3\,Sr^{2+} + 6\,OH^- \rightarrow 6\,H_2O$ (l) $+ Sr_3(PO_4)_2$ (s)   total ionic

$2\,H_3PO_4$ (aq) $+ 3\,Sr^{2+} + 6\,OH^- \rightarrow 6\,H_2O$ (l) $+ Sr_3(PO_4)_2$ (s)   net ionic

l) $HC_2H_3O_2$ (aq) $+ NaOH$ (aq) $\rightarrow$ H_2O (l) $+ NaC_2H_3O_2$ (aq)   molecular

$HC_2H_3O_2$ (aq) $+ Na^+ + OH^- \rightarrow H_2O$ (l) $+ Na^+ + C_2H_3O_2^-$ total ionic

$HC_2H_3O_2$ (aq) $+ OH^- \rightarrow H_2O$ (l) $+ C_2H_3O_2^-$ net ionic

m) $4\,HClO_3$ (aq) $+ Ni(OH)_4$ (s) $\rightarrow$ $4\,H_2O$ (l) $+ Ni(ClO_3)_4$ (aq)   molecular

$4\,HClO_3$ (aq) $+ Ni(OH)_4$ (s) $\rightarrow$ $4\,H_2O$ (l) $+ Ni^{4+} + 4\,ClO_3^-$ total ionic

$4\,HClO_3$ (aq) $+ Ni(OH)_4$ (s) $\rightarrow$ $4\,H_2O$ (l) $+ Ni^{4+} + 4\,ClO_3^-$ net ionic

8. a) $2\,C_3H_6$ (g) $+ 9\,O_2$ (g) $\rightarrow$ $6\,CO_2$ (g) $+ 6\,H_2O$ (l)

   b) C_5H_{12} (l) $+ 8\,O_2$ (g) $\rightarrow$ $5\,CO_2$ (g) $+ 6\,H_2O$ (l)

   c) C_7H_{12} (l) $+ 10\,O_2$ (g) $\rightarrow$ $7\,CO_2$ (g) $+ 6\,H_2O$ (l)

9. a) $2\,K$ (s) $+ Ba(NO_3)_2$ (aq) $\rightarrow$ $2\,KNO_3$ (aq) $+ Ba$ (s)

    b) $2\,Mg$ (s) $+ Sn(C_2H_3O_2)_4$ (aq) $\rightarrow$ $2\,Mg(C_2H_3O_2)_2$ (aq) $+ Sn$ (s)

    c) $2\,Fe$ (s) $+ PbCl_4$ (aq) $\rightarrow$ $2\,FeCl_2$ (aq) $+ Pb$ (s)

    d) Cu (s) $+ MgSO_4$ (aq) $\rightarrow$ N.R.

    e) $4\,Ag$ (s) $+ Au(ClO_3)_4$ (aq) $\rightarrow$ $4\,AgClO_3$ (aq) $+ Au$ (s)

    f) Cu (s) $+ H_2O$ (l) $\rightarrow$ N.R.

    g) Cd (s) $+ 2\,HCl$ (aq) $\rightarrow$ $CdCl_2$ (aq) $+ H_2$ (g)

    h) Ni (s) $+ H_2SO_4$ (aq) $\rightarrow$ $NiSO_4$ (aq) $+ H_2$ (g)

    i) $2\,Al$ (s) $+ 6\,H_2O$ (g) $\rightarrow$ $2\,Al(OH)_3$ (s) $+ 3\,H_2$ (g)

    j) Pb (s) $+ 2\,H_2O$ (l) $\rightarrow$ N.R.

    k) Ni (s) $+ H_2SO_4$ (aq) $\rightarrow$ $NiSO_4$ (aq) $+ H_2$ (g)

    l) I_2 (s) $+ FeCl_3$ (aq) $\rightarrow$ N.R.

    m) F_2 (g) $+ 2\,NaCl$ (aq) $\rightarrow$ $2\,NaF$ (aq) $+ Cl_2$ (g)

    n) $2\,Cl_2$ (g) $+ CoI_4$ (aq) $\rightarrow$ $CoCl_4$ (aq) $+ 2\,I_2$ (s)

    o) Br_2 (l) $+ NaCl$ (aq) $\rightarrow$ N.R.

MODULE 7. *Redox Reactions and Stoichiometry*

I. Reduction and Oxidation

Reduction is defined as the gain of electrons.   For example, $Li^+ + e^- \rightarrow Li$.

Oxidation is defined as the loss of electrons. For example, $Mg \rightarrow Mg^{2+} + 2e^-$

There can be no oxidation without an accompanying reduction or vice-versa. In order to determine which specie in a redox reaction has been oxidized and which has been reduced, one must first determine the oxidation number for each element. For example,

$$\overset{0}{C}_{(s)} + \overset{0}{O_2}_{(g)} \rightarrow \overset{+4-2}{CO_2}_{(g)}$$

Carbon has been oxidized (oxidation number has increased from 0 to +4, i.e., it has lost e^-)

Oxygen has been reduced (oxidation number has decreased from 0 to -2, i.e., it has gained e^-)

Reducing Agent (Reductant) is the reagent that donates the electron(s). Reducing agents are always oxidized.

Oxidizing Agent (Oxidant) is the reagent that accepts the electron(s). Oxidizing agents are always reduced.

II. Balancing Redox Reactions

Some redox reactions, such as single replacement and combustion reactions, are so simple that the equations can be balanced easily by inspection. However, many of the redox reactions that are encountered are more complex and special methods to balance them are empolyed. The method that is discussed below to balance more complex redox equations is the Ion-Electron Method.

A. Ion-Electron Method of Balancing Redox Reactions

With this method, the overall reaction is divided into two half-reactions, one for oxidation and one for reduction. The equations for the two half-reactions are balanced separately and then added to give the overall balanced equation.   These redox reactions are either carried out in acidic or basic media.

Example Problems:

1. Complete and balance the following equation under acidic conditions.

$$MnO_4^- + N_2H_4 \rightarrow Mn^{2+} + NO_3^- \quad \textit{[NOTE: Spectator ions are not shown.]}$$

   [NOTE: Bold printing will emphasize the part(s) of the equation that have been "changed" with each step.]

Step 1. Separate the unbalanced equations into half-reactions.

$$MnO_4^- \rightarrow Mn^{2+}$$
$$N_2H_4 \rightarrow NO_3^-$$

Step 2. Balance the atoms (other than O and H) in each half reaction.

$$MnO_4^- \rightarrow Mn^{2+}$$
$$N_2H_4 \rightarrow \mathbf{2\,NO_3^-}$$

Step 3. Balance the O's with H_2O. For each O present on one side of the equation add 1 H_2O to the other side.

$$MnO_4^- \rightarrow Mn^{2+} + \mathbf{4\,H_2O}$$
$$\mathbf{6\,H_2O} + N_2H_4 \rightarrow 2\,NO_3^-$$

Step 4. Balance the H's with H^+. For each H present on one side of the equation add 1 H^+ to the other side.

$$8 \text{ H}^+ + \text{MnO}_4^- \rightarrow \text{Mn}^{2+} + 4 \text{ H}_2\text{O}$$
$$6 \text{ H}_2\text{O} + \text{N}_2\text{H}_4 \rightarrow 2 \text{ NO}_3^- + 16 \text{ H}^+$$

Step 5. Balance the charge (i.e., the total charge on the left side of the equation must be equal to that of the right side of the equation) in each half-reaction by adding electrons to the appropriate side.

$$5 \text{ e}^- + 8 \text{ H}^+ + \text{MnO}_4^- \rightarrow \text{Mn}^{2+} + 4 \text{ H}_2\text{O} \qquad \text{total charge: } -5 + 8 - 1 \rightarrow +2$$
$$6 \text{ H}_2\text{O} + \text{N}_2\text{H}_4 \rightarrow 2 \text{ NO}_3^- + 16 \text{ H}^+ + 14 \text{ e}^- \qquad \text{total charge: } 0 \rightarrow -2 + 16 - 14$$

Step 6. Balance the electron transfer by multiplying the coefficients of each balanced half-reaction by appropriate integers so that the total number of electrons is the same in each half-reaction.

(In this particular case, for the first half-reaction in step 5 multiply the coefficients of the chemical equation by 14 and for the second half-reaction in step 5 multiply the coefficients of the chemical equation by 5.)

$$70 \text{ e}^- + 112 \text{ H}^+ + 14 \text{ MnO}_4^- \rightarrow 14 \text{ Mn}^{2+} + 56 \text{ H}_2\text{O}$$
$$30 \text{ H}_2\text{O} + 5 \text{ N}_2\text{H}_4 \rightarrow 10 \text{ NO}_3^- + 80 \text{ H}^+ + 70 \text{ e}^-$$

Step 7. a) Add the resulting half-reactions,

$$70 \text{ e}^- + 112 \text{ H}^+ + 14 \text{ MnO}_4^- + 30 \text{ H}_2\text{O} + 5 \text{ N}_2\text{H}_4 \rightarrow 14 \text{ Mn}^{2+} + 56 \text{ H}_2\text{O} + 10 \text{ NO}_3^- + 80 \text{ H}^+ + 70 \text{ e}^-$$

b) eliminate any common terms to obtain the balanced equation.

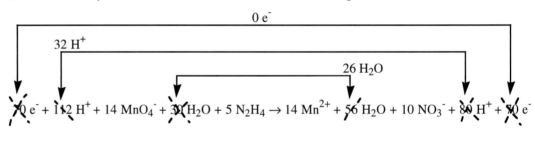

$$32 \text{ H}^+ + 14 \text{ MnO}_4^- + 5 \text{ N}_2\text{H}_4 \rightarrow 14 \text{ Mn}^{2+} + 26 \text{ H}_2\text{O} + 10 \text{ NO}_3^-$$

2. Complete and balance the equation given above in problem 1 under basic conditions.

In basic solutions, the amount of H^+ present is very small; the dominant species are OH^- and H_2O. Strictly speaking, these should be used to balance the reactions. However, the simplest way is to do the following. Repeat steps 1 - 7 given above for the acidic medium equation balancing. After step 7 we have the following:

$$32 \text{ H}^+ + 14 \text{ MnO}_4^- + 5 \text{ N}_2\text{H}_4 \rightarrow 14 \text{ Mn}^{2+} + 26 \text{ H}_2\text{O} + 10 \text{ NO}_3^-$$

Step 8. Add as many OH^- as there are H^+ to *both* sides of the equation.

$$32 \text{ OH}^- + 32 \text{ H}^+ + 14 \text{ MnO}_4^- + 5 \text{ N}_2\text{H}_4 \rightarrow 14 \text{ Mn}^{2+} + 26 \text{ H}_2\text{O} + 10 \text{ NO}_3^- + 32 \text{ OH}^-$$

Step 9. Convert $x\, OH^- + x\, H^+$ (on the same side of the equation) into $x\, H_2O$.

$$32 \text{ H}_2\text{O} + 14 \text{ MnO}_4^- + 5 \text{ N}_2\text{H}_4 \rightarrow 14 \text{ Mn}^{2+} + 26 \text{ H}_2\text{O} + 10 \text{ NO}_3^- + 32 \text{ OH}^-$$

Step 10. If H_2O appears on both sides of the equation, subtract the appropriate amount of H_2O from each side of equation so that H_2O only appears on one side of the equation.

$$6 \text{ H}_2\text{O} + 14 \text{ MnO}_4^- + 5 \text{ N}_2\text{H}_4 \rightarrow 14 \text{ Mn}^{2+} + 10 \text{ NO}_3^- + 32 \text{ OH}^-$$

3. Complete and balance the following disproportionation reaction under acidic conditions.

$$Cl_2 \rightarrow ClO_3^- + Cl^-$$

Step 1. Separate the unbalanced equations into half-reactions.

$$Cl_2 \rightarrow ClO_3^-$$
$$Cl_2 \rightarrow Cl^-$$

Step 2. Balance the atoms (other than O and H) in each half reaction.

$$Cl_2 \rightarrow \mathbf{2}\,ClO_3^-$$
$$Cl_2 \rightarrow \mathbf{2}\,Cl^-$$

Step 3. Balance the O's with H_2O. For each O present on one side of the equation add 1 H_2O to the other side.

$$\mathbf{6\,H_2O} + Cl_2 \rightarrow 2\,ClO_3^-$$
$$Cl_2 \rightarrow 2\,Cl^-$$

Step 4. Balance the H's with H^+. For each H present on one side of the equation add 1 H^+ to the other side.

$$6\,H_2O + Cl_2 \rightarrow 2\,ClO_3^- + \mathbf{12\,H^+}$$
$$Cl_2 \rightarrow 2\,Cl^-$$

Step 5. Balance the charge (i.e., the total charge on the left side of the equation must be equal to that of the right side of the equation) in each half-reaction by adding electrons to the appropriate side.

$$6\,H_2O + Cl_2 \rightarrow 2\,ClO_3^- + 12\,H^+ + \mathbf{10\,e^-}$$
$$\mathbf{2\,e^-} + Cl_2 \rightarrow 2\,Cl^-$$

Step 6. Balance the electron transfer by multiplying the coefficients of each balanced half-reaction by appropriate integers so that the total number of electrons is the same in each half-reaction.

$$6\,H_2O + Cl_2 \rightarrow 2\,ClO_3^- + 12\,H^+ + 10\,e^-$$
$$5 \times (2\,e^- + Cl_2 \rightarrow 2\,Cl^-) \;\text{------->}\; 10\,e^- + 5\,Cl_2 \rightarrow 10\,Cl^-$$

Step 7. a) Add the resulting half-reactions,

$$6\,H_2O + 6\,Cl_2 \rightarrow 2\,ClO_3^- + 12\,H^+ + 10\,Cl^-$$

   b) have lowest possible multiple of each coefficient (divide all coefficients by 2)

$$3\,H_2O + 3\,Cl_2 \rightarrow ClO_3^- + 6\,H^+ + 5\,Cl^-$$

4. Complete and balance the following reaction under basic conditions.

$$Mn^{2+} + H_2O_2 \rightarrow MnO_2$$

Step 1. $Mn^{2+} \rightarrow MnO_2$
$H_2O_2 \rightarrow H_2O$ (Any substance that only has H's and/or O's usually gets converted into H_2O)

Step 2. This step is not necessary

Step 3. $Mn^{2+} + \mathbf{2\,H_2O} \rightarrow MnO_2$
$H_2O_2 \rightarrow \mathbf{2}\,H_2O$

Step 4. $Mn^{2+} + \mathbf{2\,H_2O} \rightarrow MnO_2 + \mathbf{4\,H^+}$
$\mathbf{2\,H^+} + H_2O_2 \rightarrow \mathbf{2}\,H_2O$

Step 5. $Mn^{2+} + 2\,H_2O \rightarrow MnO_2 + 4\,H^+ + 2\,e^-$

$2\,e^- + 2\,H^+ + H_2O_2 \rightarrow 2\,H_2O$

Step 6.   This step is already done

Step 7.   a) $Mn^{2+} + 2\,H_2O + 2\,H^+ + H_2O_2 \rightarrow MnO_2 + 4\,H^+ + 2\,H_2O$

b) $Mn^{2+} + H_2O_2 \rightarrow MnO_2 + 2\,H^+$

Step 8. $2\,OH^- + Mn^{2+} + H_2O_2 \rightarrow MnO_2 + 2\,H^+ + 2\,OH^-$

Step 9. $2\,OH^- + Mn^{2+} + H_2O_2 \rightarrow MnO_2 + 2\,H_2O$

Step 10.   Not necessary, so balanced equation is:

$2\,OH^- + Mn^{2+} + H_2O_2 \rightarrow MnO_2 + 2\,H_2O$

III. Redox Stoichiometry

There are two common methods for solving redox stoichiometry problems. If a balanced chemical equation is given, then the mole and molarity method is the best method to use to solve the problem; however, if a balanced chemical equation is not given, then the equivalents and normality method is the best method to use to solve the problem.

A. Mole and Molarity Method to Solving Redox Stoichiometry

To use Mole and Molarity Method to solve redox stoichiometry problems, a balanced chemical reaction is needed. Then using the following concept map, which was previously shown in the Stoichiometry Module, can be used to solve problems.

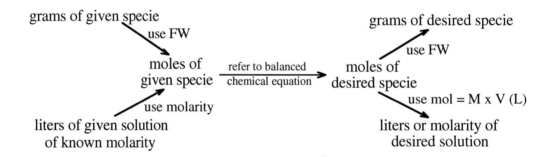

Example Problems:

1.   If 30.00 mL of a K_2SO_3 (FW = 158.3) solution of unknown molarity are required to react with 16.25 mL of 0.2315 M $K_2Cr_2O_7$ (FW = 294.) according to the following balanced redox reaction, in which spectator ions are not shown,

$$3\,SO_3^{2-} + Cr_2O_7^{2-} + 8\,H^+ \rightarrow 3\,SO_4^{2-} + 2\,Cr^{3+} + 4\,H_2O$$

then calculate the molarity of the K_2SO_3.

$$? \text{ mol } K_2SO_3 = 16.25 \text{ mL } K_2Cr_2O_7 \left(\frac{0.2315 \text{ mol } K_2Cr_2O_7}{1000. \text{ mL } K_2Cr_2O_7}\right)\left(\frac{3 \text{ mol } K_2SO_3}{1 \text{ mol } K_2Cr_2O_7}\right) = 0.01129$$

$$M = \frac{\text{mole } K_2SO_3}{\text{L } K_2SO_3 \text{ soln}} = \frac{0.01129 \text{ mol}}{30.00 \text{ mL}\left(\frac{10^{-3} \text{ L}}{1 \text{ mL}}\right)} = 0.3763 \text{ M}$$

2. If 2.00 g of a sample containing an unknown amount of $FeCl_2$ was titrated to its equivalence point with 20.0 mL of 0.0204 M $K_2Cr_2O_7$ (FW = 294.), according to the following balanced redox reaction,

$$6\ Fe^{2+}\ +\ Cr_2O_7{}^{2-}\ +\ 14\ H^+\ \rightarrow\ 6\ Fe^{3+}\ +\ 2\ Cr^{3+}\ +\ 7\ H_2O$$

[Spectator ions: K^+ and Cl^-]

then:

a) How many mol of iron (in the form of Fe^{2+}) were present in the sample?

$$?\ mol\ Fe = 20.0\ mL\ K_2Cr_2O_7 \left(\frac{0.0204\ mol\ K_2Cr_2O_7}{1000.\ mL\ K_2Cr_2O_7}\right)\left(\frac{6\ mol\ FeCl_2}{1\ mol\ K_2Cr_2O_7}\right)\left(\frac{1\ mol\ Fe^{2+}}{1\ mol\ FeCl_2}\right) = 2.45\ x\ 10^{-3}$$

b) How many grams of iron were present in the sample?

$$?\ g\ Fe\ =\ 2.45\ x\ 10^{-3}\ mol\ Fe^{2+}\left(\frac{55.9\ g}{1\ mol\ Fe^{2+}}\right) = 0.137\ g\ Fe^{2+}$$

c) What is the % Fe in the sample?

$$\%\ Fe\ =\ \frac{0.137\ g}{2.00\ g}\ x\ 100 = 6.85\ \%$$

B. Equivalents and Normality Method to Solving Redox Stoichiometry

The concepts of equivalents and normality were devised to simplify calculations in chemical analyses so as to retain a one-to-one relationship between the oxidizing agent and the reducing agent. Thus for redox reactions,

$$eq_{red} = eq_{ox}$$

An equivalent of one reactant is the mass [i.e., equivalent weight (EW)] that will exactly react with an equivalent of another reactant. *Equivalent Weight* (units -- g/eq) is defined as:

$$EW\ =\ \frac{FW\ (g/mol)}{n\ (eq/mol)} \qquad units\ for\ EW = \frac{g}{eq}$$

For substances undergoing a redox reaction, *n = # of e^- transferred / mol*

It is not uncommon for the equivalent weight of a substance undergoing a redox reaction to vary (*see example problem 1 a and b below*).

Normality, along with equivalents, can also be used in redox calculations. Recall that normality can be defined as follows:

$$N\ =\ \frac{equivalent\ of\ solute\ (eq)}{liter\ of\ solution\ (L)} \quad or \quad N = n\ x\ M$$

$$where\ eq = n\ x\ mol$$

Example Problems:

1. Considering the following half reactions, what is the equivalent weight of $KMnO_4$ (FW = 158.0)?

a) $MnO_4{}^- \ +\ 8\ H^+\ +\ 5\ e^- \rightarrow\ Mn^{2+} + 4\ H_2O$

1 mol $KMnO_4$ = 158.0 g $KMnO_4$ 1 mol $KMnO_4$ = 5 eq $KMnO_4$

$$EW\ =\ \frac{FW\ (g/mol)}{n\ (eq/mol)}\ =\ \frac{158.0\ (g/mol)}{5\ (eq/mol)}\ =\ 31.60\ g/eq$$

b) $MnO_4^- \rightarrow MnO_2$

Instead of balancing the following half-reaction, it is easier to find the electrons that are transferred by calculating the change in oxidation numbers in Mn (note: O is not undergoing a change in oxidation number)

ox. # -- Mn (in MnO_4^-) = +7

ox. # -- Mn (in MnO_2) = +4

------> # e^- transferred = 3

1 mol $KMnO_4$ = 158.0 g $KMnO_4$ = 3 eq $KMnO_4$

$$EW = \frac{FW \text{ (g/mol)}}{n \text{ (eq/mol)}} = \frac{158.0 \text{ (g/mol)}}{3 \text{ (eq/mol)}} = 52.67 \text{ g/eq}$$

2. What is the equivalent weight of KBr (FW = 103.) in the following half-reaction, $Br^- \rightarrow Br_2$, in acidic medium?

The balanced redox equation is: $2 Br^- \rightarrow Br_2 + 2 e^-$. Since the concept of equivalents was to devised to keep a one-to-one relationship between reducing and oxidizing agents we need to have only one mole of Br^-; therefore, we must divide the balanced equation by 2:

$Br^- \rightarrow \frac{1}{2} Br_2 + 1 e^-$

1 mol KBr = 103. g $KMnO_4$ = 1 eq KBr

$$EW = \frac{FW \text{ (g/mol)}}{n \text{ (eq/mol)}} = \frac{103. \text{ (g/mol)}}{2 \text{ (eq/mol)}} = 103. \text{ g/eq}$$

3. What is the normality of a solution prepared by dissolving 1.50 g of $K_2Cr_2O_7$ (FW = 294) in enough water to make 250. mL of solution?

Before we can calculate the normality of $K_2Cr_2O_7$, we must know the type of redox reaction it is going to undergo and the medium (acidic or basic). Consider that $K_2Cr_2O_7$ will undergo the following half reaction in acidic medium: $Cr_2O_7^{2-} \rightarrow Cr^{3+}$. The following is the balanced redox half-reaction.

$$Cr_2O_7^{2-} + 14 H^+ + 6 e^- \rightarrow 2 Cr^{3+} + 7 H_2O$$

[NOTE: Very often spectator ions in redox reactions are not shown, K^+ is a spectator ion.]

The following equalities are true concerning the above balance redox half-reaction:

1 mol $K_2Cr_2O_7$ = 294 g $K_2Cr_2O_7$ = 6 eq $K_2Cr_2O_7$

$$N = \frac{eq\ K_2Cr_2O_7}{L\ soln} = \frac{1.50\ g\ K_2Cr_2O_7 \left(\dfrac{6\ eq\ K_2Cr_2O_7}{294\ g\ K_2Cr_2O_7}\right)}{250\ mL\ soln \left(\dfrac{10^{-3}\ L}{1\ mL}\right)} = 0.122\ N$$

The following relationships can be used to solve redox stoichiometry problems in which balanced redox equations are not given.

$$eq_{red} = eq_{ox}$$

$$eq = n \times mol = N \times L = (n \times M) \times L = \frac{g}{EW}$$

The number of electrons transferred per mol of oxidant or reductant, n, can be obtained by balancing each redox half reaction (without balancing the electron transfered in each half reaction - to keep a one-to-one mole ratio of oxidant and reductant) or by calculating changes in oxidation number.

Example Problems:

1. Consider the following unbalanced chemical equation (where the specator ions are not shown) to answere the following questions.

$$SO_3^{2-} + Cr_2O_7^{2-} \rightarrow SO_4^{2-} + Cr^{3+}$$

a) How many mL of a 0.3762 M K_2SO_3 (FW = 158.3) solution are required to react with 17.57 mL of 0.3995 M $K_2Cr_2O_7$ (FW = 294.) ?

Since M or both reactants are given, we will use the following definitions for eq:

$$(n \times M)_{SO_3^{2-}} \times V_{SO_3^{2-}} = (n \times M)_{Cr_2O_7^{2-}} \times V_{Cr_2O_7^{2-}}$$

To find n we must find the number of electrons transferred in each half-reaction. The easiest way to do this is to find the change in oxidation number that is taking place.
For the $Cr_2O_7^{2-} \rightarrow Cr^{3+}$ half reaction, Cr is the specie that is undergoing a change in its oxidation state.

ox. # -- Cr (in $Cr_2O_7^{2-}$) = +6
ox. # -- Cr (in Cr^{3+}) = +3   -----> # e⁻ transferred = 3 x 2 = 6

The 2 is due to the fact that 1 mol of $Cr_2O_7^{2-}$ yields 2 mol of Cr^{3+}

For the $SO_3^{2-} \rightarrow SO_4^{2-}$ half reaction, S is the specie that is undergoing a change in its oxidation state.

ox. # -- S (in SO_3^{2-}) = +4
ox. # -- S (in SO_4^{2-}) = +6   ------> # e⁻ transferred = 2

Thus,

$$(n \times M)_{SO_3^{2-}} \times V_{SO_3^{2-}} = (n \times M)_{Cr_2O_7^{2-}} \times V_{Cr_2O_7^{2-}}$$

$$(2 \text{ eq/mol} \times 0.3762 \text{ M}) \times V_{SO_3^{2-}} = (6 \text{ eq/mol} \times 0.3995 \text{ M}) \times 17.57 \text{ mL}$$

$$V_{SO_3^{2-}} = \frac{6 \times 0.3995 \times 17.57}{2 \times 0.3762} = 55.97 \text{ mL}$$

b) How many mL of a 0.05795 M $K_2Cr_2O_7$ (FW = 158.3) solution are required to react with 2.365 g of K_2SO_3 (FW = 158.3).

$$(n \times M)_{Cr_2O_7^{2-}} \times L_{Cr_2O_7^{2-}} = \frac{g_{SO_3^{2-}}}{EW_{SO_3^{2-}}}$$

As obtained in example a above, n for $Cr_2O_7^{2-}$ = 6 and for SO_3^{2-} = 2

$$(6 \text{ eq/mol} \times 0.05795 \text{ M}) \times L_{Cr_2O_7^{2-}} = \frac{2.365 \text{ g}}{\dfrac{158.3 \text{ (g/mol)}}{2 \text{ (eq/mol)}}}$$

$$L_{Cr_2O_7^{2-}} = \frac{2.365}{\dfrac{158.3}{2} \times 6 \times 0.05795} = 0.08594 \text{ L} \text{ ------> } 85.94 \text{ mL}$$

EXERCISES

Balancing Redox Reactions and Identifying Reducing and Oxidizing Agents

1. Balance the following half-reactions.

    a) $BiO_3^- \rightarrow Bi^{3+}$ (acidic media)

    b) $I_2 \rightarrow IO_3^-$ (acidic media)

    c) $Pb^{2+} \rightarrow PbO_2$ (acidic media)

    d) $NO_3^- \rightarrow NH_4^+$ (acidic media)

    e) $H_4IO_6^- \rightarrow I_2$ (basic media)

    f) $Fe \rightarrow Fe(OH)_2$ (basic media)

    g) $Mn(OH)_2 \rightarrow MnO_4^-$ (basic media)

    h) $CN^- \rightarrow CNO^-$ (basic media)

2. Classify each of the half-reactions in question 1 as an oxidation or reduction

3. Complete and balance the following redox reactions using the ion-electron method.

    a) $Cu + NO_3^- \rightarrow Cu^{2+} + NO_2$ ox.   (acidic media)

    b) $Zn + SO_4^{2-} \rightarrow Zn^{2+} + SO_2$ (acidic media)

    c) $Zn + NO_3^- \rightarrow Zn^{2+} + NH_4^+$ (acidic media)

    d) $IO_3^- + AsO_3^{3-} \rightarrow I^- + AsO_4^{3-}$ (acidic media)

    e) $CrO_4^{2-} + S^{2-} \rightarrow S + CrO_2^-$ (basic media)

    f) $MnO_4^- + SO_3^{2-} \rightarrow MnO_2 + SO_4^{2-}$ (basic media)

    g) $ClO_3^- + N_2H_4 \rightarrow Cl^- + NO$ (basic media)

    h) $SO_3^{2-} + MnO_2 \rightarrow S_2O_6^{2-} + Mn^{2+}$ (basic media)

4. For those reactions in question 3, what atom is being oxidized and which is being reduced?

5. For those reactions in question 3, what is the oxidizing agent and what is the reducing agent?

Redox Stoichiometry (Mole and Molarity Method)

6. Consider the following balanced redox equation:

$$8 H^+ + Cr_2O_7^{2-} + 3 SO_3^{2-} \rightarrow 2 Cr^{3+} + 3 SO_4^{2-} + 4 H_2O$$

    a) How many mol of Na_2SO_3 (FW = 126.) are required to completely react with 20.3 mL of a 0.500 M $K_2Cr_2O_7$ (FW = 294.) solution under acidic conditions?

    b) How many grams of Na_2SO_3 (FW = 126.) are required to completely react with 40.3 mL of a 0.300 M $K_2Cr_2O_7$ (FW = 294.) solution under acidic conditions?

    c) If a 10.0 mL sample of Na_2SO_3 (FW = 126.) was titrated with 2.63 mL of a 3.08 M $K_2Cr_2O_7$ (FW = 294.) under acidic conditions, then calculate the molarity of the Na_2SO_3.

    d) How many mL of a 2.43 M Na_2SO_3 (FW = 126.) are required to completely react with 2.63 mL of a 3.08 M $K_2Cr_2O_7$ (FW = 294.) solution under acidic conditions?

    e) How many mL of a 3.48 M $K_2Cr_2O_7$ (FW = 294.) acidic solution are required to completely react with 2.37 g of Na_2SO_3 (FW = 126.)?

7. Consider the following balanced redox equation:

$$H_2O + 2\ MnO_4^- + 3\ SO_3^{2-} \rightarrow 2\ MnO_2 + 3\ SO_4^{2-} + 2\ OH^-$$

a) How many mol of Na_2SO_3 (FW = 126.) are required to completely react with 20.3 mL of a 0.500 M $KMnO_4$ (FW =158.) solution under basic conditions?

b) How many grams of Na_2SO_3 (FW = 126.) are required to completely react with 40.3 mL of a 0.300 M $KMnO_4$ (FW =158.) solution under basic conditions?

c) If a 10.0 mL sample of Na_2SO_3 (FW = 126.) was titrated with 2.63 mL of a 3.08 M $KMnO_4$ (FW =158.) under basic conditions, then calculate the molarity of the Na_2SO_3.

d) How many mL of a 1.22 M Na_2SO_3 (FW = 126.) are required to completely react with 2.63 mL of a 3.08 M $KMnO_4$ (FW =158.) solution under basic conditions?

e) How many mL of a 3.48 M $KMnO_4$ (FW =158.) basic solution are required to completely react with 2.37 g of Na_2SO_3 (FW = 126.)?

Equivalent Weight and Normality

8. Given the following redox half-reaction, $Fe^{2+} \rightarrow Fe$, calculate:
a) The equivalent weight for $FeSO_4$ (FW = 152.).
b) The normality of a 1.00 M $FeSO_4$ (FW = 152.) solution.

9. Given the following redox half-reaction, $Fe^{2+} \rightarrow Fe^{3+}$, calculate:
a) The equivalent weight for $FeSO_4$ (FW = 152.).
b) The normality of a 1.00 M $FeSO_4$ (FW = 152.) solution.

10. Given the following redox half-reaction, $ClO_3^- \rightarrow Cl^-$, calculate:
a) The equivalent weight for $KClO_3$ (FW = 122.).
b) The normality of a 1.00 M $KClO_3$ (FW = 122.) solution.

Redox Stoichiometry (Equivalents and Normality Method)

11. Consider the following unbalanced redox equation:

$$Cr_2O_7^{2-} + SO_3^{2-} \rightarrow Cr^{3+} + SO_4^{2-}$$

a) How many grams of Na_2SO_3 (FW = 126) are required to completely react with 40.3 mL of a 0.300 N $K_2Cr_2O_7$ solution under acidic conditions?

b) If a 10.0 mL sample of Na_2SO_3 was titrated with 26.3 mL of a 0.308 N $K_2Cr_2O_7$ under acidic conditions, then calculate the normality of the Na_2SO_3.

12. Consider the following unbalanced redox equation:

$$MnO_4^- + Zn \rightarrow MnO_2 + Zn(OH)_2$$

a) How many grams of Zn (AW = 65.4) are required to completely react with 40.3 mL of a 0.300 N $KMnO_4$ (FW = 158.) solution under basic conditions?

b) How many grams of Zn (AW = 65.4) are required to completely react with 40.3 mL of a 0.300 M $KMnO_4$ (FW = 158.) solution under basic conditions?

c) If a 10.0 mL sample of $KMnO_4$ (FW = 158.) completely reacted 1.30 g of Zn (AW = 65.4) under basic conditions, then calculate the normality of the $KMnO_4$ (FW = 158.) solution.

d) If a 10.0 mL sample of $KMnO_4$ (FW = 158.) completely reacted 1.30 g of Zn (AW = 65.4) under basic conditions, then calculate the molarity of the $KMnO_4$ (FW = 158.) solution.

MULTIPLE CHOICE PRACTICE EXAM FOR MODULE 7

1. In which of the following *unbalanced* reactions is H_2O_2 acting as a reducing agent?

    a. $Mn^{2+} + H_2O_2 \rightarrow MnO_2$

    b. $PbS + H_2O_2 \rightarrow PbSO_4$

    c. $CrO_4^{2-} + H_2O_2 \rightarrow Cr^{3+}$

    1) only a   2) only b   3) only c   4) only a and c
    5) In none of the above reactions

2. What is the coefficient in front of the boldfaced substance in the balanced form of the following redox reaction carried out under *acidic* conditions?

    $$Mn^{2+} + \mathbf{H_2O_2} \rightarrow MnO_2$$

    1) 5   2) 2   3) 3   4) 4   5) 1

3. What is the coefficient in front of the boldfaced substance in the balanced form of the following redox reaction carried out under *basic* conditions?

    $$S_2O_3^{2-} + \mathbf{I_2} \rightarrow SO_4^{2-} + I^-$$

    1) 1   2) 2   3) 3   4) 4   5) 5

4. For the following *unbalanced* redox reaction in *acidic* conditions, which of the following is a correctly balanced **reduction** half-reaction?

    $$S^{2-} + NO_3^- \rightarrow S + NO$$

    1) $S^{2-} \rightarrow S + 2\,e^-$ 2) $3\,e^- + 4\,H^+ + NO_3^- \rightarrow NO + 2\,H_2O$

    3) $2\,e^- + S^{2-} \rightarrow S$ 4) $2\,e^- + 6\,H^+ + 2\,NO_3^- \rightarrow 2\,NO + 3$
        H_2O

    5) None of the above choices

Consider the following balanced redox reaction when answering questions 5 - 6

$$4\,ClO_3^- + 3\,N_2H_4 \rightarrow 4\,Cl^- + 6\,NO + 6\,H_2O$$

5. How many grams of N_2H_4 (FW = 32.0) are needed to react with 0.250 L of 0.122 M $KClO_3$?

    1) 24.5   2) 49.2   3) 0.976   4) 1.30   5) 0.732

6. How many mL of a 12.0 M N_2H_4 are needed to react with 45.0 mL of 0.122 M $KClO_3$?

    1) 0.343   2) 0.610   3) 23.1   4) 0.458   5) 1.83

Consider the following unbalanced redox half-reaction when answering questions 7 - 8
$$NiO_2 \rightarrow Ni(OH)_2$$

7. How many electrons are transferred in the above *unbalanced* redox half-reaction when it is carried out under *basic* conditions?

    1) 1   2) 2   3) 3   4) 4   5) 5

8. What is the equivalent weight of NiO_2 in the above *unbalanced* redox half-reaction when it is carried out under *basic* conditions?

    1) 90.7   2) 181.   3) 45.4   4) 22.7   5) 363.

Consider the following unbalanced redox half-reaction when answering questions 9 - 10

$$Cr_2O_7^{2-} \rightarrow Cr^{3+}$$

9. How many grams of $K_2Cr_2O_7$ (FW = 294) are needed to prepare 0.250 L of 0.122 N $K_2Cr_2O_7$?

    1) 0.0305   2) 53.8   3) 5.08 x 10^{-3} 4) 8.97   5) 1.49

10. Calculate the normality of a 0.422 M $K_2Cr_2O_7$ solution which undergoes the above redox half-reaction?

    1) 0.422   2) 2.53   3) 0.844   4) 0.141   5) 0.070

Consider the following unbalanced redox equation under acidic conditions when answering questions 11 - 17

$$Cu + NO_3^- \rightarrow Cu^{2+} + NO$$

11. When the $NO_3^- \rightarrow NO$ half-reaction is balanced (by itself), which of the following statements would be true?
    1) There are 7 electrons on the right side of the equation.
    2) This is the oxidation half reaction.
    3) There are 16 H^+ on the right side of the equation.
    4) Two of the above statements are correct.
    5) None of the above statements are correct.

12. When the $Cu \rightarrow Cu^{2+}$ half-reaction is balanced (by itself), which of the following statements would be true?
    1) There are two electrons on the left side of the equation.
    2) This is the oxidation half reaction.
    3) There are 3 Cu on the left side.
    4) Two of the above statements are correct.
    5) None of the above statements are correct.

13. When the complete reaction is balanced, which of the following statements would be true?
    1) There were a total of 6 electrons transferred.
    2) There are 2 H_2O on the right side of the equation.
    3) There are 8 H^+ on the left side of the equation.
    4) Two of the above statements are correct.
    5) All of the above statements are correct.

14. How many grams of Cu (AW = 63.5) are needed to react with 0.250 L of 0.122 N KNO_3?

    1) 1.66   2) 3.87   3) 8.20   4) 0.968   5) 1.94

15. How many mL of a 12.0 N KNO_3 are needed to react with 12.0 g of Cu (AW = 63.5)?

    1) 10.5   2) 15.7   3) 31.5   4) 5.25   5) 2.62

16. How many mL of a 12.0 M KNO_3 are needed to react with 12.0 g of Cu (AW = 63.5)?

    1) 10.5   2) 15.7   3) 31.5   4) 5.25   5) 2.62

17. What is the equivalent weight of KNO_3 (FW = 101) for this particular reaction?

    1) 101.   2) 202.   3) 310.   4) 33.7   5) 50.6

MODULE 7 - ANSWERS

1. a) $2e^- + 6H^+ + BiO_3^- \rightarrow Bi^{3+} + 3H_2O$

    b) $6H_2O + I_2 \rightarrow 2IO_3^- + 12H^+ + 10e^-$

    c) $2H_2O + Pb^{2+} \rightarrow PbO_2 + 4H^+ + 2e^-$

    d) $8e^- + 10H^+ + NO_3^- \rightarrow NH_4^+ + 3H_2O$

    e) $14e^- + 4H_2O + 2H_4IO_6^- \rightarrow I_2 + 16OH^-$

    f) $2OH^- + Fe \rightarrow Fe(OH)_2 + 2e^-$

    g) $6OH^- + Mn(OH)_2 \rightarrow MnO_4^- + 4H_2O + 5e^-$

    h) $2OH^- + CN^- \rightarrow CNO^- + H_2O + 2e^-$

2. Oxidations: b, c, f, g, h   Reductions: a, d, e

3. a) $4H^+ + Cu + 2NO_3^- \rightarrow Cu^{2+} + 2NO_2 + 2H_2O$

    b) $4H^+ + Zn + SO_4^{2-} \rightarrow Zn^{2+} + SO_2 + 2H_2O$

    c) $10H^+ + 4Zn + NO_3^- \rightarrow 4Zn^{2+} + NH_4^+ + 3H_2O$

    d) $IO_3^- + 3AsO_3^{3-} \rightarrow I^- + 3AsO_4^{3-}$

    e) $4H_2O + 2CrO_4^{2-} + 3S^{2-} \rightarrow 3S + 2CrO_2^- + 8OH^-$

    f) $H_2O + 2MnO_4^- + 3SO_3^{2-} \rightarrow 2MnO_2 + 3SO_4^{2-} + 2OH^-$

    g) $4ClO_3^- + 3N_2H_4 \rightarrow 4Cl^- + 6NO + 6H_2O$

    h) $2H_2O + 2SO_3^{2-} + MnO_2 \rightarrow S_2O_6^{2-} + Mn^{2+} + 4OH^-$

4. a) Ox: Cu, Red: N   b) Ox: Zn, Red: S   c) Ox: Zn, Red: N   d) Ox: As, Red: I   e) Ox: S, Red: Cr
    f) Ox: S, Red: Mn   g) Ox: N, Red: Cl   h) Ox: S, Red: Mn

5. a) Ox: N in NO_3^- Red: Cu   b) Ox: S in SO_4^{2-} Red: Zn
    c) Ox: N in NO_3^- Red: Zn   d) Ox: I in IO_3^- Red: As in AsO_3^{3-}
    e) Ox Cr in CrO_4^{2-} Red: S in S^{2-} f) Ox: Mn in MnO_4^- Red: S in SO_3^{2-}
    g) Ox: Cl in ClO_3^- Red: N in N_2H_4 h) Ox: Mn in MnO_2 Red: S in SO_3^{2-}

6. a) 0.0304 mol   b) 4.57 g   c) 2.43 M   d) 10.0 mL   e) 1.80 mL

7. a) 0.0152 mol   b) 2.29 g   c) 1.22 M   d) 9.96 mL   e) 3.60 mL

8. a) 76.0 g/eq   b) 2.00 N

9. a) 152. g/eq   b) 1.00 N

10. a) 20.3 g/eq   b) 6.00 N

11. a) 0.762 g   b) 0.810 N

12. a) 0.395 g   b) 1.19 g   c) 3.97 N   d) 1.32 M

MODULE 8.   *Gases*

I.   Substances that Exist as Gases

The following table lists all the elements that exist as gases and some common compounds that also exist as gases under "standard" laboratory conditions (T = 25°C and P = 760 torr).

Elements	Compounds
H_2	HF
N_2	HCl
O_2	HBr
O_3 (ozone, an allotrope of O_2)	HI
F_2	CO
Cl_2	CO_2
He	NH_3
Ne	NO_2
Ar	SO_2
Kr	H_2S
Xe	HCN
Rn	CH_4 (methane)

II.   Properties of Gases

a)   *Compressibility.* Gases can be compressed into smaller volumes; i.e., their densities can be increased by applying pressure.

b)   *Indefinite shape or volume.* A gas can be made to fit the vessel in which it is placed.

c)   *Expansion.* Gases expand without limits so that gas samples completely and uniformly occupy the volume of a container.

d)   *Mixibility or diffusion.* Gases diffuse into each other completely.

e)   *Low density.* Because the density of a gas is small, it is measured in g/L

f)   The amounts and properties of gases are described in terms of T = temperature (in K), P = pressure, V = volume they occupy, and n = the number of moles present.

III. Characteristics of Ideal Gases

The equations that will be used in this module, apply only to ideal gases or those behaving very closely as ideal gases. An ideal gas is considered to have the following characteristics:

a)   has a negligible volume,

b)   has no attractive forces between molecules,

c)   undergoes elastic collisions.

Boost

Real Gases such as H_2, N_2, etc. can behave as ideal gases by avoiding: a) extremely low temperatures, b) very small volumes, & c) very high pressures.

IV. Pressure

Pressure - force per unit area

Common units of pressure - atmosphere (atm), torr, millimeters of mercury (mm Hg), Pascal (Pa)

$$1 \text{ atm} = 760 \text{ torr} = 760 \text{ mm Hg} = 1.01 \times 10^5 \text{ Pa}$$

NOTE: At sea level the pressure is 760 torr, above sea level it is less than 760 torr, and below sea level it is greater than 760 torr.

Barometer - a device used for measuring pressure

Manometer - A partially filled glass tube of mercury
with one arm open to the atmosphere
(side P_1) and the other arm (side P_2)
attached to a container of gas.

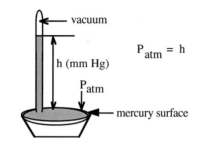

Schematic of a barometer

Example Problem:

The difference in the height of mercury from one
arm of a manometer to the other arm is 27 mm
(see Figure B). If the atmospheric pressure is
1.02 atm, then what is the pressure of the gas in
the container that is attached to the manometer?

$$P_{gas} = P_{atm} + \Delta h$$

$$P_{gas} = \left(1.02 \text{ atm} \times \frac{760 \text{ mm Hg}}{1 \text{ atm}}\right) + 27 \text{ mm Hg}$$

$$P_{gas} = 802 \text{ mm Hg} = 802 \text{ torr}$$

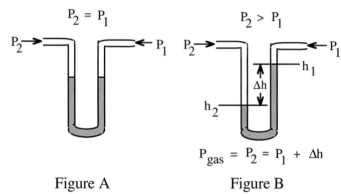

Figure A   Figure B

Schematic of a manometer

V. Standard Temperature and Pressure (STP) & Standard Molar Volume

> STP = 0°C (273 K) and 1 atm (760 torr)
>
> at STP, 1 mol of an ideal gas occupies 22.4 L

VI. Gas Laws

A. Boyle's Law: $V \propto \dfrac{1}{P}$ (at contant T and n)   {where $\propto$ means proportional}

Example: If the pressure of a gas at constant temperature and composition is doubled, its volume
will be cut in half.

B. Charles' Law: $V \propto T$ (K)   (at contant P and n)

Example: If the temperature (in K) of a gas at constant pressure and composition is tripled, its
volume will triple.

C. Avogadro's Law: $V \propto n$ (at contant T and P)

Example: If the number of moles of a gas at constant temperature and pressure is quadrupled, its
volume will quadruple.

At the same T & P, equal volumes of gases contain the same number of moles and molecules (at
STP, 1 mole gas = 22.4 L).

Example Problem:

Which occupies a larger volume at STP, 2.0 grams of He or 1.0 gram of H_2?

Since $V \propto n$, the gas that contains the greatest number of moles will have the largest volume.

$$? \text{ mol He} = 2.0 \text{ g He}\left(\frac{1 \text{ mol He}}{4.0 \text{ g He}}\right) = 0.5 \text{ mol He}$$

$$? \text{ mol } H_2 = 1.0 \text{ g } H_2 \left(\frac{1 \text{ mol } H_2}{2.0 \text{ g } H_2} \right) = 0.5 \text{ mol } H_2$$

Both occupy the same volume at STP since there are an equal number of moles of each gas; futhermore each gas occupies a volume of 11.2 L_{STP} (0.5 mol x 22.4 $\frac{L}{mol}$).

VII. Combined Gas Laws

$$\frac{P_1 V_1}{T_1} = \frac{P_2 V_2}{T_2} \qquad \text{T must be in K} \qquad \text{(at constant n)}$$

Any unit of pressure and volume can be used as long as P_1 and P_2 & V_1 and V_2 have the same units. T_1 and T_2 *must be* in K.

Example Problems:

1. A sample of neon occupies 105 L at 27°C under a pressure of 985 torr. What volume would it occupy at STP?

$$\frac{P_1 V_1}{T_1} = \frac{P_2 V_2}{T_2} \quad ----> \quad \frac{985 \text{ torr x } 105 \text{ L}}{(27 + 273) \text{ K}} = \frac{760 \text{ torr x } V_2}{273 \text{ K}}$$

$$V_2 = \frac{985 \times 105 \times 273}{300 \times 760} = 124 \text{ L}$$

2. If the pressure of a gas (at 27°C) is tripled and its volume is cut in half, what will the resulting temperature (in °C) be?

The initial pressure (P_1) and volume (V_1) are not given; however, we know that the initial pressure was tripled ($P_2 = 3P_1$) and the initial volume was cut in half ($V_2 = \frac{1}{2}V_1$)

$$\frac{P_1 V_1}{T_1} = \frac{P_2 V_2}{T_2} \quad ----> \quad \frac{P_1 V_1}{(27 + 273) \text{ K}} = \frac{3P_1 \times \frac{1}{2}V_1}{T_2}$$

$$T_2 = \frac{3P_1 \times \frac{1}{2}V_1 \times (27 + 273)}{P_1 \times V_1} = 450 \text{ K}$$

$$K = °C + 273 \quad ----> 450 = °C + 273$$

$$°C = 450 - 273 = 177°C$$

3. If the pressure of a 5.00 L sample of a gas is reduced from 5.00 atm to 70 mm Hg at a constant temperature, then what will its new volume (in mL) be?

Since this change in condition was done at a constant temperature ($T_1 = T_2$), the combined gas law becomes:

$$P_1 V_1 = P_2 V_2 ---> (5.00 \text{ atm}) (5.00 \text{ L}) = \left(70 \text{ mm Hg x } \frac{1 \text{ atm}}{760 \text{ mm Hg}} \right) \text{x } V_2$$

$$V_2 = \frac{5.00 \times 5.00 \times 760}{70} = 271 \text{ L} \rightarrow 271 \text{ L} \left(\frac{1 \text{ mL}}{10^{-3} \text{ L}} \right) = 2.71 \times 10^5 \text{ mL}$$

VIII. Ideal Gas Equation

$$PV = nRT \qquad\qquad R \text{ (gas constant)} = 0.0821 \frac{L \cdot atm}{mole \cdot K} = 62.4 \frac{L \cdot torr}{mole \cdot K}$$

Example Problems:

1. Calculate the pressure in atm of 0.652 moles of oxygen gas occupying a 10.0 L cylinder at 30°C.

$$PV = nRT \longrightarrow P\,(10.0\text{ L}) = 0.652 \text{ mol } \times 0.0821 \frac{L \cdot atm}{mole \cdot K} \times (30 + 273)\text{ K}$$

$$P = \frac{0.652 \times 0.0821 \times 303}{10.0} = 1.62 \text{ atm}$$

2. Calculate the number of moles that a sample of neon gas occupies its pressure at 25°C is 500 torr and its volume is 400 mL.

$$PV = nRT \longrightarrow 500 \text{ torr } \times \left(400 \text{ mL} \times \frac{10^{-3}\text{ L}}{1 \text{ mL}}\right) = n \times 62.4 \frac{L \cdot torr}{mole \cdot K} \times (25 + 273)\text{K}$$

$$n = \frac{500 \times 400 \times 10^{-3}}{62.4 \times 298} = 0.0108 \text{ mol Ne}$$

IX. Molecular Weight and Density of Gases

$$PV = nRT \qquad\qquad n = \frac{g}{M} \qquad\qquad d = \frac{g}{V} \qquad\qquad \text{[Note, M = molecular weight]}$$

$$\downarrow$$

$$PV = \left(\frac{g}{M}\right)RT \qquad \longrightarrow \qquad d = \frac{g}{V} = \frac{PM}{RT}$$

Example Problems:

1. Analysis of a gaseous sample shows that it contains 85.7% carbon and 14.3% hydrogen by mass. If 0.188 g of this compound occupies 109 mL at 25°C and 760 torr, what is the molecular formula of this compound?

First find its molecular weight by using the following formula,

$$PV = \left(\frac{g}{M}\right)RT \longrightarrow 760 \text{ torr} \times 0.109 \text{ L} = \left(\frac{0.188 \text{ g}}{M}\right) \times 62.4 \frac{L \cdot torr}{mol \cdot K} \times (25 + 273)\text{ K}$$

$$M = \frac{0.188 \times 62.4 \times 298}{760 \times 0.109} = 42.2 \text{ g/mol}$$

Now determine empirical formula from mass percent data.   Assume that % = g.

Convert g ---> moles $C_{\frac{85.7}{12.0}} H_{\frac{14.3}{1.01}} = C_{7.14}H_{14.2}$

Divide by the smallest number:

$$C_{\frac{7.14}{7.14}} H_{\frac{14.2}{7.14}} = CH_{1.99}$$

Since 1.99 is within 0.08 of a whole number, the empirical formula is: CH_2

The molecular formula can be obtained using the following formula:

$$\left(\frac{\text{molecular formula weight}}{\text{empirical formula weight}}\right) \times \text{empirical formula} = \text{molecular formula} \longrightarrow \left(\frac{42.2}{14.0}\right) \times CH_2 = C_3H_6$$

2. Find the density (in g/L) of oxygen gas at STP.

$$d = \frac{PM}{RT} = \frac{1 \text{ atm} \times 32.0 \frac{g}{mol}}{0.0821 \frac{L \cdot atm}{mol \cdot K} \times 273 \text{ K}} = 1.43 \text{ g/L}$$

3. Assuming that they are at the same temperature and pressure, which gas has the greatest density, CH_4 or H_2?

$$d = \frac{PM}{RT} \quad \text{--->} \quad d \propto M \text{ (at constant T and P)}$$

Since the molecular weight of CH_4 is greater than that of H_2, its density is greater.

X. Dalton's Law of Partial Pressures

At constant volume and temperature, the total pressure exerted by a mixture of ideal gases is the sum of the partial pressures of those gases.

P_A = 200 torr P_B = 250 torr $P_T = P_A + P_B$ = 450 torr

gas A   gas B   Place A & B in same container   gas A & B   At constant T and V conditions

$$P_T = P_A + P_B + P_C + ... = \frac{n_A RT}{V} + \frac{n_B RT}{V} + \frac{n_C RT}{V} + ... = (n_A + n_B + n_C + ...)\left(\frac{RT}{V}\right)$$

There is a simple relation that exists between total pressure and individual partial pressures. Consider a sample containing gases A and B. Dividing P_A by P_T we obtain:

$$\frac{P_A}{P_T} = \frac{\dfrac{n_A RT}{V}}{\dfrac{(n_A + n_B)RT}{V}} = \frac{n_A}{n_A + n_B} = X_A$$

where X_A is called *mole fraction of A*

Mole fraction is a dimensionless quantity that expresses the ratio of moles of one component to the number of total moles. The mole fraction can be any number between 0 and 1. Note that the sum of mole fractions must be equal to one. If two components are present, then:

$$X_A + X_B = 1$$

Rearranging the above equation ($P_A/P_T = X_A$), we can express the partial pressure of A and B as:

$$P_A = \left(\frac{n_A}{n_A + n_B}\right)P_T = X_A P_T \qquad\qquad P_B = \left(\frac{n_B}{n_A + n_B}\right)P_T = X_B P_T$$

Therefore, in a sample containing two gases (A & B), the total pressure of the sample is given by:

$$P_T = P_A + P_B = (n_A + n_B)\left(\frac{RT}{V}\right) = X_A P_T + X_B P_T$$

Gases that are insoluble and that don't react with water can be collected over water. The partial pressure exerted by the water vapor above the liquid is called its vapor pressure. Every liquid shows characteristic vapor pressures that vary with temperature. Thus, a gas collected over water is saturated with water vapor; and at atmospheric pressure (P_T = atmospheric pressure), we can write:

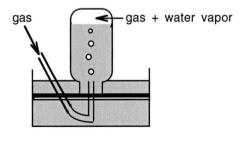

$$P_T = P_{gas} + P_{H_2O} \quad \text{---->} \quad P_{gas} = P_T - P_{H_2O}$$

Table 1.   Vapor Pressure of Water (P_{H_2O}) in torr Near Room Temperature

Temp (°C)	P_{H_2O}	Temp (°C)	P_{H_2O}	Temp (°C)	P_{H_2O}
20	17.5	23	21.1	26	25.2
21	18.7	24	22.4	27	26.7
22	19.8	25	23.8	28	28.4

Example Problems:

1. A 10.0 L flask contains 3.2 g of methane gas (CH_4) and 0.300 mole of hydrogen gas at 25°C.

    a) What is the pressure in atm inside the flask?

    $$P_T = (n_{CH_4} + n_{H_2}) \frac{RT}{V}$$

    $$? \text{ mol } CH_4 = 3.2 \text{ g } CH_4 \left(\frac{1 \text{ mol } CH_4}{16.0 \text{ g } CH_4} \right) = 0.200 \text{ mol } CH_4$$

    $$P_T = (0.200 + 0.300) \text{ mol} \left(\frac{0.0821 \frac{L \cdot atm}{mol \cdot K} \times (25 + 273) \text{ K}}{10.0 \text{ L}} \right) = 1.22 \text{ atm}$$

    b) What is the partial pressure of each component in the mixture?

    $$P_{CH_4} = \frac{(n_{CH_4})RT}{V} = \frac{0.200 \text{ mol} \times 0.0821 \frac{L \cdot atm}{mol \cdot K} \times 298 \text{ K}}{10.0 \text{ L}} = 0.489 \text{ atm}$$

    $$P_{H_2} = \frac{(n_{H_2})RT}{V} = \frac{0.300 \text{ mol} \times 0.0821 \frac{L \cdot atm}{mol \cdot K} \times 298 \text{ K}}{10.0 \text{ L}} = 0.734 \text{ atm}$$

    Proof that $P_T = P_{CH_4} + P_{H_2} = 0.489 + 0.734 = 1.22$ atm

2. If a gas sample whose total pressure is 3.00 atm contains 2.00 mol of O_2 and 4.00 mol of N_2, then what is the partial pressure (in atm) of O_2 in the sample?

    $$P_{O_2} = X_{O_2} P_T = \left(\frac{2.00}{2.00 + 4.00} \right) 3.00 \text{ atm} = 1.00 \text{ atm}$$

3. The volume of a sample of oxygen gas collected over water at 24°C and 752 torr is 1.52 L. How many moles of oxygen are there in the sample?

    From Table 1, P_{H_2O} (at 24°C) = 22.4

    $$P_T = P_{O_2} + P_{H_2O} \; \text{--->} \; 752 = P_{O_2} + 22.4 \; \text{----->} \; P_{O_2} = 752 - 22.4 = 730 \text{ torr}$$

    $$PV = nRT \; \text{--->} \; 730 \text{ torr} \times 1.52 \text{ L} = n \times 62.4 \frac{L \cdot torr}{mol \cdot K} \times (24 + 273) \text{ K}$$

    $$n = \frac{730 \times 1.52}{62.4 \times 297} = 0.0599 \text{ mol } O_2$$

XI. Graham's Law: Diffusion and Effusion of Gases

Diffusion - the intermingling of gases

Effusion - the leaking out of a gas through a small hole or orifice

$$\frac{Rate_A}{Rate_B} = \sqrt{\frac{MW_B}{MW_A}} \qquad \text{where Rate refers to the rate of effusion} \; \text{-->} \; \frac{V}{t} \Rightarrow \frac{mL}{sec}, \frac{L}{min}, \text{etc.}$$

Example Problems:

1. Calculate the ratio of effusion of CH_4 to that of SO_2.

$$\frac{Rate_{CH_4}}{Rate_{SO_2}} = \sqrt{\frac{MW_{SO_2}}{MW_{CH_4}}} = \sqrt{\frac{64 \text{ g/mol}}{16 \text{ g/mol}}} = \frac{2}{1}$$

CH_4 effuses through an orifice twice as fast as SO_2

2. A 100 mL sample of hydrogen effuses through an orifice four times faster than that of an unknown gas. Calculate the molecular weight of the unknown gas.

$$\frac{Rate_{H_2}}{Rate_{Unk}} = \sqrt{\frac{MW_{Unk}}{MW_{H_2}}}$$

$$\frac{4}{1} = \sqrt{\frac{MW_{Unk}}{2 \text{ g/mol}}} \quad \text{----- square both sides ---->} \quad \left(\frac{4}{1}\right)^2 = \frac{MW_{Unk}}{2 \text{ g/mol}}$$

$MW_{Unk} = 16 \times 2 = 32$ g/mol

3. If methane gas (CH_4) effuses through an orifice at a rate of 400 mL/min, then at what rate (in mL/min) will sulfur trioxide gas effuse through the same orifice.

$$\frac{Rate_{CH_4}}{Rate_{SO_3}} = \sqrt{\frac{MW_{SO_3}}{MW_{CH_4}}} \quad ----> \quad \frac{400 \text{ mL/min}}{Rate_{SO_3}} = \sqrt{\frac{80.1 \text{ g/mol}}{16.0 \text{ g/mol}}} \quad ---->$$

$$\frac{400 \text{ mL/min}}{Rate_{SO_3}} = 2.24 \quad ----> \quad Rate_{SO_3} = \frac{400}{2.24} = 179 \text{ mL/min}$$

XII. **Stoichiometry in Reactions Involving Gases**

A. **Gay-Lussac's Law (Law of Combining Volumes)**

At constant temperature and pressure, the volumes of reacting gases can be expressed as the simple whole number ratio of the moles of gases that are reacting (i.e., $V \propto N$ at constant T & P). If the reaction is carried out at STP, then 1 mol gas = 22.4 L.

	H_2 (g)	+	Cl_2 (g)	→	2 HCl (g)
	1 mol		1 mol		2 mol
	1 volumes		1 volume		2 volumes
@ STP	1(22.4 L)		1(22.4) L		2(22.4 L)

Example Problems:

1. What volume (in L) of HCl (g) will form when 50 L of chlorine gas are reacted with excess hydrogen at constant T and P?

$$H_2 \text{ (g)} + Cl_2 \text{ (g)} \rightarrow 2 \text{ HCl (g)}$$

$$? \text{ L HCl} = 50 \text{ L Cl}_2\left(\frac{2 \text{ L HCl}}{1 \text{ L Cl}_2}\right) = 100 \text{ L}$$

2. If 112. g of hydrogen that is 95% pure are reacted with excess nitrogen gas at STP, then how many liters of ammonia will be produced?

$$3 \text{ H}_2 \text{ (g)} + \text{N}_2 \text{ (g)} \rightarrow 2 \text{ NH}_3 \text{ (g)}$$

$$? \text{ L NH}_3 = 112. \text{ g sample}\left(\frac{95 \text{ g H}_2}{100 \text{ g sample}}\right)\left(\frac{1 \text{ mol H}_2}{2.02 \text{ g H}_2}\right)\left(\frac{2 \text{ mol NH}_3}{3 \text{ mol H}_2}\right)\left(\frac{22.4 \text{ L}_{STP} \text{ NH}_3}{1 \text{ mol NH}_3}\right) = 786.6 \text{ L}$$

B. **Using the Ideal Gas Equation in Solving Stoichiometry Problems**

Depending on what is given and/or asked to be solved for, each arrow in the following concept map represents a step in the solution to the problem.

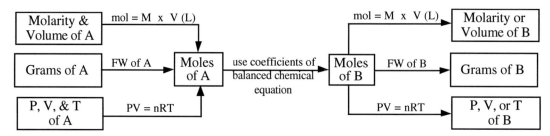

Example Problems:

Use the following balanced decomposition chemical equation when answering questions 1 - 3:

$$2\ KClO_{3\,(s)} \quad \rightarrow \quad 2\ KCl_{\,(s)} + \quad 3\ O_{2\,(g)}$$
$$FW \qquad 122.6 \qquad\qquad 74.6 \qquad\quad 32.0$$

1. If 3.72 g of pure $KClO_3$ is completely decomposed, then how many mL of oxygen would be produced at 705 torr and 32.0°C?

$$?\ mol\ O_2\ = 3.72\ g\ KClO_3 \left(\frac{1\ mol\ KClO_3}{122.6\ g\ KClO_3} \right)\left(\frac{3\ mol\ O_2}{2\ mol\ KClO_3} \right) = 0.0455\ mol\ O_2$$

$$PV = nRT \dashrightarrow 705\ torr\ x\ V = 0.0455\ mol\ x\ 62.4\ \frac{L \cdot torr}{mol \cdot K}\ x\ (32.0 + 273)\ K$$

$$V\ =\ \frac{0.0455\ x\ 62.4\ x\ 305}{705}\ =\ 1.23\ L\ \dashrightarrow\ 1.23\ x\ 10^3\ mL$$

2. When a student decomposed a 1.800 g mixture containing impure potassium chlorate, 0.405 L of oxygen at 25°C and 745 torr were liberated. The residue left behind after heating weighed 1.282 g.

    a) Calculate the value for the gas constant R in L·torr/mol·K from this data.

    To find R we need: P, V, T (which are given) and n -- which we need to solve for.

    From the Law of Conservation of Mass we can find how much O_2 was liberated:

    $$g\ of\ O_2 = 1.800 - 1.282\ g = 0.518\ g\ O_2$$

    $$?\ mol\ O_2\ =\ 0.518\ g\ O_2 \left(\frac{1\ mol\ O_2}{32.0\ g\ O_2} \right) = 0.0162\ mol$$

    $$PV = nRT\ \dashrightarrow (745\ torr)(0.405\ L) =\ 0.0162\ mol\ x\ R\ x\ (25 + 273)\ K$$

    $$R\ =\ \frac{745\ x\ 0.405}{0.0162\ x\ 298}\ =\ 62.5\ \frac{L \cdot torr}{mol \cdot K}$$

    This data shows that the value for R can be indeed experimentally obtained and that the value that is obtained should be 62.4 L·torr/mol·K. If it is not, then there has been an experimental error.

    b) How many grams of pure potassium chlorate were in the original sample?

    $$?\ g\ KClO_3 = 0.0162\ mol\ O_2 \left(\frac{2\ mol\ KClO_3}{3\ mol\ O_2} \right)\left(\frac{122.6\ g\ KClO_3}{1\ mol\ KClO_3} \right) = 1.32\ g\ KClO_3$$

c) What percentage of the mixture was potassium chlorate?

$$\% \ KClO_3 \ = \ \frac{g \ pure \ KClO_3}{g \ sample} \ x \ 100 \ = \ \frac{1.32 \ g}{1.80 \ g} \ x \ 100 \ = \ 73.3\%$$

3. When a 4.72 g sample of $KClO_3$ that is 60.0% pure is completely decomposed, then how many mL of O_2 collected over water at 25.0°C and a barometric pressure of 747.2 torr should be collected? (P_{H_2O} at 25.0°C = 23.8 torr)

$$? \ mol \ O_2 = 4.72 \ g \ sample \left(\frac{60.0 \ g \ KClO_3}{100 \ g \ sample} \right) \left(\frac{1 \ mol \ KClO_3}{122.6 \ g \ KClO_3} \right) \left(\frac{3 \ mol \ O_2}{2 \ mol \ KClO_3} \right) = 0.0346 \ mol \ O_2$$

$$P_T = P_{O_2} + P_{H_2O} \ ---> 747.2 = \ P_{O_2} + 23.8 \ ---> P_{O_2} \ = 747.2 - 23.8 \ = 723.4 \ torr$$

$$PV = nRT \ ---> (723.4 \ torr) \ x \ V \ = \ (0.0346 \ mol) \left(62.4 \frac{L \cdot torr}{mol \cdot K} \right) (25.0 + 273) \ K$$

$$V \ = \ \frac{0.0346 \ x \ 62.4 \ x \ 298}{723.4} \ = 0.889 \ L \ ------> \ \ 889 \ mL$$

4. 27.0 mL of a solution of unknown phosphoric acid concentration when reacted with excess Na, produced 6.46 L of hydrogen gas at pressure of 695 torr and 23°C. Given this information, what is the molarity of the phosphoric acid solution?

$$6 \ Na_{(s)} \ + \ 2 \ H_3PO_4 \ _{(aq)} \ \rightarrow \ 2 \ Na_3PO_4 \ _{(s)} \ + \ \ 3 \ H_2 \ _{(g)}$$

$$PV = nRT \ ---> \ (695 \ torr) \ (6.46 \ L) \ = \ n \ x \ \left(62.4 \frac{L \cdot torr}{mol \cdot K} \right) \ (23 + 273) \ K$$

$$n \ = \ \frac{695 \ x \ 6.46}{62.4 \ x \ 296} \ = 0.243 \ mol \ H_2$$

$$? \ mol \ H_3PO_4 = 0.243 \ mol \ H_2 \left(\frac{2 \ mol \ H_3PO_4}{3 \ mol \ H_2} \right) = 0.162 \ mol \ H_3PO_4$$

$$? \ M \ H_3PO_4 \ = \ \frac{0.162 \ mol \ H_3PO_4}{27.0 \ x \ 10^{-3} \ L} \ = 6.00 \ M$$

5. Consider the following chemical equation: $Cr_x(CO)_{y \ (s)} \rightarrow \ x \ Cr_{(s)} \ + \ y \ CO_{(g)}$. When 0.1120 g of $Cr_x(CO)_y$ is decomposed at 27°C, 0.155 L of CO at a pressure of 369 torr is generated. Given this information, what is the empirical formula of $Cr_x(CO)_y$.

First find grams of CO generated, this will also be the grams of CO present in $Cr_x(CO)_y$.

$$PV = \left(\frac{g}{M} \right) RT \ --> (369 \ torr) \ (0.155 \ L) = \left(\frac{g}{28.0 \ g/mol} \right) \left(62.4 \frac{L \cdot torr}{mol \cdot K} \right) (27 + 273) \ K$$

$$g \ = \ \frac{369 \ x \ 0.155 \ x \ 28.0}{62.4 \ x \ 300} \ = 0.0855 \ g \ CO$$

Using the Law of Conservation of Mass we can then find g of Cr in sample:

0.1120 - 0.0855 = 0.0265 g of Cr

Now that we have grams of Cr and CO we can proceed by converting g into moles:

$Cr_{\frac{0.0265}{52.0}} \ (CO)_{\frac{0.0855}{28.0}} \ ----> \ Cr_{0.000510} \ (CO)_{0.00305}$

Divide by the smallest number:

$Cr_{\frac{0.000510}{0.000510}} \ (CO)_{\frac{0.00305}{0.000510}} \ ----> \ Cr(CO)_{5.98}$

Since 5.98 is within 0.08 of a whole number, the empirical formula is: $Cr(CO)_6$

EXERCISES

Pressure, Gas Laws, & Combined Gas Laws

1. If the pressure applied on the left arm (P_2) of the manometer was 1.5 atm, then what is the pressure applied to the right arm (P_1) of the manometer?   Assume that each division is 0.5 cm (ruler not shown to scale).

2. At STP, what volume would each of the following gases occupy?
   a) 3.75 g of Cl_2 (FW = 71.0)
   b) 7.65 g of NO (FW = 30.0)
   c) 1 mol of Ne (FW = 20.2)
   d) 1 mol Ar (FW = 40.0)

3. A gas occupies a volume of 100 mL. What happens to its volume as a result of each of the following changes?
   a) Increasing the pressure (@ constant T & n) from 1 atm to 4 atm.
   b) Decreasing the pressure (@ constant T & n) from 760 torr to 190 torr.
   c) Increasing the temperature (@ constant P & n) from 25°C to 100°C.
   d) Decreasing the temperature (@ constant P & n) from 50 K to 25 K.
   e) Decreasing the number of moles (@ constant T & P) from 3 mol to 1 mol.
   f) Increasing the number of moles (@ constant T & P) from 5 mol to 50 mol.

4. What would the pressure (in torr) of 1.00 mole of gas at STP be, if the temperature is increased to 27.0°C and its volume is increased to 500 L?

5. A 1200 L sample of a gas at 0.00°C exerts a pressure of 75.0 torr. What volume (in L) would it occupy at 273°C and 600 torr?

6. A 366 mL sample of a gas at 27.0°C exerts a pressure of 1.75 atm. What pressure (in torr) would it exert if the volume is decreased to 105 mL at a constant temperature?

7. A 22,400 mL sample of a gas at 50.0°C exerts a pressure of 1.20 atm. What pressure (in torr) would it exert if the volume is changed to 300 L and its temperature is decreased to 30.0°C?

8. If the pressure of a gas (at 25.0°C) is cut to a third of its original pressure and its volume is quadrupled, what will be the resulting temperature (in °C)?

Ideal Gas Equation, Molecular Weights of Gases, and Gas Densities

9. Calculate the pressure (in atm) of 0.652 mole sample of neon gas occupying a 20.0 L cylinder at 25°C.

10. At 100°C and a pressure of 3.675 atm, what volume (in L) would be occupied by 1.20 mole of He?

11. A 400 mL sample of a gas at 75.0°C exerts a pressure of 584 torr, how many moles of gas are in the sample?

12. What pressure (in torr) would a 9.60 g sample of SO_2 occupying a volume of 5.25 L at 36°C exert?

13. An 8.87 g sample of a gas at 30°C confined in a 5.25 L tank exerts a pressure of 799 torr; what is its molecular weight?

14. What volume (in L) is a 2.20 g sample of hydrogen gas at 50.0°C occupying at 443 torr?

15. What is the density (in g/L) of SO_2 at STP?

16. What is the molecular weight a gas whose density at STP is 7.78 g/L?

17. At a pressure of 760 torr what temperature (in °C) would the density of nitrogen gas be 1.25 g/L?

18. Compared to its density at STP, what would happen to the density (increase, decrease, or remain the same) of H_2 under the following changes in condition?
    a) temperature increase.
    b) pressure increase.

Dalton's Law of Partial Pressures

19. A 5.5 L flask contains 0.50 mol of hydrogen and 0.60 mol of helium at 0°C:
    a) What is the pressure (in atm) inside the flask?
    b) What is the partial pressure of each component?

20. The pressure inside of a 2.50-L tank containing helium and argon at 25°C is 12.2 atm.
    a) If there are 0.75 mol of helium in the tank, then how many moles of argon are in the sample?
    b) What is the partial pressure (in atm) of each component?

21. A 22.4 L tank contains 1.00 mol of Ar and 1.00 mol of krypton at 0°C. What is the total pressure (in atm) inside the container?

22. If the total pressure inside a 10.0 L tank containing 0.100 mol of hydrogen, 0.200 mol of helium, and 0.300 mol of neon is 1.48 atm, what is the temperature (in °C) inside the tank?

23. A 20,000 mL tank contains 1.00 g of helium and 1.00 g of neon at 0°C:
    a) What is the pressure (in atm) inside the tank?
    b) What is the partial pressure (in atm) of neon?

24. A 2.00 L gas tank at 27.0°C contains nitrogen, helium, and argon. The partial pressure of nitrogen, helium, and argon is 1.23 atm, 2.46 atm, and 3.69 atm, respectively. Given this information,
    a) What is the pressure (in atm) inside the tank?
    b) How many moles of each gas are present inside the container?

25. A 10.0 L sample of a gas was collected over water at 27.0°C and at a pressure of 1.48 atm. (Refer to table 1 to obtain the vapor pressure of water.)
    a) What is the partial pressure (in torr) of the gas?
    b) How many moles of gas were collected?

26. A 3.46 L sample of a gas was collected over water at 21°C and at an atmospheric pressure of 718 torr. After the gas sample was dried, it weighed 4.20 g, what is the molecular weight of the gas? (Refer to table 1 to obtain the vapor pressure of water.)

27. A 5.25 L sample of argon was collected over water at 30°C and at a pressure of 830 torr. (Vapor Pressure of water at 30°C is 31.8 torr.)
    a) What is the partial pressure (in torr) of argon?
    b) How many grams of argon were collected?

Graham's Law

28. Calculate the ratio of effusion of helium to that of sulfur dioxide under identical conditions.

29. A sample of fluorine gas effuses through an orifice 1.37 times faster than that of an unknown gas. Calculate the molecular weight of the unknown gas.

30. If helium effuses through an orifice at a rate of 400 mL/min, then at what rate (in mL/min) will hydrogen gas effuse through that same orifice?

31. At a given temperature and pressure, how many times faster than fluorine gas would neon escape through an orifice?

32. If chlorine gas effuses through an orifice at a rate of 700 mL/min and an unknown gas effuses through that same orifice at a rate of 957 mL/min, then what is the molecular weight of the gas?

Stoichiometry in Reactions Involving Gases

33. Consider the following balanced chemical equation:

$$CH_{4\ (g)} + 2\ O_{2\ (g)} \rightarrow CO_{2\ (g)} + 2\ H_2O_{\ (l)}$$

a) What volume (in L) of methane gas (CH_4) will combine with 25.0 L of oxygen at a pressure of 760 torr and a temperature of 50°C?

b) At STP, how many L of carbon dioxide will be produced if 10.0 mol of methane reacts with excess oxygen?

c) How many moles of methane are needed to react with 44.8 L of oxygen at STP?

34. Consider the following balanced chemical equation:

$$2\ K_{(s)} + 2\ HCl_{(aq)} \rightarrow 2\ KCl_{(s)} + H_{2\ (g)}$$

a) What volume (in L) of hydrogen gas at STP can be produced by reacting 2.00 moles of potassium with excess HCl?

b) 500 mL of a 4.00 M HCl solution were reacted with excess potassium. If the pressure of the dry hydrogen collected was 450 torr at a temperature of 25.0°C, then

   A. How many grams of hydrogen were produced?
   B. How many liters of hydrogen were produced?

35. Consider the following balanced chemical equation:

$$Ba(ClO_3)_{2\ (s)} \xrightarrow{\ \Delta\ } 3\ O_{2\ (g)} + BaCl_{2\ (s)}$$
$$FW \quad\ \ 304 \qquad\qquad\quad 32.0 \qquad 208$$

a) If a 100. g sample $Ba(ClO_3)_2$ is decomposed, then what volume (in mL) of oxygen gas should be collected at STP?

b) If a 100. g sample of 75.0% pure $Ba(ClO_3)_2$ is decomposed, then what volume (in mL) of oxygen gas should be collected at STP?

c) A 3.00 g sample of barium chlorate that was 83.0% pure was heated until all of it decomposed. If the pressure of the dry oxygen collected was 732 torr at a temperature of 25.0°C, then

   A. How many grams of oxygen were produced?
   B. How many liters of oxygen were produced?

d) A 2.00 g sample of impure barium chlorate was heated until all of it decomposed. A volume of 200 mL of oxygen gas collected over water was obtained at a pressure of 758 torr and a temperature of 25.0°C. (vapor pressure of water at 25.0°C = 23.8 torr)

   A. How many moles of oxygen were produced?
   B. How many grams of barium chlorate were in the original sample?
   C. What percentage of the mixture was barium chlorate?

36. A 5.00 g sample of an unknown compound containing C and H when combusted in the presence of oxygen produced 8.09 L of CO_2 (FW = 44.0) at a pressure of 758 torr and a temperature 24°C. Given this information, calculate the empirical formula of this unknown compound. [HINT: 1) Find g of CO_2 using ideal gas equation, 2) Find g of C in CO_2, 3) use law of conservation of mass to find g of H, 4) convert g of each element into moles, 5) divide by the smallest number, 6) if whole numbers are not obtained, multiply by the smallest whole number that will produce a whole number.]

MULTIPLE CHOICE PRACTICE EXAM FOR MODULE 8

1. Which of the following statements is true?
    1) Gases have high densities.
    2) Gases are not compressible
    3) Gases have a definite volume.
    4) Two or more of the statements are correct.
    5) None of the statements are correct.

2. A gas would tend to behave more ideally under which of the following conditions?
    1) 5°C and 10 torr   2) 500°C and 1 torr   3) 50°C and 100 torr
    4) 5°C and 1 torr   5) 500°C and 10 torr

3. Consider the manometer set-up to the right. If the atmospheric pressure was 758.8 torr, then what is the pressure (in torr) exerted by gas A?
    1) 753.6   2) 764.0   3) 706.8
    4) 810.8   5) 758.8

4. At STP, which of the following occupies the greatest volume?
    1) 4.0 g of He   2) 44.8 L of H_2 3) 32.0 g of CH_4 4) 2.5 mol of Ar
    5) All occupy the same volume at STP.

5. If the volume of a gas at 30.0°C and 10.0 L is reduced to 9.0 L under a constant pressure, then what is the resulting temperatrure (in °C)?
    1) -30   2) 0   3) 24   4) 27   5) 36

6. A helium balloon has a volume of 1.50 x 10^3 L at 0.901 atm and 25°C. When this ballon is taken to an altitude of 20 km, the temperature is -50°C and the atmospheric pressure is 76.0 mm Hg. What is the volume (in L) of this balloon at 20 km?
    1) 2.20 x 10^2 2) 1.25 x 10^2 3) 1.01 x 10^4 4) 1.80 x 10^2 5) 1.33 x 10^2

7. What would happen to the volume of a gas if: its pressure were doubled, its number of moles were quadrupled, and its temperature was decreased from 100 K to 25 K?
    1) double   2) quadruple   3) increase by a factor of 8
    4) cut in half   5) decrease by a factor of 4

8. What is the molecular weight of a 0.0564 g sample of an unknown gas inside a 25.0 mL container whose temperature is 100°C and whose pressure is 750 torr ?
    1) 85.0   2) 22.2   3) 60.0   4) 18.8   5) 70.0

9. Calculate the density of Ar (in g/L) at STP.
    1) 1.00   2) 0.561   3) 0.891   4) 1.58   5) 1.78

10. At STP, which gas has the greatest density?
    1) H_2 2) CH_4 3) Kr   4) N_2 5) Cl_2

11. The density of which of the following gases is 1.96 g/L at STP?
    1) O_2 (M = 32.0)   2) SO_2 (M = 64.1)   3) CO_2 (M = 44.0)
    4) N_2 (M = 28.0)   5) AsH_3 (M = 77.9)

12. If a 1 L sample of a gas at STP is subjected to an increase in pressure and a decrease in temperature, its density will _____.
    1) decrease   2) increase   3) remain the same   4) become zero
    5) increase or decrease depending on the relative increase in P & decrease in T

13. If 150. mL of Ar at atmospheric pressure of 758 torr were collected over water at 20.0°C, then what volume (in mL) would this argon sample occupy at STP? (Vapor Pressure of H_2O @ 20.0°C = 17.5 torr)
    1) 136   2) 140   3) 157   4) 161   5) 166

14. If a gas sample whose total pressure is 3.00 atm contains 4.00 g of H_2 and 16.0 g of He, then what is the partial pressure (in atm) of H_2 in the sample?
    1) 0.600   2) 2.00   3) 18.0   4) 1.00   5) 1.50

15. What is the pressure exerted (in torr) by a 100. L sample containing 4.0 g of H_2 and 16.0 g of He at 25.0°C?
    1) 3.72×10^3 2) 1.12×10^3 3) 1.47   4) 760   5) 562

16. A mixture containing CO_2, Ar, and CO has a total pressure of 1.82 atm at 25°C. If the partial pressure of CO_2 is 360 torr and that of CO is 664 torr, then what is the partial pressure (in torr) of Ar?
    1) 8020   2) 359   3) 0.258   4) 301   5) 5345

17. If 100. mL of He escapes through an orifice in 36 sec and 100. mL of unknown X takes 72 sec to escape through the same orifice, then what is the molecular weight of unknown X?
    1) 1.0   2) 2.0   3) 4.0   4) 8.0   5) 16.0

18. Which of the following gases (under the same conditions) would escape most rapidly from an orifice?
    1) Cl_2 2) F_2 3) CO_2 4) N_2 5) O_2

19. At STP, what volume (in L) of PH_3 $_{(g)}$ should be produced if 100. g of Ca_3P_2 (FW = 182) reacted with excess H_2O?
    $$Ca_3P_2 \,_{(s)} \;+\; 6\,H_2O \,_{(l)} \;\rightarrow\; 3\,Ca(OH)_3 \,_{(s)} \;+\; 2\,PH_3 \,_{(g)}$$
    1) 12.3   2) 6.15   3) 24.6   4) 40.8   5) 81.5

20. At 300 K and 760 torr, what volume (in L) of HCl $_{(g)}$ would be produced by the reaction of 2.4 L of H_2 with 1.5 L of Cl_2?
    $$H_2 \,_{(g)} \;+\; Cl_2 \,_{(g)} \;\rightarrow\; 2\,HCl \,_{(g)}$$
    1) 1.5   2) 2.4   3) 4.8   4) 7.8   5) 3.0

21. A 2.50 g sample of impure $KClO_3$ was heated until all of the potassium chlorate decomposed. If 496 mL of O_2 at 25.0°C and 790 torr were liberated, then calculate the percent purity of the original potassium chlorate sample.
    $$2\,KClO_3 \,_{(s)} \;\rightarrow\; 2\,KCl \,_{(s)} \;+\; 3\,O_2 \,_{(g)}$$
    FW   122.6   74.6   32.0
    1) 32.2   2) 103   3) 27.0   4) 69.0   5) 89.1

22. How many liters of O_2 at 800 torr and 25.0°C would be produced by the decomposition of a 25.0 g sample of 65.0% pure $KMnO_4$ (FW = 158)?
    $$8\,KMnO_4 \,_{(s)} \;\rightarrow\; 4\,K_2MnO_4 \,_{(s)} \;+\; 2\,Mn_2O_3 \,_{(s)} \;+\; 5\,O_2 \,_{(g)}$$
    1) 2.39   2) 1.49   3) 3.67   4) 2.29   5) 15.1

MODULE 8 - ANSWERS

1. 1160 mm Hg

2. a) 1.18 L   b) 5.71 L   c) 22.4 L   d) 22.4 L

3. a) 25.0 mL   b) 400 mL   c) 125 mL   d) 50.0 mL   e) 33.3 mL   f) 1000 mL

4. 37.4 torr

5. 300 L

6. 4.64×10^3 torr

7. 63.9 torr

8. 124°C

9. 0.798 atm

10. 10.0 L

11. 1.08×10^{-2} mol

12. 551 torr

13. 40.0 g/mol

14. 49.6 L

15. 2.86 g/L

16. 174 g/mol

17. 0.00°C

18. a) decrease   b) increase

19. a) 4.5 atm   b) $P_{H_2} = 2.0$ atm, $P_{He} = 2.5$ atm

20. a) 0.50 mol   b) $P_{He} = 7.3$ atm, $P_{Ar} = 4.9$ atm

21. 2.0 atm

22. 27.0°C

23. a) 0.335 atm   b) $P_{He} = 0.280$ atm, $P_{Ne} = 0.055$ atm

24. a) 7.38 atm   b) mol N_2 = 0.100, mol He = 0.200, mol Ar = 0.300

25. 1.10×10^3 torr   b) 0.587

26. 31.8 g/mol

27. a) 798 torr   b) 8.87 g

28. 4 to 1

29. 71.3 g/mol

30. 566 mL/min

31. 1.37 times faster

32. 38.0 g/mol

33. a) 12.5 L   b) 224 L   c) 1.00 mol

34. a) 22.4 L   b) A. 2.02 g   B. 41.3 L

35. a) 2.21×10^4 mL   b) 1.66×10^4 mL   c) A. 0.786 g   B. 0.624 L
    d) A. 7.90×10^{-3} mol; B. 0.801 g; C. 40.0%

36. CH_3

MODULE 9.   *Quantum Theory and The Electronic Structure of Atoms*

I.   Electromagnetic (EM) Radiation

When an electric current is applied to a tube filled with a gas (e.g., neon), electrons jump to higher energy levels and fall again, emitting electromagnetic radiation. Most radiation cannot be seen. Only that radiation that is in the visible region of the electromagnetic spectrum can be detected by our eyes.

A. Wave Nature of EM Radiation

Electromagnetic (EM) radiation travels in waves through space at the speed of light (c), 3.00×10^8 m/s. An electromagnetic wave is depicted in the figure to the right. The distance between peaks (or other equivalent points) of consecutive waves is called the *wavelength* (λ). The number of waves that pass a particular point in 1 second is called the frequency (ν). Wavelength and frequency have the following relationship:

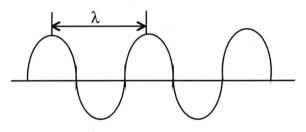

$$\nu = \frac{c}{\lambda}$$

λ ---> m or cm or Å --> Angstrom

$$1\,\text{Å} = 10^{-10}\,\text{m} = 10^{-8}\,\text{cm}$$

c ---> 3.00×10^8 m/sec = 3.00×10^{10} cm/sec

ν ---> Hertz = Hz = cycle/sec = 1/sec = sec⁻

B. Particle Nature of EM Radiation

Einstein discovered that he could explain a phenomenon known as the photoelectric effect (ejection of electrons from the surface of a metal when light shines on it) by postulating that light had both wave and particle properties. These light particles are called **photons**.

Planck's Equation (gives the energy of a photon):

$$E = h\nu = h\left(\frac{c}{\lambda}\right)$$

E = Energy (Joule = J or erg)
h = Planck's Constant = 6.63×10^{-34} J·sec = 6.63×10^{-27} erg·sec
c = speed of light = 3.00×10^8 m/sec = 3.00×10^{10} cm/sec
ν = frequency (sec⁻)
λ = wavelength (m or cm or Å)

<u>Example Problems:</u>

1. If the wavelength of violet light is 4.07×10^3 Å, then calculate its frequency.

$$\nu = \frac{c}{\lambda} = \frac{3.00 \times 10^8 \text{ m/sec}}{\left(4.07 \times 10^3 \text{ Å} \times \dfrac{10^{-10}\text{ m}}{1\text{Å}}\right)} = 7.37 \times 10^{14} \text{ sec}^-$$

2. If the frequency of a ray of light is 2.50×10^{13} Hz, then calculate its wavelength in: a) cm b) Å.

NOTE: 2.50×10^{13} Hz $= 2.50 \times 10^{13}$ sec⁻

a) $\nu = \dfrac{c}{\lambda}$ ---> 2.50×10^{13} sec⁻ $= \dfrac{3.00 \times 10^{10} \text{ cm/sec}}{\lambda}$

$$\lambda = \frac{3.00 \times 10^{10}}{2.50 \times 10^{13}} = 1.20 \times 10^{-3} \text{ cm}$$

b) $? \text{ Å} = 1.20 \times 10^{-3} \text{ cm} \left(\dfrac{1\text{ Å}}{10^{-8}\text{ cm}}\right) = 1.20 \times 10^5 \text{ Å}$

3. Calculate the energy (in J) of violet light whose frequency is 7.37×10^{14} sec⁻ .

$E = h\nu = (6.63 \times 10^{-34} \text{ J·sec})(7.37 \times 10^{14} \text{ sec}^-) = 4.89 \times 10^{-19}$ J

4. What is the wavelength (in Å) of a ray whose energy is 6.16×10^{-14} erg?

$$E = h\left(\frac{c}{\lambda}\right) \quad ----> \quad 6.16 \times 10^{-14} \text{ erg} = 6.63 \times 10^{-27} \text{ erg·sec} \left(\frac{3.00 \times 10^8 \text{ m/sec}}{\lambda}\right)$$

$$\lambda = \frac{6.63 \times 10^{-27} \times 3.00 \times 10^8}{6.16 \times 10^{-14}} = 3.23 \times 10^{-5} \text{ m}$$

$$? \text{ Å} = 3.23 \times 10^{-5} \text{ m} \left(\frac{1 \text{ Å}}{10^{-10} \text{ m}}\right) = 3.23 \times 10^5 \text{ Å}$$

C. Types of EM Radiation

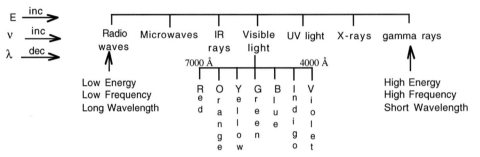

Visible Region of EM Radiation is from ~4000 - 8000 Å or 4.00 x 10⁻⁷ - 8.00 x 10⁻⁷ m

II. The Wave Nature of Electrons

L. de Broglie predicted that a particle with mass, m, and velocity, v, should have a wavelength associated with it.

$$\lambda = \frac{h}{mv} \qquad h = \text{Planck's Constant}, \quad m = \text{mass}, \quad v = \text{velocity}$$

<u>Example Problem:</u> If an electron travelling at 3.00×10^8 cm/sec has a mass of 9.06×10^{-28} g, then calculate its wavelength in cm.

$$[\text{NOTE:} \quad \text{erg} = \frac{g \cdot cm^2}{sec^2}]$$

a) $\lambda = \dfrac{h}{mv} = \dfrac{6.63 \times 10^{-27} \text{ erg·sec}}{9.06 \times 10^{-28} \text{ g} \times 3.00 \times 10^8 \text{ cm/sec}} = 2.49 \times 10^{-8}$ cm

III. The Bohr Atom, Quantization of Energy, & Atomic Spectra

a) The Bohr Atom - assumes that electrons revolve around the nucleus of an atom in circular orbits, like planets around the sun.

b) Quantization of Energy - When an electron is promoted from a lower energy level to a higher energy level or orbit (by the excitation of an atom), it only absorbs a definite amount (or quantized amount) of energy. When the electron falls back to its original energy level, it emits exactly the same amount of energy it absorbed in moving from the lower energy level to the higher energy level.

electronic transition from n = 1 to n = 4
(this process requires energy)

nucleus —

n = 1   n = 2
        n = 3   n = 4

electronic transition from n = 4 to n = 1
(this process releases energy)

n = principal energy levels or orbit (as n increases the levels get closer to one another)

Maximum # of e⁻ / level = $2n^2$

The Bohr Model of the atom only predicts the correct electronic structure for the first 18 elements.

Example Problems:

1. What is the maximum number of electrons that principal energy levels (orbits) 1 to 4 can hold?

n	maximum number of electrons
1	2 e⁻ ---> $2(1^2)$
2	8 e⁻ ---> $2(2^2)$
3	18 e⁻ ---> $2(3^2)$
4	32 e⁻ ---> $2(4^2)$

2. Draw a diagram for the atomic structure of $^{11}_{5}B$, indicating the # of p, n, and e⁻ (arranged in the appropriate principal energy levels):

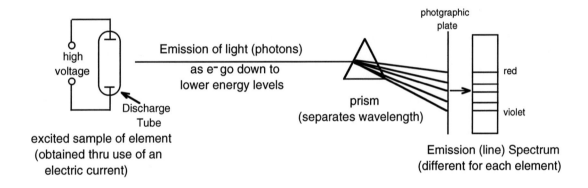

c) Emission (or bright line) Spectra - when electric current is passed through a gas in a vacuum tube (thus exciting the electrons in an atom to higher energy levels) at very low pressures, the light (photons) that the gas emits (due to electrons coming back down to their original levels) can be dispersed by a prism into distinct lines. Each line corresponds to light with a *specific* wavelength, frequency, and energy.

Diffraction gratings can also be used to separate different wavelengths in which the least energetic ones (just the opposite of a prism) are bent the most.

Example Problem: Which of the visible wavelengths are bent the most by: a) a prism   b) a diffraction grating?

                              a) violet   b) red

J. Balmer - discovered that the wavelengths of various lines in the hydrogen spectrum can be related mathematically by the following empirical equation.

$$\frac{1}{\lambda} = (R)\, Z^2 \left(\frac{1}{n_i^2} - \frac{1}{n_o^2} \right)$$

R = Rydberg Constant = 1.097×10^7 m⁻ = 1.097×10^5 cm⁻
n_o = outer energy level
n_i = inner energy level
Z = atomic number
λ = wavelength in m or cm

This equation can be applied to any hydrogen-like species (i.e., species that contain only one electron - He^+, Li^{2+}, etc.).

<u>Example Problem:</u>   When an electron from a sample of He^+ goes from energy level $2 \rightarrow 1$:

a) What wavelength (in m) is associated with this transition?

$$\frac{1}{\lambda} = (1.097 \times 10^7 \text{ m}^-) \, 2^2 \left(\frac{1}{1^2} - \frac{1}{2^2}\right) \quad \text{---->} \quad \frac{1}{\lambda} = 3.29 \times 10^7 \text{ m}^-$$

$$\lambda = \frac{1}{3.29 \times 10^7 \text{ m}^-} = 3.04 \times 10^{-8} \text{ m}$$

b) What wavelength (in Å) is associated with this transition?

$$? \text{ Å} = 3.04 \times 10^{-8} \text{ m} \left(\frac{1 \text{ Å}}{10^{-10} \text{ m}}\right) = 3.04 \times 10^2 \text{ Å}$$

c) Is this transition in the visible portion of the EM spectrum?

No, because 3.04×10^2 Å is not in the visible region (4000Å - 8000Å)

d) What is the frequency associated with this transiton?

$$\nu = \frac{c}{\lambda} = \frac{3.00 \times 10^8 \text{ m/sec}}{3.04 \times 10^{-8} \text{ m}} = 9.87 \times 10^{15} \text{ s}^-$$

e) What is the energy (in Joules) associated with this transition?

$$E = h\nu = (6.63 \times 10^{-34} \text{ J·sec}) (9.87 \times 10^{15} \text{ sec}^-) = 6.54 \times 10^{-18} \text{ J}$$

IV. Quantum Mechanical Picture of the Atom

Bohr made a significant contribution to the understanding of atoms, and his suggestion that the energy of an electron in an atom is quantized remains unchallenged. His theories, however, did not provide for a complete description of the electronic behavior in atoms such as the emission spectra of atoms with more than one electron and the dual nature of matter. One important consequence of the dual nature of matter was expressed by the **Heisenberg Uncertainty Principle**. This principle states that it is impossible to determine accurately both the momentum (defined as the mass x velocity) and position of an electron (or other very small particles) simultaneously. An extension of the Heisenberg Uncertainty Principle states that both the energy and position of an electron can't be known accurately at the same time. Application of the Heisenberg Uncertainty Principle, we see that in reality electrons do not orbit the nucleus in a well-defined path, as Bohr thought. If it did, we could more precisely determine their position (from the radius of the orbit) and their momentum (for its kinetic energy) at the same time.

Since submicroscopic particles were found not to obey the laws of classical mechanics, a search to describe their behavior lead to the birth of quantum mechanics (a highly mathematical branch of chemistry/physics) which treats these small particles as waves. Schrödinger, using a complex mathematical treatment, formulated an equation that described the behavior and energies of submicroscopic particles. The Schrödinger equation requires advanced calculus to solve, however, it is important to note that this equation incorporates both the particle behavior (in terms of mass) and the wave behavior (in terms of a wave function which depends on the location in space of the small particles) of these small particles.

<u>Basic Ideas of Quantum Mechanics</u>

1. Atoms & molecules can exist only in certain energy states. When an atom or molecule changes its energy state, it must emit or absorb just enough energy to bring it to the new energy state (the quantum condition).

2. The energy lost (or gained) by an atom as it goes from higher to lower (or lower to higher) energy states is equal to the energy of the photon emitted (or absorbed) during transition.

3. Since a particle can behave as a wave, many of the concepts and mathematical equations from wave theory are used.

4. The allowed energy states called orbitals of atoms and molecules can be described by sets of four numbers called quantum numbers.

5. Since the exact energy of these orbitals can be calculated, the exact postion of the electron is not known (a consequence of the Heisenberg Uncertainty Principle).

A. Quantum Numbers

Four quantum numbers are used to describe the electronic arrangements (electronic configuration) of atoms in space. These regions in space where the electrons can be found are called atomic orbitals.

1. **Principal Quantum Number (n)** describes the main energy level an electron occupies. It may be any positive integer.

$$n = 1, \quad 2, \quad 3, \quad 4.........$$
$$K, \quad L, \quad M, \quad N \text{ (corresponding to shells in the Bohr atom)}$$

2. **Angular Momentum, Subsidiary or Azimuthal Quantum Number (l)** designates a specific kind of atomic orbital (*sublevel*) that an electron occupies.

$$l = 0, \quad 1, \quad 2, \quad 3, \quad .... \text{ (n-1)}$$
$$s, \quad p, \quad d, \quad f \quad \text{(kind of sublevel)}$$

If n = 1 the only one permissible value for l is 0, which tells us there is only one sublevel, the s sublevel in the first energy level, and no p, d, or f sublevels.

If n = 2 there are two permissible values for l, 0 and 1, which tells us there are only s and p sublevels in the second energy level.

3. **Magnetic Quantum Number (m_l)** designates the spatial orientation of an atomic orbital. This quantum number tells us how many distinct regions of space (atomic orbitals) are associated with a specific sublevel.

$$m_l = -l,...0,...+l$$

If $l = 1$ (designating the p sublevel), $m_l = -1, 0, +1$ meaning that there are three distinct regions of space (atomic orbitals) associated with a p sublevel.

4. **Electron Spin Quantum Number (m_s)** designates the spin of an electron (either up or down) and the orientation of the magnetic field produced by this spin.

$$m_s = \pm \frac{1}{2}$$

This means that each atomic orbital can accomodate no more than 2 e⁻, one with $m_s = +\frac{1}{2}$ and the other with $m_s = -\frac{1}{2}$.

Pauli Exclusion Principle - no two electrons in an atom may have identical sets of 4 quantum numbers (3 of the 4 may be the same, but m_s must be different).

Permissible Values of the Quantum Numbers Through n = 4.

$n = 1,2,...$ $l = 0,1, ..(n-1)$ $m_l = -l,..,0,..+l$ $m_s = \pm\frac{1}{2}$ $2\,\dfrac{e^-}{orbital}$

n	l	m_l	m_s	e⁻ capacity of sublevel	e⁻ capacity of energy level
1 (K)	0 (1s)	0	$+\frac{1}{2}, -\frac{1}{2}$	2	2
2 (L)	0 (2s)	0	$+\frac{1}{2}, -\frac{1}{2}$	2	8
	1 (2p)	-1, 0, +1	$\pm\frac{1}{2}$ for each value of m_l	6	
3 (M)	0 (3s)	0	$+\frac{1}{2}, -\frac{1}{2}$	2	18
	1 (3p)	-1, 0, +1	$\pm\frac{1}{2}$ for each value of m_l	6	
	2 (3d)	-2,-1, 0, +1, +2	"	10	
4 (N)	0 (4s)	0	$+\frac{1}{2}, -\frac{1}{2}$	2	32
	1 (4p)	-1, 0, +1	$\pm\frac{1}{2}$ for each value of m_l	6	
	2 (4d)	-2,-1, 0, +1, +2	"	10	
	3 (4f)	-3, -2,-1, 0, +1, +2, +3	"	14	

<u>Example Problem:</u>   Indicate in each case below whether or not the following sets of four quantum numbers (n, l, m_l, m_s) are permissible or not.

a) $(0, 1, 1, -\frac{1}{2})$ --> Not a permissible set, n has to be a positive integer (1, 2,...)

b) $(3, 1, 2, +\frac{1}{2})$ --> Not a permissible set, m_l (in this case) can only equal -1, 0, +1

c) $(1, 2, 2, +\frac{1}{2})$ --> Not a permissible set, l (in this case) can only equal 0

d) $(3, 2, -2, +\frac{1}{2})$ --> This is a permissible set of four quantum numbers.

B. Orbital Diagrams & Quantum Numbers

In orbital diagrams, lines are used for orbitals and arrows are used to represent electrons. The orbitals are labelled by using a number (representing the principal quantum number, n) and a letter (representing the subsidiary quantum number, l).

Consider the following orbital diagram for the 2p orbitals. The 2 represents n = 2. If n = 2, l can be equal to 1 or 0. In this particular case, l = 1 which is represented by the letter p. If l = 1, then m_l = -1, 0, +1 (meaning that there are three kinds of p orbitals) this is represented by three lines. By convention, the first line represents the most negative value of m_l, the next line represents the second most negative value of m_l, etc. Since each orbital can hold a maximum of 2 electrons, the electrons can either be spin up (m_s = $+\frac{1}{2}$) or spin down ($-\frac{1}{2}$).

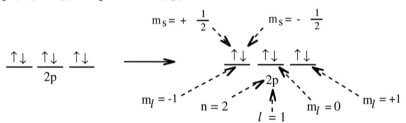

<u>Example Problem:</u>   For the following orbital diagram give the four quantum numbers (n, l, m_l, m_s) associated with the electrons labelled A thru D.

Electron: A $(2, 0, 0, -\frac{1}{2})$; B $(3, 1, -1, +\frac{1}{2})$; C $(3, 2, -2, +\frac{1}{2})$; D $(3, 2, +1, -\frac{1}{2})$

n	Orbital Diagrams for n = 1 to 4			total # of e⁻
1	↑↓ 1s			2
2	↑↓ 2s	↑↓ ↑↓ ↑↓ 2p		8
3	↑↓ 3s	↑↓ ↑↓ ↑↓ 3p	↑↓ ↑↓ ↑↓ ↑↓ ↑↓ 3d	18
4	↑↓ 4s	↑↓ ↑↓ ↑↓ 4p	↑↓ ↑↓ ↑↓ ↑↓ ↑↓ 4d	↑↓ ↑↓ ↑↓ ↑↓ ↑↓ ↑↓ ↑↓ 4f	32

l	0	1	2	3
orbital	s	p	d	f
m_l	0	-1 0 +1	-2 -1 0 +1 +2	-3 -2 -1 0 +1 +2 +3
# of e⁻	2	6	10	14

where ↑ —> $m_s = +\frac{1}{2}$ and ↓ --> $m_s = -\frac{1}{2}$

C. Atomic Orbitals

An orbital is a region in which there is a high probability of finding the electron. For any atom, each orbital can hold a maximum of two electrons. Within each atom, these atomic orbitals, taken together, can be represented as a diffuse cloud of electrons.

Shapes of Atomic Orbitals

Orbitals

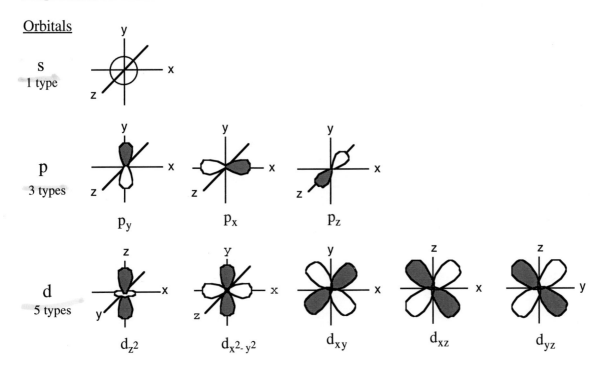

s
1 type

p
3 types

p_y p_x p_z

d
5 types

d_{z^2} $d_{x^2-y^2}$ d_{xy} d_{xz} d_{yz}

f   Refer to textbook (you will not be held responsible for the shape of the 7-f orbitals)
7 types

Example Problems:
1. What is the difference between a 1s orbital and a 2s orbital?
      Both are spherical; however, the 1s orbital is smaller (closer to the nucleus) than the 2s orbital.

2. What is the shape of a $3d_{z^2}$ orbital?
      A $3d_{z^2}$ orbital has the same shape as the d_{z^2} orbital given above.

3. What is the shape of a $1p_x$ orbital?
      There is no such thing as a 1p orbital. p orbitals start in the 2nd energy level (2p, 3p, 4p,...).

4. An electron with quantum numbers: $n = 3$, $l = 1$, $m_l = 0$, $m_s = +\frac{1}{2}$ is in what orbital?
      The electron is in one of the 3p orbitals.

V. Electronic Configuration

Electronic Configuration - the electronic arrangement of atoms.

Each electron in an atom can be given a position in space by defining the principal energy level or shell and sublevel or subshell (orbital) which the electron occupies. For example,

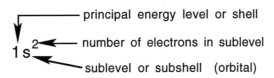

principal energy level or shell

number of electrons in sublevel

1 s^2

sublevel or subshell (orbital)

The principal energy levels are designated by the whole numbers 1, 2, 3, 4, 5, 6, and 7.   The sublevels are labeled: *s, p, d, and f.*   Each orbital can hold a maximum of 2 electrons:

Orbitals	Different types	Max. # of e⁻ (total)
s	1	2
p	3	6
d	5	10
f	7	14

A. The Energies of Orbitals

The *Aufbau Principle* states that electrons will fill the lowest energy atomic orbital available first. This order can be easily obtained by following the periodic table. Start at the top of the periodic table and follow the arrows as you move across and then down the table through subsequent periods (1 - 7) as shown below.

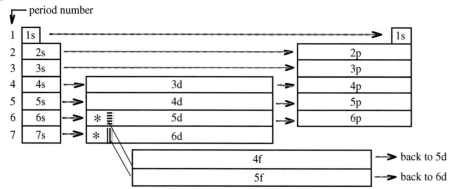

* 1 electron fills these d orbitals first, then the f orbitals get filled before
these d orbitals get completely filled.

The specific electronic configuration (i.e., arrangement) for each element is given below:

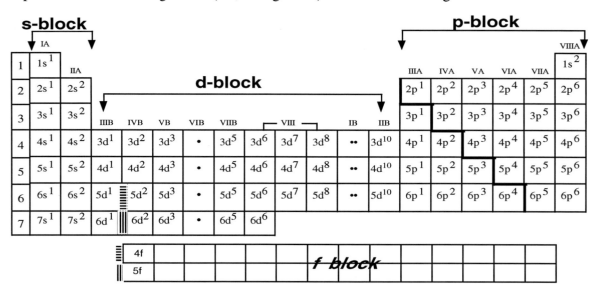

where, • VIB and •• IB elements are notable exceptions to the rule. There are other exceptions to the rules for the B elements in the main part of the periodic table; however, you will not be held responsible for them. There are many exceptions to the rule in the f block.

The larger the principal energy level is, the further away the electron is from the nucleus. For electrons having the same principal quantum number, their proximity to the nucleus is: s, p, d, f. The closer an electron is to the nucleus, the less energy it possess and the harder it is to remove that electron from the atom.   For example, this means that more energy is required to separate a 3s electron from an atom than it is to separate a 3p electron from an atom.

Orbitals having the same n and *l* quantum numbers but different m*l* and m$_s$ quantum numbers are degenerate (i.e., possess the same energy).

Example Problems:

1. Arrange the following orbitals - 3s, 3p, 1s, 4s, 4f - in order of their proximity to the nucleus?

    closest --> furthest: 1s, 3s, 3p, 4s, 4f

2. Which of the following - $2p_x$, $2p_y$, $2p_z$, $3p_x$, $4p_y$, and $5p_z$ - orbitals are degenerate?

    $2p_x$, $2p_y$, and $2p_z$ are all degenerate (i.e., they all have the same energy).

B. Writing Electronic Configurations

Follow the periodic table until you reach the element in question. For example,

a) H $1s^1$ b) He $1s^2$ c) Li $1s^2 2s^1$

d) P $1s^2 2s^2 2p^6 3s^2 3p^3$ e) V $1s^2 2s^2 2p^6 3s^2 3p^6 4s^2 3d^3$

Example Problem: Write the electronic configuration and a possible set of four quantum numbers n, l, m_l, m_s that an electron filling the last orbital can have for: a) Na b) C

a) Na: $1s^2 2s^2 2p^6 3s^1$

  last orbital being filled -- 3s --> $n = 3$, $l = 0$, $m_l = 0$, $m_s = -\frac{1}{2}$ or $+\frac{1}{2}$

  $(3, 0, 0, -\frac{1}{2})$ or $(3, 0, 0, +\frac{1}{2})$

b) C: $1s^2 2s^2 2p^2$

  last orbital being filled -- 2p --> $n = 2$, $l = 1$, $m_l = -1, 0$, or -1, $m_s = -\frac{1}{2}$ or $+\frac{1}{2}$

  $(2, 1, -1, -\frac{1}{2})$; $(2, 1, -1, +\frac{1}{2})$; $(2, 1, 0, +\frac{1}{2})$; $(2, 1, 0, -\frac{1}{2})$; $(2, 1, 1, +\frac{1}{2})$; or $(2, 1, 1, -\frac{1}{2})$

C. Writing Abbreviated Electronic Configurations

In the *abbreviated notation*, the electronic configuration of the noble gas (VIIIA) in the previous row of the element in question is omitted; in its place, the symbol for the noble gas (enclosed in brackets) is used as the starting point followed by the rest of the electronic configuration.

Example Problem: For each of the following elements - P and V - write their abbreviated electronic configuration.

  a) P   [Ne] $3s^2 3p^3$ Ne is the noble gas in the row previous to where P is found. Instead of writing the electronic configuration for Ne ($1s^2 2s^2 2p^6$) in its place, [Ne] is used as the starting point followed by the rest of the electronic configuration.

  b) V   [Ar] $4s^2 3d^3$

D. Orbital Diagram for the Elements

When writing orbital diagrams, lines are used to represent orbitals and arrows are used to represent electrons. The one-type of s orbital is represented by one line, the three-types of p orbitals are represented by three lines, the five-types of d orbitals are represented by five lines, and the seven-types of f orbitals are represented by seven lines. The following rules for writing orbital diagrams are to be followed:

  1) an orbital can hold a maximum of 2 electrons, and these must have opposite spin (*Pauli Exclusion Principle*). Pauli's Exclusion Principle can also be stated as: no 2 electrons can have the same set of 4 quantum numbers.

  2) all orbitals of a given sublevel (i.e., degenerate orbitals) must be occupied by a single electron, having the same spin, before being paired (*Hund's Rule*).

Example Problem: For each of the following elements - Si and Co - write their orbital diagram.

a) Si $\underset{1s}{\uparrow\downarrow}$ $\underset{2s}{\uparrow\downarrow}$ $\underset{2p}{\uparrow\downarrow \quad \uparrow\downarrow \quad \uparrow\downarrow}$ $\underset{3s}{\uparrow\downarrow}$ $\underset{3p}{\uparrow \quad \uparrow \quad \_\_}$

b) Co $\underset{1s}{\uparrow\downarrow}$ $\underset{2s}{\uparrow\downarrow}$ $\underset{2p}{\uparrow\downarrow \quad \uparrow\downarrow \quad \uparrow\downarrow}$ $\underset{3s}{\uparrow\downarrow}$ $\underset{3p}{\uparrow\downarrow \quad \uparrow\downarrow \quad \uparrow\downarrow}$ $\underset{4s}{\uparrow\downarrow}$ $\underset{3d}{\uparrow\downarrow \quad \uparrow\downarrow \quad \uparrow \quad \uparrow \quad \uparrow}$

E. Exceptions to Electronic Configurations and Orbital Diagrams

Certain elements do not follow the rules given above. These elements are in groups VIB and IB of the periodic table. (There are other elements that do not follow the rules, however, you will not be held accountable for knowing those.)

VIB	IB
Cr	Cu
Mo	Ag
W*	Au

* W is actually not an exception to the rules.

The elements in VIB prefer to have the d sublevel halfway filled and the elements in IB prefer to have the d sublevel completely filled, while the s orbital has only one electron (i.e., s orbital is half-filled).

a) Cr $\underset{1s}{\uparrow\downarrow}$ $\underset{2s}{\uparrow\downarrow}$ $\underset{2p}{\uparrow\downarrow \quad \uparrow\downarrow \quad \uparrow\downarrow}$ $\underset{3s}{\uparrow\downarrow}$ $\underset{3p}{\uparrow\downarrow \quad \uparrow\downarrow \quad \uparrow\downarrow}$ $\underset{4s}{\uparrow}$ $\underset{3d}{\uparrow \quad \uparrow \quad \uparrow \quad \uparrow \quad \uparrow}$

$1s^2\ 2s^2\ 2p^6\ 3s^2\ 3p^6\ 4s^1\ 3d^5$

b) Cu $\underset{1s}{\uparrow\downarrow}$ $\underset{2s}{\uparrow\downarrow}$ $\underset{2p}{\uparrow\downarrow \quad \uparrow\downarrow \quad \uparrow\downarrow}$ $\underset{3s}{\uparrow\downarrow}$ $\underset{3p}{\uparrow\downarrow \quad \uparrow\downarrow \quad \uparrow\downarrow}$ $\underset{4s}{\uparrow}$ $\underset{3d}{\uparrow\downarrow \quad \uparrow\downarrow \quad \uparrow\downarrow \quad \uparrow\downarrow \quad \uparrow\downarrow}$

$1s^2\ 2s^2\ 2p^6\ 3s^2\ 3p^6\ 4s^1\ 3d^{10}$

F. Electronic Configuration of Ions

First write the electronic configuration for the atom, which has no charge. Then for the negative ions (anions) place as many electrons in the last orbital being filled as the charge on the ion. For positive ions (cations), remove electrons from the least stable [last orbital(s) - highest energy] orbital(s) as the charge on the ion. [*Note: For the elements having their outermost electrons in d orbitals, the electrons are removed first from the s orbital and then from the d orbitals. For elements having outermost p, d, and s electrons, first remove electrons from the p orbital(s), then s orbital, and then from the d orbital(s).*]

Example Problem: Write the electronic configuration for each of the following ions.

a) O^{2-} $1s^2\ 2s^2\ 2p^6$

b) Ca^{2+} $1s^2\ 2s^2\ 2p^6\ 3s^2\ 3p^6\ 4s^0$ or $1s^2\ 2s^2\ 2p^6\ 3s^2\ 3p^6$

c) Fe^{3+} $1s^2\ 2s^2\ 2p^6\ 3s^2\ 3p^6\ 4s^0\ 3d^5$ or $1s^2\ 2s^2\ 2p^6\ 3s^2\ 3p^6\ 3d^5$
     [Note: electrons are removed from the s orbital first, then from the d]

d) Ga^{3+} $1s^2\ 2s^2\ 2p^6\ 3s^2\ 3p^6\ 4s^0\ 3d^{10}\ 4p^0$ or $1s^2\ 2s^2\ 2p^6\ 3s^2\ 3p^6\ 3d^{10}$
     [Note: electrons are removed from the p orbital first, then from the s]

G. Paramagnetism and Diamagnetism

Any atom or ion is **paramagnetic** if it has one or more unpaired electrons. It is **diamagnetic** if it has no unpaired electrons. For example, H is paramagnetic (1 unpaired e^-) and He is diamagnetic (no unpaired e^-).

<u>Example Problem</u>: How many unpaired electrons do the following species - Cl^-, N, Cr, Ga^{3+} - have (also indicate if the specie is paramagnetic or diamagnetic)?

a) Cl^- $\underset{1s}{\uparrow\downarrow}$ $\underset{2s}{\uparrow\downarrow}$ $\underset{2p}{\uparrow\downarrow \quad \uparrow\downarrow \quad \uparrow\downarrow}$ $\underset{3s}{\uparrow\downarrow}$ $\underset{3p}{\uparrow\downarrow \quad \uparrow\downarrow \quad \uparrow\downarrow}$

   0 unpaired electron   (diamagnetic)

b) N $\underset{1s}{\uparrow\downarrow}$ $\underset{2s}{\uparrow\downarrow}$ $\underset{2p}{\uparrow \quad \uparrow \quad \uparrow}$

   3 unpaired electrons (paramagnetic)

c) Cr $\underset{1s}{\uparrow\downarrow}$ $\underset{2s}{\uparrow\downarrow}$ $\underset{2p}{\uparrow\downarrow \quad \uparrow\downarrow \quad \uparrow\downarrow}$ $\underset{3s}{\uparrow\downarrow}$ $\underset{3p}{\uparrow\downarrow \quad \uparrow\downarrow \quad \uparrow\downarrow}$ $\underset{4s}{\uparrow}$ $\underset{3d}{\uparrow \quad \uparrow \quad \uparrow \quad \uparrow \quad \uparrow}$

   6 unpaired electrons (paramagnetic)

d) Ga^{3+} $\underset{1s}{\uparrow\downarrow}$ $\underset{2s}{\uparrow\downarrow}$ $\underset{2p}{\uparrow\downarrow \quad \uparrow\downarrow \quad \uparrow\downarrow}$ $\underset{3s}{\uparrow\downarrow}$ $\underset{3p}{\uparrow\downarrow \quad \uparrow\downarrow \quad \uparrow\downarrow}$ $\underset{4s}{\quad}$ $\underset{3d}{\uparrow\downarrow \quad \uparrow\downarrow \quad \uparrow\downarrow \quad \uparrow\downarrow \quad \uparrow\downarrow}$

   0 unpaired electrons (diamagnetic)

H. Isoelectronic Species

Species with the same electronic configuration are said to be isoelectronic. For example, F^-, Ne, Na^+, Mg^{2+}, and Al^{3+} are isoelectronic because they all have the same electronic configuration ($1s^2 2s^2 2p^6$).

<u>Example Problems</u>:

1. Is Sc^{3+} isoelectronic with Ca^{2+} ?

   Yes, both have the same electronic configuration. $1s^2 2s^2 2p^6 3s^2 3p^6$

2. Indicate whether or not each of the following ions -- Rb^+, Se^-, Sn^{4+} -- are isoelectroinc with Kr?

   Kr $1s^2 2s^2 2p^6 3s^2 3p^6 4s^2 3d^{10} 4p^6$

   Rb^+ $1s^2 2s^2 2p^6 3s^2 3p^6 4s^2 3d^{10} 4p^6$ (yes)

   Se^- $1s^2 2s^2 2p^6 3s^2 3p^6 4s^2 3d^{10} 4p^5$ (no)

   Sn^{4+} $1s^2 2s^2 2p^6 3s^2 3p^6 4s^2 3d^{10} 4p^6 5s^0 4d^{10} 5p^0$ (no)

EXERCISES

Calculations Involving the Dual Nature of Electromagnetic Radiation & Small Particles

1. If the wavelength of light associated with a ray is 3.70×10^{-6} m, then what is its frequency in $\sec^-$?

2. If the wavelength of light associated with a ray is 3700 Å, then what is its frequency in hertz?

3. If the frequency of light associated with a ray is 5.60×10^{15} $\sec^-$, then calculate its wavelength in:
   a) m,   b) cm,   c) Å

4. Calculate the energy (in erg) of a light ray whose frequency is 7.37×10^{15} $\sec^-$.

5. Calculate the energy (in J) of a light ray whose wavelength is 3700 Å.

6. Calculate the energy (a) in J & b) in cal) of a light ray whose wavelength is 3.70×10^{-6} cm. (1 cal = 4.184 J)

7. A ray whose energy is 7.36×10^{-13} erg has what wavelength in: a) m,   b) cm,   c) Å

8. A ray whose energy is 6.16×10^{-19} J has what wavelength in: a) m,   b) cm,   c) nm,   d) Å

9. If a ray has a wavelength of 4400 Å, would it be visible to the naked eye?

10. Arrange the following electromagnetic rays -- Microwaves, Green Light, Blue Light, X-rays -- in order of: a) increasing frequency,   b) decreasing wavelength,   and   c) increasing energy

11. If a proton moving at 3.00×10^8 cm/sec has a mass of 1.67×10^{-24} g, then calculate the wavelength associated with it in: a) cm   b) Å.   Also, compare the wavelength in Å of a proton to that of an electron travelling at the same speed (see example problem in the "The Wave Nature of Electrons" section).

The Bohr Atom, Quantization of Energy, and Atomic Spectra

12. How many electrons are in each principal energy level for each of the following atoms?
    a) Be   b) C   c) Na   d) Ar

13. What is the wavelength (in cm) of a photon emitted when a sample of hydrogen goes from energy level $4 \rightarrow 2$? Is this transition in the visible portion of the EM spectrum?

14. A photon emitted from a sample of Li^{2+} as it goes from energy level $5 \rightarrow 3$, has
    a)   What wavelength (m)?   b)   What frequency (hertz)?
    c)   What Energy (in J)?   d)   More or Less energy than visible light?

15. A photon emitted from a sample of hydrogen gas as it goes from energy level $6 \rightarrow 5$, has
    a)   What wavelength (cm)?   b)   What frequency ($\sec^-$)?
    c)   What Energy (in erg)?   d)   More or Less energy than visible light?

16. An electron in hydrogen in principal energy level n_o, makes a transition down to the second orbit. If the photon emitted has a wavelength of 4.860×10^2 nm, calculate n_o?

Quantum Mechanical Picture of the Atom

17. An electron in a certain atom is in the $n = 2$ quantum level. List the possible values of l and m_l that it can have.

18. An electron with a value of $l = 2$, is in what orbital?

19. What are the possible values that m_l can have if $l = 4$?

20. Indicate in each case below whether or not the following sets of four quantum numbers n, l, m_l, m_s are permissible or not.

    a) $2, 3, 3, -\frac{1}{2}$ b) $2, 3, 3, -1$ c) $1, 2, 1, -\frac{1}{2}$ d) $2, 0, 0, -\frac{1}{2}$

21. How many total electrons can fit in the $n = 3$ quantum level?

22. What is the electron capacity in the $l = 3$ sublevel?

23. For the following orbital diagram give the four quantum numbers (n, l, m_l, m_s) associated with the electrons labelled A thru D.

A $\underset{1s}{\underset{\uparrow\downarrow}{}}$ $\underset{2s}{\underset{\uparrow\downarrow}{}}$ $\underset{2p}{\underset{\uparrow\downarrow\ \ \uparrow\downarrow\ \ \uparrow\downarrow}{}}$ $\underset{3s}{\underset{\uparrow\downarrow}{}}$ $\underset{3p}{\underset{\uparrow\downarrow\ \ \uparrow\downarrow\ \ \uparrow\downarrow}{}}$ $\underset{3d}{\underset{\uparrow\downarrow\ \ \uparrow\downarrow\ \ \uparrow\downarrow\ \ \uparrow\downarrow\ \ \uparrow\downarrow}{}}$

with labels A (1s), B (3p), C (first 3d), D (last 3d)

24. What is the name of the atomic orbital depicted to the right?

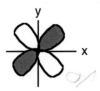

25. What possible values of n can the atomic orbital depicted to the right have?

26. What possible values of m_l can the atomic orbital depicted to the right have?

27. An electron with quantum numbers: $n = 2$, $l = 1$, $m_l = 0$, $m_s = +\frac{1}{2}$ is in what orbital?

28. What is the difference between a $2p_x$ and a $2p_z$ orbital?

29. What is the difference between a $3d_{xy}$ and a $5d_{xy}$ orbital?

Electronic Configurations

30. Using the periodic table as your guide, which orbital starts getting filled after the following sublevels are completely filled?
    a) 2p   b) 6p   c) 4d   d) 4f   e) 5f

31. Which of the following - $3d_{xz}$, $3p_x$, 3s, $3d_{yz}$, $3p_z$ - orbitals are degenerate?

32. For each of the following elements give a possible set of four quantum numbers n, l, m_l, m_s that an electron filling the last orbital can have.
    a) Na   b) Al   c) Ar   d) Mg

33. Write both the electronic configuration and the abbreviated electronic configuration for each of the following:
    a) Tin   b) Mn   c) Y^{2+} d) Se^{1-} e) silver
    f) Sn^{2+} g) Ge^{4+} h) As^{3-} i) Mo   j) Au^{1+}

34. Write orbital diagrams for each of the following. Also indicate how many unpaired electrons each specie has and if the specie is paramagnetic or diamagnetic.
    a) P   b) Al^{3+} c) Ti   d) S^{2-} e) Na

35. Indicate whether or not each of the following are isoelectroinc with Ga^{3+}?
    a) Ar   b) K^+ c) Zn^{2+} d) Cu^{1+} e) Ge^{4+}

MULTIPLE CHOICE PRACTICE EXAM FOR MODULE 9

1. What is the wavelength (in m) of an x-ray whose frequency is 6.21×10^{18} Hz?
    1) 5.37×10^{-28} 2) 4.83×10^{-9} 3) 2.07×10^{10} 4) 1.86×10^{27} 5) 4.83×10^{-11}

2. If the wavelength of a photon of ultraviolet light is 500 Å, then what is its energy (in erg)?
    1) 9.95×10^{-26} 2) 1.10×10^{-30} 3) 3.98×10^{-11} 4) 3.98×10^{-21} 5) 1.10×10^{-32}

3. Which of the following is the most energetic?
    1) IR rays   2) yellow light   3) radio waves   4) blue light   5) red light

4. How many electrons are in the third energy level of Si?
    1) 0   2) 1   3) 4   4) 8   5) 18

5. Which of the following statements is (are) true?
    a. quantization of energy causes excitation of an electron.
    b. an excited electron can return to a lower energy level by releasing energy.
    c. an atom can be excited by emitting a photon.
    1) only a   2) only b   3) only c   4) only b and c   5) only a and b

6. What is wavelength (in m) emitted when a sample of Li^{2+} undergoes an electronic transition from the 3rd energy level to the 2nd energy level?
    1) 7.2×10^{-6} 2) 1.4×10^{7} 3) 1.5×10^{6} 4) 7.2×10^{-8} 5) 6.6×10^{-7}

7. Which of the following is a permissible set of four quantum numbers (n, l, m_l, m_s)?
    1) $(1,1,0,+\frac{1}{2})$ 2) $(0,1,2,+\frac{1}{2})$ 3) $(2,1,0,+\frac{1}{2})$ 4) $(2,1,2,-\frac{1}{2})$ 5) $(2,2,2,-\frac{1}{2})$

8. An electron having having the following four quantum numbers (n = 4, l = 3, m_l = 1, $m_s = -\frac{1}{2}$) is in one of the _____ orbitals.
    1) 4s   2) 4p   3) 4d   4) 4f   5) 4g

9. Which of the following sets of orbitals are degenerate (i.e., have the same energy)?
    a. $3p_x$ & $3p_z$ b. $3d_{xy}$ & $3p_y$ c. $4d_y$ & $3p_y$
    1) only a   2) only b   3) only a & b   4) only b and c   5) a, b, and c

10. For the following orbital diagram of the 3d orbitals, give the four quantum numbers (n, l, m_l, m_s) associated with the electron labelled A?

    A
    $\underline{\uparrow\downarrow}$ $\underline{\uparrow\downarrow}$ $\underline{\uparrow\downarrow}$ $\underline{\uparrow\downarrow}$ $\underline{\uparrow\downarrow}$
    3d

    1) $(3,1,0,+\frac{1}{2})$ 2) $(3,2,+1,+\frac{1}{2})$ 3) $(3,1,2,+\frac{1}{2})$ 4) $(3,2,+2,-\frac{1}{2})$ 5) $(3,0,2,-\frac{1}{2})$

11. The following is an example of what type of atomic orbital?
    1) $7d_{xy}$ 2) $2d_{x2-y2}$ 3) $4d_{x2-y2}$
    4) Two of the above choices are correct.
    5) None of the above choices are correct.

    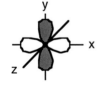

12. The electronic configuration for Zn^{2+} is:
    1) $1s^2 2s^2 2p^6 3s^2 3p^6 4s^0 3d^{10}$ 2) $1s^2 2s^2 2p^6 3s^2 3p^6 4s^2 3d^8$ 3) $1s^2 2s^2 2p^6 3s^2 3p^6 4s^2 3d^{10}$
    4) $1s^2 2s^2 2p^6 3s^2 3p^6 4s^0 4d^{10}$ 5) $1s^2 2s^2 2p^6 3s^2 3p^6 4s^2 3d^{10} 4p^2$

13. The orbital diagram for N⁻ is:

1) $\frac{\uparrow\downarrow}{1s}$ $\frac{\uparrow\downarrow}{2s}$ $\frac{\uparrow\uparrow}{}$ $\frac{\uparrow}{}$ $\frac{\uparrow}{2p}$ 2) $\frac{\uparrow\downarrow}{1s}$ $\frac{\uparrow\downarrow}{2s}$ $\frac{\uparrow\downarrow}{}$ $\frac{\uparrow}{}$ $\frac{\uparrow}{2p}$

3) $\frac{\uparrow\downarrow}{1s}$ $\frac{\uparrow\downarrow}{2s}$ $\frac{\uparrow}{}$ $\frac{\uparrow}{}$ $\frac{\uparrow}{2p}$ 4) $\frac{\uparrow\uparrow}{1s}$ $\frac{\uparrow\uparrow}{2s}$ $\frac{\uparrow\uparrow}{}$ $\frac{\uparrow}{}$ $\frac{\uparrow}{2p}$

5) $\frac{\uparrow\downarrow}{1s}$ $\frac{\uparrow\downarrow}{2s}$ $\frac{\uparrow\downarrow}{}$ $\frac{\uparrow\downarrow}{}$ $\frac{\uparrow}{2p}$

14. Which orbital starts getting filled after the 4d orbital has been completely filled ?
   1) 5f   2) 4f   3) 5p   4) 5s   5) 5d

15. Which of the following statements is correct?
   a. Pauli's Exclusion Principle states that no two electrons in the same atom can have an identical set of four quantum numbers.
   b. Aufbau's Principle describes the order in which electrons fill atomic orbitals. Electrons fill lower energy atomic orbitals first.
   c. Hund's Rule states that electrons in degenerate orbitals must first be paired and then spread.
   d. The Heisenberg Uncertainty Principle states that both the energy and position of an electron can be determined simultaneously with great accuracy.

   1) only a   2) only b   3) only d   4) only a and b   5) only a, b, and d

16. How many unpaired electron(s) does Cr have ?
   1) 2   2) 3   3) 4   4) 5   5) 6

17. Which of the following are isoelectronic with Ar?
         a. Zn^{2+} b. K^+ c. P^{3-}

   1) only a   2) only b   3) only c   4) only b and c   5) a, b, and c

18. Which of the following species are paramagnetic?
         a. Cl^- b. Cl c. K^+

   1) only a   2) only b   3) only c   4) only a and c   5) a, b, and c

19. Which of the following species have no unpaired electrons?
         a. Cl^- b. Zn^{2+} c. K^+

   1) only a   2) only b   3) only c   4) only a and c   5) a, b, and c

20. Which of the following have exceptional electronic configurations?
         a. Ga   b. Cu   c. Mo   d. Au

   1) only b   2) only a   3) only b and d   4) only b, c, and d   5) all of them

MODULE 9 - ANSWERS

1. 8.11×10^{13} sec$^-$ 2. 8.11×10^{14} Hz   3. a) 5.36×10^{-8} m   b) 5.36×10^{-6} cm   c) 5.36×10^{2} Å
4. 4.89×10^{-11} erg   5. 5.38×10^{-19} J   6. a) 5.38×10^{-18} J   b) 1.28×10^{-18} cal
7. a) 2.70×10^{-6} m   b) 2.70×10^{-4} cm   c) 2.70×10^{4} Å
8. a) 3.23×10^{-7} m   b) 3.23×10^{-5} cm   c) 3.23×10^{2} nm   d) 3.23×10^{3} Å
9. yes, because the visible spectrum is from 4000Å - 8000Å
10. a) microwave < green < blue < X-ray   b) microwave > green > blue > X-ray   c) microwave < green < blue < X-ray
11. a) 1.32×10^{-11} cm   b) 1.32×10^{-3} Å   wavelength comparison: the larger mass particle (proton) has a smaller wavelength (1.32×1^{-3} Å) than the electron 2.44Å).
12. a) n =1 --> 2 e$^-$, n =2 --> 2 e$^-$ b) n =1 --> 2 e$^-$, n =2 --> 4 e$^-$ c) n =1 --> 2 e$^-$, n =2 --> 8 e$^-$, n = 3 --> 1 e$^-$
    d) n =1 --> 2 e$^-$, n =2 --> 8 e$^-$, n = 3 --> 8 e$^-$
13. 4.86×10^{-5} cm, this transition would be in the visible portion of the EM spectrum
14. a) 1.43×10^{-7} m   b) 2.11×10^{15} Hz   c) 1.39×10^{-18} J   d) more energy than visible light (shorter λ)
15. a) 7.46×10^{-4} cm   b) 4.02×10^{13} sec$^-$ c) 2.67×10^{-13} erg   d) less energy than visible light (longer λ)
16. 4
17. $l = 0, 1$ $m_l = -1, 0, 1$
18. d-orbital
19. $m_l = -4, -3, -2, -1, 0, 1, 2, 3, 4$
20. a) not permissible   b) not permissible   c) not permissible   d) permissible
21. 18 e$^-$
22. 14 e$^-$
23. A = $(1,0,0,+\frac{1}{2})$ B = $(3,1,+1+\frac{1}{2})$ C = $(3,2,-1,-\frac{1}{2})$ D = $(3,2,+2,-\frac{1}{2})$
24. d_{xy}
25. any whole # greater than 2 --> 3, 4, 5, ...
26. $m_l = -2, -1, 0, 1, 2$
27. In one of the three-2p orbitals
28. Their orientation in space is different, the $2p_x$ orbital is oriented along the x-axis whereas the $2p_z$ orbital is oriented along the y axis. The n and l quantum numbers are the same; however, m_l quantum number is not the same.
29. Their shape is the same, however, the $5d_{xy}$ orbital is larger in size (i.e., further away from the nucleus)
30. a) 3s   b) 7s   c) 5p   d) 5d   e) 6d
31. $3d_{xz}$ & $3d_{yz}$ are degenerate and $3p_x$ & $3p_z$ are degenerate
32. a) $(3, 0, 0, -\frac{1}{2})$ or $(3, 0, 0, +\frac{1}{2})$
    b) $(3, 1, -1, -\frac{1}{2})$ or $(3, 1, -1, +\frac{1}{2})$ or $(3, 1, 0, -\frac{1}{2})$ or $(3, 1, 0, +\frac{1}{2})$ or $(3, 1, 1, -\frac{1}{2})$ or $(3, 1, 1, +\frac{1}{2})$
    c) same as b   d) same as a
33. a) $1s^2\ 2s^2\ 2p^6\ 3s^2\ 3p^6\ 4s^2\ 3d^{10}\ 4p^6\ 5s^2\ 4d^{10}\ 5p^2$ [Kr] $5s^2\ 4d^{10}\ 5p^2$
    b) $1s^2\ 2s^2\ 2p^6\ 3s^2\ 3p^6\ 4s^2\ 3d^5$ [Ar] $4s^2\ 3d^5$
    c) $1s^2\ 2s^2\ 2p^6\ 3s^2\ 3p^6\ 4s^2\ 3d^{10}\ 4p^6\ 5s^0\ 4d^1$ [Kr] $5s^0\ 4d^1$
    d) $1s^2\ 2s^2\ 2p^6\ 3s^2\ 3p^6\ 4s^2\ 3d^{10}\ 4p^5$ [Ar] $4s^2\ 3d^{10}\ 4p^5$
    e) $1s^2\ 2s^2\ 2p^6\ 3s^2\ 3p^6\ 4s^2\ 3d^{10}\ 4p^6\ 5s^1\ 4d^{10}$ [Kr] $5s^1\ 4d^{10}$
    f) $1s^2\ 2s^2\ 2p^6\ 3s^2\ 3p^6\ 4s^2\ 3d^{10}\ 4p^6\ 5s^2\ 4d^{10}\ 5p^0$ [Kr] $5s^2\ 4d^{10}\ 5p^0$
    g) $1s^2\ 2s^2\ 2p^6\ 3s^2\ 3p^6\ 4s^0\ 3d^{10}\ 4p^0$ [Ar] $4s^0\ 3d^{10}\ 4p^0$
    h) $1s^2\ 2s^2\ 2p^6\ 3s^2\ 3p^6\ 4s^2\ 3d^{10}\ 4p^6$ [Ar] $4s^2\ 3d^{10}\ 4p^6$
    i) $1s^2\ 2s^2\ 2p^6\ 3s^2\ 3p^6\ 4s^2\ 3d^{10}\ 4p^6\ 5s^1\ 4d^5$ [Kr] $5s^1\ 4d^5$
    j) $1s^2\ 2s^2\ 2p^6\ 3s^2\ 3p^6\ 4s^2\ 3d^{10}\ 4p^6\ 5s^2\ 4d^{10}\ 5p^6\ 6s^0\ 4f^{14}\ 5d^{10}$ [Xe] $6s^0\ 4f^{14}\ 5d^{10}$

34. a) ↑↓   ↑↓   ↑↓ ↑↓ ↑↓   ↑↓   ↑ ↑ ↑   3 unpaired e$^-$
        1s   2s   2p   3s   3p   paramagnetic

    b) ↑↓   ↑↓   ↑↓ ↑↓ ↑↓   0 unpaired e$^-$
        1s   2s   2p   diamagnetic

    c) ↑↓   ↑↓   ↑↓ ↑↓ ↑↓   ↑↓   ↑↓ ↑↓ ↑↓   ↑↓   ↑ ↑ __ __ __   2 unpaired e$^-$
        1s   2s   2p   3s   3p   4s   3d   paramagnetic

    d) ↑↓   ↑↓   ↑↓ ↑↓ ↑↓   ↑↓   ↑↓ ↑↓ ↑↓   0 unpaired e$^-$
        1s   2s   2p   3s   3p   diamagnetic

    f) ↑↓   ↑↓   ↑↓ ↑↓ ↑↓   ↑   1 unpaired e$^-$
        1s   2s   2p   3s   paramagnetic

35. a) no   b) no   c) yes   d) yes   e) yes

MODULE 10.   *Chemical Periodicity*

I. Periodic Table

Mendeleev's arrangement of the periodic table is the one that is basically used today. Elements are arranged in order of increasing atomic numbers in successive sequences so that elements with similar chemical properties & those that form similar type compounds, fall in the same column.

	IA	IIA	IIIB	IVB	VB	VIB	VIIB		VIII		IB	IIB	IIIA	IVA	VA	VIA	VIIA	VIIIA
1	H																H	He
2	Li	Be											B	C	N	O	F	Ne
3	Na	Mg											Al	Si	P	S	Cl	Ar
4	K	Ca	Sc	Ti	V	Cr	Mn	Fe	Co	Ni	Cu	Zn	Ga	Ge	As	Se	Br	Kr
5	Rb	Sr	Y	Zr	Nb	Mo	Tc	Ru	Rh	Pd	Ag	Cd	In	Sn	Sb	Te	I	Xe
6	Cs	Ba	La	Hf	Ta	W	Re	Os	Ir	Pt	Au	Hg	Tl	Pb	Bi	Po	At	Rn
7	Fr	Ra	Ac	Rf	Db	Sg	Bh	Hs	Mt	Uun	Uuu	Uub						

	Ce	Pr	Nd	Pm	Sm	Eu	Gd	Tb	Dy	Ho	Er	Tm	Yb	Lu
	Th	Pa	U	Np	Pu	Am	Cm	Bk	Cf	Es	Fm	Md	No	Lr

Periods - horizontal rows

Family or Group - vertical rows

Metals - elements to the left of bold staircase

Nonmetals - elements to the right of the bold staircase. H is a nonmetal.

Metalloids - elements just on either side of bold staircase (those that are in bold-face)

Alkali Metals - Group IA (Except H)

Alkaline Earth Metals - Group IIA

Chalcogens - Group VIA

Halogens - Group VIIA (except H)

Noble or Rare Gases - Group VIIIA

Representative or Main Group Elements - A (s & p block) elements

Transition Elements - d block elements

   1st transition series - 4th period transition elements

   2nd transition series - 5th period transition elements

   3rd transition series - 6th period transition elements

   4th transition series - 7th period transition elements

Inner Transition Elements - f block elements

Lanthanides - * elements (Z = 58 - 71)

Actinides - † elements (Z = 90 - 103)

Example Problems:
1. Which of the following elements are transition elements: a) Uub, b) Ce, c) Ga, d) Rb,   e) Sc
      Uub and Sc
2. Which of the following elements are metalloids: a) B, b) Ga c) Ge, d) Po
      B, Ge, and Po

II. Nomenclature for New Elements

Until their identification is verified and named by the IUPAC (International Union of Pure and Applied Chemistry), newly synthesized elements are given names and symbols consistent with the following prefixes that denote their atomic number.

Prefixes: 0 - nil, 1 - un, 2- bi, 3 - tri, 4 - quad, 5 - pent, 6 - hex, 7 - sept, 8 - oct, 9 - enn

Suffix: ium

For example, the symbol and name for the element with an atomic number of 117 is:

Example Problem: Once discovered, give the name and symbol that elements with the following atomic numbers would have: a) 138, b) 117, c) 124, and d) 119.

a) 138 - Uto - Untrioctium   b) 117 - Uus - Ununseptium
c) 124 - Ubq - Unbiquadium   d) 119 - Uue - Ununennium

III. Predicting Physical Properties

In some cases, we can predict physical properties, such as boiling point, of elements by taking an average of the boiling point of the elements immediately above and below the element in question.

Example Problem: From the following data, predict the a) melting point and b) boiling point of Br_2.

	mp	bp
Cl_2	-101	114
Br_2	?	?
I_2	35	184

a) $mp(Br_2) = \dfrac{-101 + 35}{2} = -33°C$ (actual mp = -7.2°C)

b) $bp(Br_2) = \dfrac{114 + 184}{2} = 149°C$ (actual bp = 59°C)

IV. Lewis Dot Representation of the Representative Elements

The symbol for the element represents the nucleus and all but the outermost shell (i.e., the occupied outermost s and p electrons). The electrons in the outermost, *valence*, shell are represented by dots that are placed on four sides of an imaginary square (no more than 2 dots/side). The group number in the periodic table gives the number of valence electrons for elements in that group. Helium is an exception, it has 2 valence electrons; hydrogen has 1 valence electron.

There are two ways in which the Lewis dot structure for the elements can be written: 1) Electrons are spread to all four sides of the imaginary square before being paired;

$\longrightarrow \boxed{X} \longleftarrow$ dots can be placed on any of the
                                                4 sides of the imaginary square.

2) Paired and unpaired (as is indicated by the electronic configuration of the valence shell) electrons are shown as dots on the four sides of an imaginary square.

A generalized example of the two methods is shown below:

IA	IIA	IIIA	IVA	VA	VIA	VIIA	VIIIA
E·	·E·	·Ė·	·Ė·	:Ė·	:Ė·	:Ė:	:Ë:
	or	or	or				except
	:E	:E·	:E·				·He· or He:

Example Problem: Write the Lewis dot structure of Te.
                  Te is in group VIA, it therefore has 6 valence electrons ----> :Të·

V. Periodic Properties

A. **Atomic Radii** - refers to the size of the element. It is obvious that as one goes down the periodic table, an additional shell of electrons is added, making the elements larger. Going across the periodic table, the elements are larger on the left than on the right. The explanation for this phenomenon is that as one progresses through a period (for example, from lithium to fluorine), electrons are being added to the same shell while the nucleus of the atom is becoming increasingly more positive, that is, more attractive to electrons. So fluorine can attract electrons towards its nucleus better than lithium can, making fluorine a much smaller element.

Given a list of elements, the element with the smallest atomic radii will be the one that is at the most upper right hand corner of the periodic table.

Example Problem: Arrange the following atoms in order of increasing atomic radii: N, Mg, Al, Si.
$$N < Si < Al < Mg$$

B. **Ionization Energy (IE)** - refers to the ability of an atom in the gas phase to lose an electron and form a positive ion.   Generally, the larger the atom, the smaller the interaction between an electron on the outer shell and the nucleus of the atom. This lessened interaction allows for easier removal of electrons. For elements having partially filled s and p orbitals these trends do apply; however, there are *exceptions*. The only partial exceptions occur with the elements having electronic configurations of ns^2 (filled subshell) or ns^2np^3 (partially filled subshell); the ionization potentials (energies) of these elements are greater than those of ns^2np^1 and ns^2np^4, respectively.

Given a list of elements, the element with the largest ionization energy will be the one that is at the most upper right hand corner of the periodic table (exceptions: IIA > IIIA and VA > VIA).

IE_1 - first ionization energy (lose of 1 e^-) $E\ (g)\ +$ energy $\rightarrow E^+\ (g) + e^-$

IE_2 - second ionization energy (lose of 2nd e^-) $E^+\ (g)\ +$ energy $\rightarrow E^{2+}\ (g) + e^-$

$IE_1 < IE_2$; it is always more difficult to remove e^- from a positively charged ion than from the corresponding neutral atom.

The smaller the first ionization energy, the more readily an element will form a +1 cation. Knowledge of the relative values of IE's assists in the prediction of whether an element is likely to form ionic or molecular (covalent) compounds. Elements with low IE's (metals) form ionic compounds by becoming cations (losing electrons). Elements with intermediate IE's form molecular compounds by sharing electrons with other elements. Elements with very high IE's (VIA & VIIA) when in an ionic compound become anions (gain electrons instead).

Example Problems:

1. Arrange the following sets of elements in order of increasing first ionization energies: As, N, O, Ga, Cs, and F.
    $$Cs < Ga < As < O < N < F$$

2. Which of the following will form a +1 cation the most readily: Br, N, O, Ga, Cs, or H.
    Cs (the element with the smallest IE)

3. Which of the following will lose an electron the most readily: Ge, Ge^{2+}, In, or In^{2+}
    In (the element that is at most lower left hand corner)

4. Which of the following will lose an electron the least readily: Ga, Ga^+, Ga^{2+}, or In^{2+}
    Ga^{2+} (the highest charged cation that is at the most upper right hand corner)

C. **Electron Affinity (EA)** - refers to the ability of an atom in the gas phase to gain an electron and form a negative ion. By convention a positive value is assigned to the energy if it is absorbed (endothermic) and a negative value when it is released (exothermic). Elements with very negative EA's gain electrons easily to form anions.

$E\ (g)\ +\ e^-\ +$ energy $\rightarrow E^-\ (g)$ endothermic process --> +Energy value

$E\ (g)\ +\ e^-\ \rightarrow E^-\ (g) +$ energy   exothermic process --> -Energy value

For most elements energy is released upon becoming a -1 anion. However, EA_2, EA_3, etc. are all endothermic. For many reasons, the variations in EA's are not regular across a period. The general trend is for the EA's to be more negative from left to right and from bottom to top.

Given a list of elements, the element with the most negative electron affinity, [i.e., the one that will form a -1 anion the most readily (excluding VIIIA elements)] will be the one that is at the most upper right hand corner of the periodic table.

EA_2 - $E^-\ (g)\ +\ e^-\ +$ energy $\rightarrow E^{2-}\ (g)$ the addition of a second e^- is always endothermic

$EA_1 < EA_2$; it is always more difficult to add an e^- to a negatively charged ion than to the corresponding neutral atom.

Example Problems:

1. Arrange the following sets of elements in order of increasingly <u>negative</u> electron affinities: Li, K, C, F, and Cs

     Cs < K < Li < C < F (most negative EA)

2. Which of the following will form a -1 anion the most readily: Li, K, C, F, and I
     F (the element with the most negative EA)

3. Which of the following will gain an electron the most readily: F⁻, K, C, F, and I
     F (the element with the most negative EA)

D. **Ionic Radii** - refers to the radii of ions. An anion is always larger than the neutral atom from which it was derived. A cation is always smaller than the neutral atom from which it was derived. *With isoelectronic species (species with same electronic configuration) the ionic radii decreases with increasing atomic number.*

Example Problems:

1. Arrange the following sets of ions in order of increasing ionic radii: O^{2-}, F^-, Al^{3+}, N^{3-}.

     Al^{3+} < F^- < O^{2-} < N^{3-} $\left(\begin{array}{l}\text{since these species are isoelectronic -}\\ \text{the specie with the largest atomic number is the smallest}\end{array}\right)$

2. Which of the following has the largest radii: N, O, F, Al^{3+}, Na.
     Na

E. **Electronegativity (EN)** - refers to the relative tendency of an atom to attract electrons to itself when it is chemically combined with another atom. Commonly, electronegativities are expressed on a somewhat arbitrary scale, called the Pauling scale. For representative elements, electronegativities usually increase from left to right across periods and from bottom to top within groups. Variations among transition elements are not as regular. There are two things that should be noticed: a) the electronegativity of non-metals (except Si) is greater than that of any metal and b) any element in group IA & IIA (with the exception of H & Be) will have smaller electronegativies in comparison to any element in groups IIIA - VIIA.

IA	IIA	IIIA	IVA	VA	VIA	VIIA	VIIIA
H 2.1							He -
Li 1.0	Be 1.5	B 2.0	C 2.5	N 3.0	O 3.5	F 4.0	Ne -
Na 0.9	Mg 1.2	Al 1.5	Si 1.8	P 2.1	S 2.5	Cl 3.0	Ar -
K 0.8	Ca 1.1	Ga 1.6	Ge 1.8	As 2.0	Se 2.4	Br 2.8	Kr -
Rb 0.7	Sr 1.0	In 1.7	Sn 1.8	Sb 1.9	Te 2.1	I 2.5	Xe -
Cs 0.7	Ba 0.9	Tl 1.8	Pb 1.8	Bi 1.9	Po 2.0	At 2.2	Rn -
Fr 0.7	Ra 0.9						

Given a list of elements, the element with the largest electronegativity (excluding VIIIA elements) will be the one that is at the most upper right hand corner of the periodic table.

Example Problems:

1. Not looking at the values in the above table, arrange the following elements in order of increasing electronegativity: F, Sb, Rb, N, and As.
     Rb < Sb < As < N < F

2. Toward which atom will the electrons be shifted when the following atoms are in a chemical bond: a) H-F   b) Si-H
    a) towards F, which has the higher electronegativity
    b) towards H, which has the higher electronegativity

F. Summary of Periodic Trends

Atomic radii - decreases
IE - increases (except: IIA > IIIA & VA > VIA)
EA - increases* (the energy value becomes more negative)
EN - increases

ionic radii
isoelectronic species - ionic radii decreases as Z increases
cation vs. neutral atom - ionic radii of cation is smaller
anion vs. neutral atom - ionic radii of anion is larger

    * EA increases in terms of the ability of an atom to gain an electron is greater;
      however, the energy released is more negative (i.e., is smaller).

VI. Electronegativity, The Chemical Bond, and Polarity

A chemical bond is the force that holds a group of 2 or more atoms together. There are two main types of bonds: ionic and covalent. *Typically, a bond between non-metals is covalent and that between a metal and a non-metal is ionic.* However, as will be discussed below, the classification between a covalent and an ionic bond is also based on the difference in electronegativities of the atoms that are bonded together.

Ionic bonds form by the attraction of oppositely charged ions. *When electronegativities are not given to you, assume that the bond between a metal and a non-metal is ionic.* If the difference in electronegativity, ΔEN, of the 2 elements in a compound is greater than 1.8, an ionic bond is what holds the 2 elements together. The more electronegative element takes the electrons away from the less electronegative element, thus forming ions. The more electronegative element gains the electrons (becomes an anion) while the less electronegative element loses its electrons (becomes a cation). The larger the ΔEN between the two elements involved in an ionic bond, the more ionic the bond is.

Covalent bonds consist of a pair of electrons being shared between two atoms.   Covalent bonds can be: non-polar or polar.

A *non-polar* covalent bond consists of the pair of electrons being shared equally by both elements (i.e., when the difference in the electronegativity of the 2 elements is between 0.0 - 0.4).

A *polar* covalent bond consists of a pair of electrons being shared unequally between the two elements (i.e., when the difference in electronegativity of the 2 elements is between 0.5 - 1.8).

The larger the ΔEN between the two elements involved in a covalent bond, the more polar the bond is. The more electronegative atom has the electrons closer to itself and therefore develops a partially negative charge ($\delta-$) while the less electronegative atom develops a partially positive charge ($\delta+$). This separation of charges in a polar bond is called a *dipole*. For covalent compounds, the larger the ΔEN the larger the dipole.   Generally, those bonds having one of the more electronegative atoms (such as N, O, F, Cl, or Br) and a less electronegative atom will be polar. Ionic bonds could be considered extreme cases of polarity. Atoms with identical electronegativities, do not form dipoles.

Since bonding has not been fully discussed yet, the following is meant to give you a generalized example of each kind of bond.

Ionic Bond ($\Delta EN > 1.8$)   vs.   Covalent Bond ($\Delta EN = 0.0 - 1.8$)

$$X\cdot \; \cdot Y \longrightarrow X^+ \; :Y^{\,-}$$ $$Y\cdot \; \cdot Z \longrightarrow Y:Z = Y{-}Z$$

Covalent Bond

Electrostatic in nature, an ionic bond is one
that is formed by the transfer of one or
more electrons from one atom to the other

Atoms in a covalent bond,
are held together by the
sharing of an electron pair

Non-Polar Covalent Bond ($\Delta EN = 0.0 - 0.4$)	vs.	Polar Covalent Bond ($\Delta EN = 0.5 - 1.8$)

$$Y : Z$$

$$\overset{\delta+ \quad \delta-}{X : Z}$$

Atoms in a non-polar covalent bond are sharing the electron pair equally

The more electronegative element pulls the electron pair closer to itself and develops a partially negative charge ($\delta-$) while the less electronegative element develops a partially positve charge ($\delta+$)

Example Problems:

1. Classify the bonds formed between the following atoms as: non-polar covalent, polar covalent, or ionic: a) Cl & Cl, b) C & O, c) Li & Cl, d) Al & I

    a) non-polar covalent because the electronegativity difference is 0.

    b) polar covalent because the electronegativity difference is 1.0 ($|2.5 - 3.5|$)

    c) ionic because the electronegativity difference is 2.0 ($|1.0 - 3.0|$). Also, a metal and a non-metal usually form an ionic bond.

    d) polar covalent because the electronegativity difference is 1.0 ($|1.5 - 2.5|$). Notice how even though one atom is a metal (Al) and the other is a nonmetal (I), the bond formed between them is covalent.

2. Without refering to their respective electronegativities, which bond formed between the following: atoms will be the least polar: Cl & I, Br & I, F & F, or Li & I?

    The least polar bond will be between those elements having very similar (or identical) electronegativities. Since the electronegativity difference between F & F is zero, the F-F bond will be the least polar.

3. Without refering to their respective electronegativities, which of the following will have the most ionic bond: Na & Cl, Na & Br, Na & F, or Cs & F?

    When considering this type of problem, the most ionic bond will be the one in which the metal is at the most bottom left hand corner (least electronegative) of the periodic table, and the non-metal is at the most upper right hand corner (most electronegative). Therefore, Cs & F will have the most ionic bond.

4. Indicate the polarity ($\delta+/\delta-$) of each atom in the molecule H-F?

    The electrons in the polar covalent bond are closer to the fluorine atom than to the hydrogen atom; therefore, the fluorine atom becomes partially negative and the hydrogen atom becomes partially positive.

    $$\overset{\delta+ \quad \delta-}{H—F}$$ The following notation means the same thing: $\overset{\longrightarrow}{H—F}$

5. Which compound is more polar, Br-F or Br-Cl? Also, indicate the polarity ($\delta+/\delta-$) of each atom in the molecule.

    Relative to Br, since F is more electronegative than Cl, Br-F is more polar than Br-Cl

    $$\overset{\delta+ \quad \delta-}{Br—F} \qquad\qquad \overset{\delta+ \quad \delta-}{Br—Cl}$$

VII. **Metals and Nonmetals**

Most metals are solids (except: Hg which is a liquid)

Nonmetals which are: (a) gases - VIIIA (noble gases), H_2, F_2, Cl_2, O_2, N_2; (b) liquids - Br_2; (c) solids - C, P_4, S_8, Se, I_2, (B, Si, As, Te, At_2)

Physical Properties of Metals and Nonmetals

<table>
<tr><td align="center">Metals</td><td align="center">Nonmetals</td></tr>
<tr><td>

1. High electrical conductivity that decreases with increasing temperature.
2. Metallic gray or silver luster (ex: Au and Cu)
3. Almost all are solids (ex: Hg)
4. Malleable
5. Ductile (can be drawn into wires)
6. Solid state characterized by metallic bonding

</td><td>

1. Poor electrical conductivity [ex: C (graphite)]
2. No metal luster
3. Solids, liquids, gases
4. Brittle in solid state
5. Nonductile
6. Covalently bonded molecules; noble gases are monatomic

</td></tr>
</table>

Chemical Properties of Metals and Nonmetals

<table>
<tr><td align="center">Metals</td><td align="center">Nonmetals</td></tr>
<tr><td>

1. Outer shell contains few e^-.
2. Low IE
3. Slightly negative or positive EA
4. Low EN
5. Form cations by losing e^-
6. Form ionic compounds with nonmetals

</td><td>

1. Outer shell contains 4 or more e^- (ex: H)
2. High IE
3. Very negative EA
4. High EN
5. Form anions by gaining e^- (ex: noble gases)
6. Form ionic compounds with metals (ex: noble gases) and molecular (covalent) compounds with other nonmetals

</td></tr>
</table>

EXERCISES

The Periodic Table

1. Classify the following elements into one or more of the following categories:

A. alkali metal	B. alkaline earth metal	C. representative element
D. transition element	E. inner transition element	F. lanthanide
G. actinide	H. chalogen	I. halogen
J. noble gas	K. nonmetal	L. metalloid
M. metal	N. s-block element	O. p-block element
P. d-block element	Q. f-block element	R. first period element
S. third period element	T. group IIIA element	U. 3rd transition series element

a) Li	b) Au	c) Lu	d) Ge	e) Ne	f) Th	g) Mg
h) Te	i) Ar	j) Co	k) H	l) Ga	m) Uub	n) At

2. Once discovered, give the name & symbol for the elements that have the following atomic numbers:
   a) 121   b) 128   c) 134   d) 129   e) 127

3. Once discovered, what would the atomic number for each of the following elements be:
   a) the halogen in period 7   b) the alkali metal in period 8

4. If the atomic radius of Be = 1.11Å and if atomic radius of Ca = 1.97Å, then predict what is atomic radius of Mg.

5. For the elements with the following outer shell electronic configuration, give its group, its period, and its name.
   a) $4s^1 3d^5$ b) $3s^2 3p^5$ c) $4s^1$ d) $2s^2 2p^4$ e) $5s^2 4d^1$ f) $5s^2 4d^{10} 5p^2$

6. Which elements have similar chemical properties to that of -- a) F   b) Ba?

Lewis Dot Representation of the Representative Elements

7. How many valence electrons do each of the following elements have?
   a) K   b) Al   c) C   d) As   e) Te   f) F   g) He

8. Write the Lewis structure for each of the following elements.
   a) Cs   b) Ba   c) Ga   d) Si   e) P   f) Se   g) Ne

9. Which element am I?
   a) I have 6 valence electrons and I am in period 4
   b) I am a nonmetal with the following Lewis dot structure :E
   c) I am a metalloid in period 3 with the following Lewis dot structure :X·

Periodic Properties

10. For each set (A, B, C, D) of elements, answer the following questions:
    A. Li, N, O, Cs, Po   B. Si, P, S, Ge, Sn   C. Be, B, Al, K, Ca   D. O, F, S, Cl, Se
    a) which has the smallest atomic radius?
    b) which has the largest atomic radius?
    c) which has the smallest ionization energy?
    d) which has the largest ionization energy?
    e) which will lose an electron the most readily?
    f) which has the least affinity for electrons?
    g) which has the most negative electron affinity energy value?
    h) which will gain an electron the most readily?
    i) which is most electronegative?
    j) which is least electronegative?
    k) which has the greatest attraction for an electron in a covalent bond?

11. For each set (A, B, C, D) of species, answer the following questions:
    A. Be, Be^{2+}, Li, N   B. S^{2-}, Cl^-, K^+, Ca^{2+} C. Sn, Sn^{2+}, Sn^{4+} D. O, O^-, O^{2-}
    a) which has the smallest radius?
    b) which has the largest radius?

Electronegativity, The Chemical Bond, & Polarity

12. Toward which atom will the electron be shifted when the following atoms are involved in a chemical bond?
    a) O & F   b) Al & I   c) H & H   d) As & N

13. Classify the bond between the following atoms as either: non-polar covalent, polar covalent, or ionic.
    a) O & F   b) Al & I   c) Cl & Cl   d) Mg & F   e) P & As

14. Given the following pair of atoms in each set (A, B, C), answer the following questions:
    A. Li & F,   Fr & F,   Be & F
    B. Si & Si,   At & F,   At & Cl
    C. Br & Cl,   B & Cl,   Na & Cl

    a) which bond will have the most ionic character?
    b) which bond will have the least ionic character?
    c) which bond will have the most covalent character?
    d) which bond will have the least covalent character?

15. Given the following pair of atoms in each set (A, B, C), answer the following questions:
    A. H-H,   H-Cl,   H-I
    B. C-F,   N-F,   O-F
    C. S-O,   Se-O,   Te-O

    a) which bond is the least polar?
    b) which bond is the most polar?
    c) which bond has the largest dipole?
    d) which bond has the smallest dipole?

16. Indicate the polarity (δ+/δ-) of each atom in the following bonds?
    a) H-C   b) N-C   c) C-Cl   d) C-O   e) P-Cl

MULTIPLE CHOICE PRACTICE EXAM FOR MODULE 10

1. Which of the following elements is a noble gas?
   1) H   2) Xe   3) O   4) F   5) N

2. The element manganese can be classifed as a(n):
   a. group 4 element   b. 3rd transition series element   c. d block element
   1) only a   2) only b   3) only c   4) only b and c   5) a, b, and c

3. The element Ba can be classifed as a(n):
   a. transition element   b. alkaline earth metal   c. s block element
   1) only a   2) only b   3) only c   4) only b and c   5) a, b, and c

4. The element Th can be classifed as:
   a. Lanthanide   b. f block element   c. transition element
   1) only a   2) only b   3) only c   4) only b and c   5) a, b, and c

5. Once discovered the symbol for element 114 will be:
   1) Uut   2) Unt   3) Uuq   4) Unq   5) Uuf

6. Once discovered the name for element 120 will be:
   1) Undinilium   2) Unbizeroium   3) Undizeroium   4) Undosnilium   5) Unbinilium

7. Which of the following statements will be true when element 114 is discovered?
   a. Its symbol will be Uut
   b. It will be a transition element.
   c. It will be a non-metal.
   1) only a   2) only b   3) only c   4) only a and c
   5) none of the above statements are correct.

8. Which of the following statements will be true when element 116 is discovered?
   a. It will be a representative element.
   b. It will be a halogen.
   c. It will be in group VA.
   1) only a   2) only b   3) only c   4) only a and b   5) a, b, and c

9. An element having seven valence electrons:
   a. Is in group VIIA.
   b. Is a metal.
   c. Has two unpaired electrons.
   1) only a   2) only b   3) only c   4) only a and b   5) a, b, and c

10. Elements having the electronic configuration $ns^2 np^5$ are called:
    1) noble gases   2) halogens   3) metalloids   4) group VA elements   5) chalcogens

11. What element am I?
    Though my atomic radius is smaller than Si; I have very similar properties to those of Si.
    1) Ge   2) Al   3) P   4) C   5) B

12. Which of the following atoms has the smallest atomic radius?
    1) Na   2) Al   3) Cl   4) Kr   5) Ga

13. Which of the following atoms has the largest first ionization energy?

    1) K   2) Ca   3) Ga   4) Si   5) Al

14. Which of the following atoms forms a +1 ion most readiliy?

    1) K   2) Ca   3) Ga   4) Si   5) Al

15. Which of the following atoms will gain an electron most readily?

    1) K   2) Ca   3) Ga   4) Si   5) Al

16. Which of the following atoms has the most negative electron affinity?

    1) K   2) Ca   3) Ga   4) Si   5) Al

17. Which of the following ions will form most readily?

    1) K^{1-} 2) Ca^{1-} 3) Ga^{1-} 4) Si^{1-} 5) Al^{1-}

18. Which of the following atoms is most electronegative?

    1) K   2) Ca   3) Ga   4) Si   5) Al

19. Which of the following has the largest radius?
    1) K^+ 2) Ca^{2+} 3) Cl^- 4) Ar   5) S^{2-}

20. The bond formed between which of the following has the least ionic character?
    1) F-F   2) Cl-F   3) I-F   4) O-F   5) N-F

21. The bond formed between which of the following is most polar?
    1) F-F   2) Cl-F   3) I-F   4) O-F   5) N-F

22. Which of the following bonds has the largest dipole?
    1) F-F   2) Cl-F   3) I-F   4) O-F   5) N-F

23. The polarity of which of the following bonds is illustrated correctly?

    a. $\overset{\delta+ \quad \delta-}{O-H}$ b. $\overset{\longleftarrow +}{O-H}$ c. $\overset{\delta- \quad \delta+}{O-F}$

    1) only a   2) only b   3) only c   4) only a and b   5) a, b, and c

MODULE 10 - ANSWERS

1. a) A, C, M, N   b) D, M, P, U   c) E, F, M, Q   d) C, L, O, (M)   e) C, J, K, O
    f) E, G, M, Q   g) B, C, M, N, S   h) C, H, L, O, (K)   i) C, J, K, O, S   j) D, M, P
    k) C, K, N, R   l) C, M, O, T   m) D, M, P   n) C, I, L, O

2. a) Unbiunium   Ubu   b) Unbioctium   Ubo   c) Untriquadium   Utq
    d) Unbiennium   Ube   e) Unbiseptium   Ubs

3. a) 117   b) 119

4. 1.54Å   (actual = 1.60Å)

5. a) VIB, 4th period, chromium   b) VIIA, 3rd period, chlorine   c) IA, 4th period, potassium
    d) VIA, 2nd period, oxygen   e) IIIB, 5th period, yttrium   f) IVA, 5th period, tin

6. a) Cl, Br, I, & At   b) Be, Mg, Ca, Sr, & Ra

7. a) 1   b) 3   c) 4   d) 5   e) 6   f) 7   g) 2

8. a) Cs·   b) ·Ba· or Ba: c) ·Ga· or :Ga   d) ·Si· or :Si·   e) :P·   f) :Se: g) :Ne:

9. a) Se   b) He   c) Si

10. A. a) O   b) Cs   c) Cs   d) N   e) Cs   f) Cs   g) O   h) O   i) O   j) Cs   k) O
    B. a) S   b) Sn   c) Sn   d) P   e) Sn   f) Sn   g) S   h) S   i) S   j) Sn   k) S
    C. a) B   b) K   c) K   d) Be   e) K   f) K   g) B   h) B   i) B   j) K   k) B
    D. a) F   b) Se   c) Se   d) F   e) Se   f) Se   g) F   h) F   i) F   j) Se   k) F

11. A. a) Be^{2+} b) Li
    B. a) Ca^{2+} b) S^{2-}
    C. a) Sn^{4+} b) Sn
    D. a) O   b) O^{2-}

12. a) F   b) I   c) equal sharing   d) N

13. a) polar covalent   b) polar covalent   c) non-polar covalent   d) ionic   e) non-polar covalent

14. A. a) Fr & F   b) Be & F   c) Be & F   d) Fr & F
    B. a) At & F   b) Si & Si   c) Si & Si   d) At & F
    C. a) Na & Cl   b) Br & Cl   c) Br & Cl   d) Na & Cl

15. A. a) H & H   b) H & Cl   c) H & Cl   d) H & H (no dipole)
    B. a) O & F   b) C & F   c) C & F   d) O & F
    C. a) S & O   b) Te & O   c) Te & O   d) S & O

16. a) $\overset{\delta+}{H} - \overset{\delta-}{C}$ b) $\overset{\delta-}{N} - \overset{\delta+}{C}$ c) $\overset{\delta+}{C} - \overset{\delta-}{Cl}$ d) $\overset{\delta+}{C} - \overset{\delta-}{O}$ e) $\overset{\delta+}{P} - \overset{\delta-}{Cl}$

MODULE 11. *Chemical Bonding: Basic Concepts*

I. Lewis Structure for Ions

For ions, one starts with the Lewis structure for the element and then adds or removes electrons as needed. Remember that positive ions are formed when electrons are lost by an atom while negative ions result from the gain of electrons.

Metals become cations (lose e^-). "A" metals lose their valence electrons.

Non-metals become anions (gain e^-). Non-metals gain as many electrons as is necessary to become isoelectronic with the noble gas in the same row (i.e., they gain as many electrons so as to have a full octet -- 2 electrons at each side of the imaginary square) . Noble gases are stable and do not form ions.

Example Problem: Write the Lewis dot structure for the ions produced by a) Na, b) Al, and c) O.

  a) For Na, the one valence electrons is lost (becomes isoelectronic with Ne); the resulting ion has a charge of +1.
$$Na\cdot \quad \rightarrow \quad Na^+$$

  b) For Al, the three valence electrons are lost (becomes isoelectronic with Ne); the resulting ion has a charge of +3.
$$\cdot\overset{\cdot}{Al}\cdot \ \text{ or } :Al\cdot \rightarrow \quad Al^{3+}$$

  c) For O, since the atom contains 6 valence electrons -- 2 electrons are gained so that it has a full octet (becomes isoelectronic with Ne); the resulting ion has a charge of -2.
$$:\overset{\cdot\cdot}{\underset{\cdot}{O}}\cdot \ \rightarrow \ :\overset{\cdot\cdot}{\underset{\cdot\cdot}{O}}: \ ^{2-}$$

II. Lewis Structure of Ionic Compounds

For ionic compounds, the Lewis structures are simply produced by combining the Lewis structures of the individual ions. [Representative metals lose their valence electrons and nonmetals gain as many electrons as is necessary to become isoelectronic with the noble gas in the same row.]

Example Problem: Write the Lewis structures for the ionic compounds formed by:
  a) Na & Cl;   b) Mg & Br;   c) Al & O.

  a) For NaCl, $(Na^+)\ (:\overset{\cdot\cdot}{\underset{\cdot\cdot}{Cl}}:^-)$

  b) For $MgBr_2$, $(Mg^{2+})\ (:\overset{\cdot\cdot}{\underset{\cdot\cdot}{Br}}:^-)_2$

  c) For Al_2O_3, $(Al^{3+})_2\ (:\overset{\cdot\cdot}{\underset{\cdot\cdot}{O}}:^{2-})_3$

Note how each ion (in all cases shown) has a noble gas configuration. The metals lose their valence electrons, while the nonmetals gain as many electrons as is necessary to become isoelectronic with the noble gas in the same period.

III. Lewis Structure of Covalent Compounds & Polyatomic Ions

Covalent bonds are produced when two non-metals combine chemically. When a covalent compound or polyatomic ion is formed, electrons are shared. Two elements in a covalent bond can be either single, double, or triple bonded to each other.

Single bond --> the sharing of 2 e^- between two elements is represented by: X—Y

Double bond --> the sharing of 4 e^- between two elements is represented by: X=Y

Triple bond --> the sharing of 6 e^- between two elements is represented by: X≡Y

Shared (Bonding) vs. Unshared (Lone or Non-bonding) Electron Pairs:

unshared electrons
:X≡Y:
6 shared electrons

Certain elements in a covalent bond never form multiple bonds: H, B, Be, Al, VIIA elements (when not the central element), and VIIIA elements.

Covalent Bond Formation Objective ---> Each atom in a covalent bond wants to have an octet (i.e., 8 electrons surrounding it - noble gas configuration - very stable configuration).

Exceptions to Octet:

a) Some atoms have less than an octet [H, Be, B, and Al]

IA	IIA	IIIA	
H—	— Be —	— B —	[Note: Even though Be and Al are metals, they can form covalent bonds. As discussed in the the previous module, if $\Delta EN = 0.0 - 1.8$ a covalent bond forms between the atoms.]
		— Al —	

b) Some atoms *can* have more than an octet [Central elements from rows 3, 4, 5, and 6 of the periodic table, can have more than an octet due to the availablity of low lying d-orbitals. Elements in these rows can thus have up to 18 electrons surronding it.]

Guidelines to Drawing Skeletal Lewis Structures:

a) the central element will be the element which is least electronegative -- usually the element that is written first, except H - it is never the central element. For those species having only one central element (central element having no subscript), the rest of the atoms in the formula are placed surrounding the central element.

b) Oxygen atoms do not bond to each other except in: a) O_2 and O_3 molecules, b) peroxides, which contain the O_2^{2-} group, and in rare cases, c) superoxides, which contain the O_2^- group.

c) In oxyacids (compounds containing H, O, and another element -- H_xEO_y) or an oxyacid anion, H is usually bonded to O, not to the central element.

d) For ions or molecules that have more than one central element, the most symmetrical skeleton possible is used.

Example Problem: Using the above guidlines, draw a skeletal Lewis Structure for the following:
  a) $SOCl_2$ b) CO_2 c) H_2SO_3 e) C_2H_4

```
            O                                    O            H   H
a)  Cl  S  Cl      b) O  C  O      c) H  O  S  O  H    d) H  C  C  H
```

The central element is boldfaced.

A. Lewis Structures - The Real Thing

Drawing Lewis structures by this method, use the following as a guide:

a) Draw skeletal Lewis structure.

b) Draw the Lewis electron dot structure for each atom.   [Remember that there are two methods of drawing Lewis structure for atoms, use the method in which the electrons are spread to all four sides of an imaginary square before being paired.] For the sake of keeping the drawing as neat as possible direct single electrons on adjacent atoms towards each other.

c) Draw a line from a single unpaired electron on the central element to a single unpaired electron on the surrounding atom (this constitutes the formation of a covalent bond) continue doing this until each atom has an octet (note exceptions given above: H, Be, B, Al, elements in rows 3, 4, 5, & 6).   No electrons should be left unpaired (only in rare cases will a specie contain an unpaired electron). For those atoms that can have more than an octet, if all of its single electrons are used in a covalent bond, and there are surrounding atoms with electrons still to be paired, then lone electron pairs are used in bonding. The electron pair(s) being shared must be placed between the two atoms forming the bond.

d) For polyatomic ions,

-1 charge, add 1 electron to the most electronegative atom

-2 charge, add 2 electrons (one to each of the two most electronegative atoms)

-3 charge, add 3 electrons (one to each of the three most electronegative atoms)

+1 charge, remove 1 electron from the least electronegative atom.

e) Coordinate Covalent or Dative Bond Formation (a bond formed when both of the electrons in a bond are supplied by one atom): If all the single electrons of one atom (atom 1) are used in bonding and the adjacent atom (atom 2) has single electrons which need to be shared, then the electrons on atom 2 (the one still having single electrons) are paired and atom 1 donates a pair of electrons to atom 2 thus forming a coordinate covalent bond. A coordinate covalent bond is represented by →. The arrowhead is pointed to the atom to which the electrons were donated.

Example Problem: Draw the Lewis Structure for each of the following. Also, indicate how many lone pair(s) - LP and bonding pair(s) -BP each specie has.

a) CO_2 b) CO_3^{2-} c) $BeCl_2$ d) $SOCl_2$ e) H_2SO_3 f) C_2H_4 g) NH_4^+ h) PH_5

a) $:\ddot{O}\ \cdot\dot{C}\ \cdot\ddot{O}:$ —form bonds→ $:\ddot{O}\!-\!\overline{C\!-\!O}:$ —clean up drawing→ $:\ddot{O}=C=\ddot{O}:$ 4 LP & 4 BP

b) $:\ddot{O}\ \cdot\dot{C}\ \cdot\ddot{O}:$ —add 2 e⁻'s - one to each O (most EN element)→ $:\ddot{O}\ \cdot\dot{C}\ \cdot\ddot{O}:$ —form bonds→ $:\ddot{O}\!-\!\underset{}{C}\!-\!\ddot{O}:$ (with :Ö above C)

—clean up drawing→ $\left[:\ddot{O}\!-\!\underset{}{C}\!=\!\ddot{O}: \right]^{2-}$ (with :Ö: above C)   8 LP & 4 BP

c) $:\ddot{C}l\cdot\ \cdot Be\cdot\ \cdot\ddot{C}l:$ —form bonds→ $:\ddot{C}l\!-\!Be\!-\!\ddot{C}l:$ 6 LP & 2 BP

d) $:\ddot{C}l\cdot\ \cdot\dot{S}\cdot\ \cdot\ddot{C}l:$ (with :Ö above S) —form bonds→ $:\ddot{C}l\!-\!\dot{S}\!-\!\ddot{C}l:$ (with :Ö: above S) —pair e⁻'s on O→ $:\ddot{C}l\!-\!\dot{S}\!-\!\ddot{C}l:$ (with :Ö: above S)

—form coordinate covalent bond→ $:\ddot{C}l\!-\!\dot{S}\!-\!\ddot{C}l:$ (with :Ö: ↑ above S) —clean up drawing→ $:\ddot{C}l\!-\!S\!-\!\ddot{C}l:$ (with :Ö: ↑ above S)   10 LP & 3 BP

e) $H\cdot\ \cdot\ddot{O}\cdot\ \cdot\dot{S}\cdot\ \cdot\ddot{O}\cdot\ \cdot H$ (with :Ö above S) —form bonds→ $H\!-\!\ddot{O}\!-\!\dot{S}\!-\!\ddot{O}\!-\!H$ (with :Ö above S) —pair e⁻'s on O→

$H\!-\!\ddot{O}\!-\!\dot{S}\!-\!\ddot{O}\!-\!H$ (with :Ö: above S) —form coordinate covalent bond→ $H\!-\!\ddot{O}\!-\!\dot{S}\!-\!\ddot{O}\!-\!H$ (with :Ö: ↑ above S) —clean up drawing→ $H\!-\!\ddot{O}\!-\!S\!-\!\ddot{O}\!-\!H$ (with :Ö: ↑ above S)

8 LP & 5 BP

f) $H\cdot\ \cdot\dot{C}\ \cdot\dot{C}\cdot\ \cdot H$ —form bonds→ $H\!-\!\underset{H}{\overset{H}{C}}\!-\!\underset{H}{\overset{H}{C}}\!-\!H$ —clean up drawing→ $H\!-\!\underset{H}{\overset{H}{C}}\!=\!\underset{H}{\overset{H}{C}}\!-\!H$ 0 LP & 6 BP

g)

0 LP & 4 BP

h)

B. Lewis Structures - The Quick-N-Dirty Method

This method will be illustrated by drawing the Lewis structure of SO_3.

1. Find the total number of valence electrons by adding the number of valence electrons from each atom in the formula. [For polyatomic anions add the charge to the total number of valence electrons. For polyatomic cations subtract the charge from the total number of valence electrons.]

   $$1\ S \qquad\qquad 6$$
   $$3\ O = 3(6) = \quad \underline{18}$$
   $$24$$

2. Draw a single bond from the central element to each of the elements surrounding it. [The first element in the formula is usually the central element (except for H - it is never the central element).]

   O-S-O
   |
   O

3. Subtract the electrons used so far in the structure from the total number. Each bond contains 2 electrons.

   $$3\ bonds \times 2\ e^- = 6\ e^-$$
   $$24 - 6 = 18\ e^-$$

4. The remaining electrons are spread, *as pairs*, to the surrounding elements first. Each surrounding element (except H) will receive enough electron pairs so as to have an octet. If any electrons are left over, give them to the central element.

   :Ö-S-Ö:
   |
   :Ö:

5. If the central element does not have an octet, then one or two of the single bonds are converted to double bonds or one single bond is converted to a triple bond. If possible, make 2 double bonds before making one triple bond.

   Remember exceptions to the octet rule (H, Be, B, & Al and elements from rows 3, 4, 5, and 6).

   :Ö-S-Ö: ⟶ :Ö-S-Ö:

   make a double bond so that S will have an octet

   For compounds in which lone pairs on surrounding elements must be converted into bonding pairs -- consider the following:

   - Group IVA elements in almost all cases have no lone electron pairs.
   - Group VA elements in almost all cases have one lone electron pair.
   - Group VIA elements in some cases have two lone electron pairs (when involved in a double bond or in two single bonds) and in other cases have three unpaired electrons (when involved in a single bond). Basically, only the oxygen in CO has one unpaired electron.
   - Group VIIA elements have three lone pairs (when not the central element).

Example Problem:

1. Draw Lewis Structures for:

   a) $SOCl_2$ b) C_2H_2 c) NO_3^- d) H_2SO_3 e) NH_4^+
   f) PH_5 g) $AlCl_3$ h) HCO_2H (one H is bonded to C and the other to O)

Step 1	Step 2	Step 3	Step 4	Step 5

a) $6+6+2(7) = 26$ Cl-S-Cl (with O below S) $26-6 = 20$:Cl̈-S̈-Cl̈: (with :Ö: below) -

b) $2(4)+2 = 10$ H-C-C-H $10-6 = 4$ H–C̈—C—H H–C̈⤵C—H → H-C≡C-H

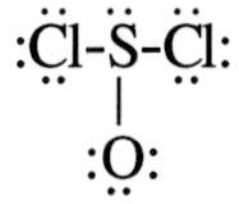

c) $5+3(6)+1 = 24$ O-N-O (with O below N) $24-6 = 18$:Ö-N-Ö: (with :Ö: below) :Ö-N-Ö: (with :Ö: below) → $\left[:Ö-N-Ö: \,\|\, :O \right]^{-}$

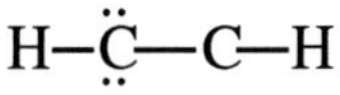

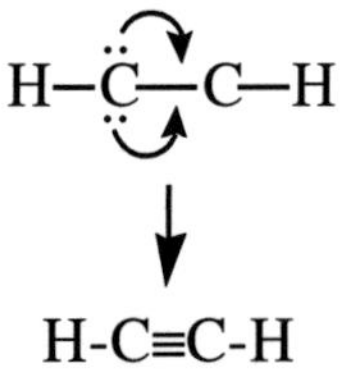

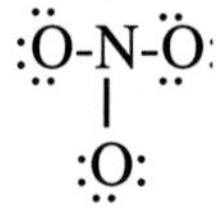

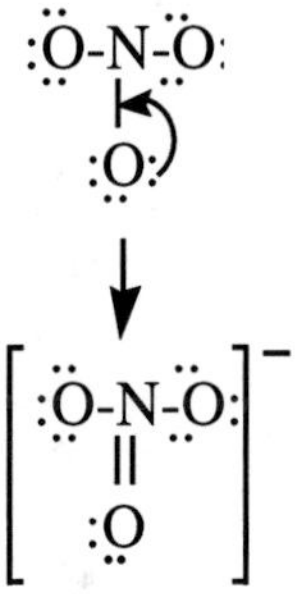

d) $2+6+3(6) = 26$ H-O-S-O-H (with O below S) $26-10 = 16$ H-Ö-S-Ö-H (with :Ö: below) -

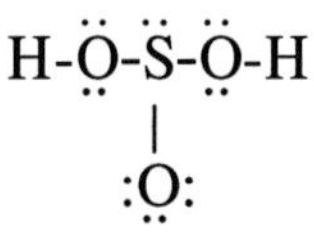

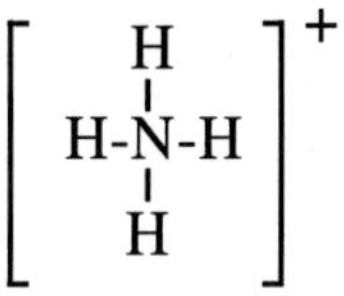

e) $5+4(1)-1 = 8$ H-N-H (with H above and H below) $8-8 = 0$ $\left[\begin{matrix} H \\ H\text{-}N\text{-}H \\ H \end{matrix} \right]^{+}$ -

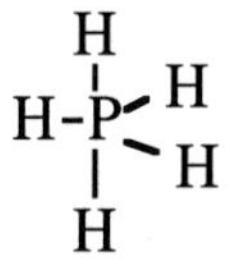

f) $5+5(1) = 10$ H-P with H's around $10-10 = 0$ H-P with H's around -

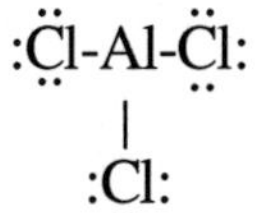

g) $3+3(7) = 24$ Cl-Al-Cl (with Cl below) $24-6 = 18$:Cl̈-Al-Cl̈: (with :Cl̈: below) -

h) $2(1)+4+2(6) = 18$ H-C-O-H (with O below C) $18-8 = 10$ H-C-Ö-H (with :Ö: below) H-C-Ö-H (with :Ö: below) → H-C-Ö-H ‖ :Ö:

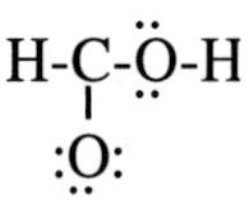

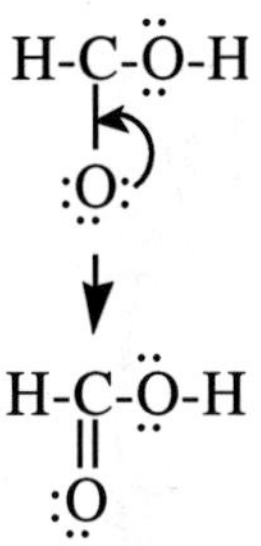

2. For each of the above structures, indicate the total number of lone pair(s) - LP and bonding pair(s) - BP that are present.

a) 10 LP & 3 BP   b) 0 LP & 5 BP   c) 8 LP & 4 BP   d) 8 LP & 5 BP

e) 0 LP & 4 BP   f) 0 LP & 5 BP   g) 9 LP & 3 BP   h) 4 LP & 5 BP

IV. Formal Charge (FC)

The concept of formal charges is basically a bookkeeping system that counts bonding electrons as though they were equally shared between atoms and helps us to write Lewis structures correctly .

Rules for Assigning Formal Charges:

FC = (atom's valence e⁻'s in nonbonded state) - (atom's valence e⁻'s in bonded state)

where, atom's valence e⁻'s in nonbonded state --> group number (of atom) for "A" elements

atom's valence e⁻'s in bonded state --> in a bonding situation, half of the electrons are given to one atom and the other half are given to the other atom; having done so, then count the number of electrons around each atom (including its lone pairs).

The sum of all the formal charges (ΣFC) is equal to the charge on the specie: a) for neutral molecules, $\Sigma FC = 0$;   b) for polyatomic ions, ΣFC = charge on the ion.

For Example, Consider the following specie:

$$\left[:C \equiv C-H \right]^{-}$$
$$\quad\quad 1 \quad 2 \quad 3$$

In a chemical bond, give half of the electrons to one atom and the other half to the other atom.

$$\left[:C \equiv C \quad H \right]^{-}$$
$$\quad 1 \quad 2 \quad 3$$

FC on C1 = 4 - 5 = -1
FC on C2 = 4 - 4 = 0
FC on H3 = 1 - 1 = 0
ΣFC = -1 + 0 + 0 = -1

Example Problem: Assign a formal charge to each of the atoms in the following species.

a) CO_3^{2-} b) BH_3 c) NH_4^+ d) $SOCl_2$

a)
$$\left[\begin{matrix} & \overset{-1}{:\ddot{O}:} & \\ \overset{-1}{:\ddot{O}} & - \overset{0}{C} = \overset{0}{\ddot{O}:} \end{matrix} \right]^{2-}$$

b)
$$\overset{0}{H} - \overset{0}{B} - \overset{0}{H}$$
$$\underset{\underset{0}{H}}{|}$$

c)
$$\left[\begin{matrix} & \overset{0}{H} & \\ \overset{0}{H} - & \overset{+1}{N} & - \overset{0}{H} \\ & \underset{\underset{0}{H}}{|} & \end{matrix} \right]^{+}$$

d)
$$\overset{0}{:\ddot{Cl}} - \overset{+1}{\underset{|}{\ddot{S}}} - \overset{0}{\ddot{Cl}:}$$
$$\underset{\underset{-1}{:\ddot{O}:}}{}$$

V. Bond Lengths

Bond length is the distance between two bonded nuclei in a molecule.   The length of a chemical bond not only depends on the nature of the bonded atoms but also on whether the bond joining the atoms is a single, double, or triple bond. As you can see from the table to your right, triple bonds are shorter than double bonds; and double bonds are shorter than single bonds.

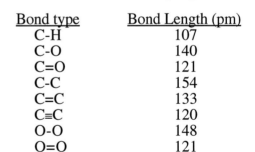

Bond type	Bond Length (pm)
C-H	107
C-O	140
C=O	121
C-C	154
C=C	133
C≡C	120
O-O	148
O=O	121

On the basis of bond length data, we would predict that for O_3,

$$:\ddot{O}-\ddot{O}=\ddot{O}:$$

that the O-O single bond distance would be 148 pm and the O=O double bond distance is 121 pm. However, experimental data shows that both oxygen-oxygen bond lengths are equal in length (128 pm); therefore, the above Lewis structure does not statisfactorily account for the observed experimental data. The concept of resonance, described below, attempts to address this problem.

VI.   Resonance

For many molecules or ions, a single Lewis structure does not satifactorily account for the chemical and physical properties of the species. The true state of the species is better represented by a combination of two or more Lewis structures. These individual structures, are called resonance contributors to the structure of that specie. *Resonance comes into play whenever there is/are multiple bonds present in a molecule or polyatomic ion.* Resonance structures differ from each other only in the arrangement of electrons; only nonbonding electrons and electrons in a multiple bond change locations in different resonance contributors. The nuclei of atoms in different resonance structures are in the same position. The more resonance structures (especially equivalent resonance structures) a species has, the more stable it is.

A.   Equivalent Resonance Structures

If one of the atoms (let's call it X) around the central element has a double bond, and there is another atom of the same kind that is singly bonded to the central element, then equivalent resonance structures exist. Equivalent resonance structures contribute equally to the real structure. The important thing to keep in mind, is that resonance structures are not *true structures*; the true structure is a composite of all the resonance structures.

Example,   The nitrate ion, NO_3^-, has the following equivalent resonance structures.

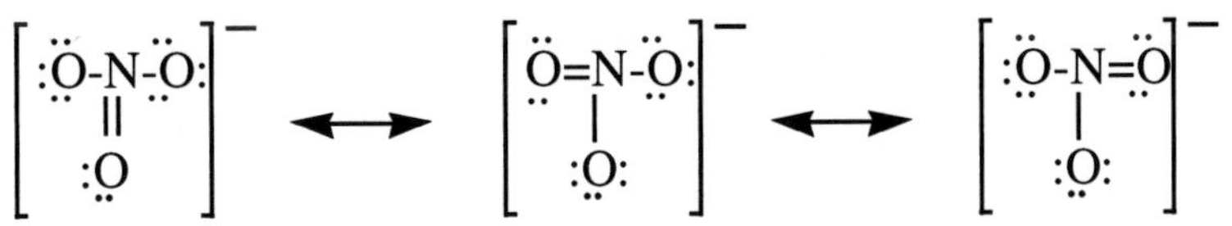

Double-headed arrows indicate resonance structures.

NO_3^- has 3 equivalent resonance structures. The nitrate ion is a *resonance hybrid* (a mixture) of the three equivalent resonance forms (each N-O bond is in-between being a single & double bond).

B.   Major vs. Minor Resonance Contributors to the Real Structure

A Major Contributor to the real structure is one in which:

a)   all elements should have an octet (except for H, Be, B, Al, and rows 3, 4, 5, & 6 elements). This is the most important factor.

b)   each element should have a low formal charge (-1, 0, or +1).

c)   the most electronegative element should have the most negative formal charge.

Resonance structures can be obtained as such:

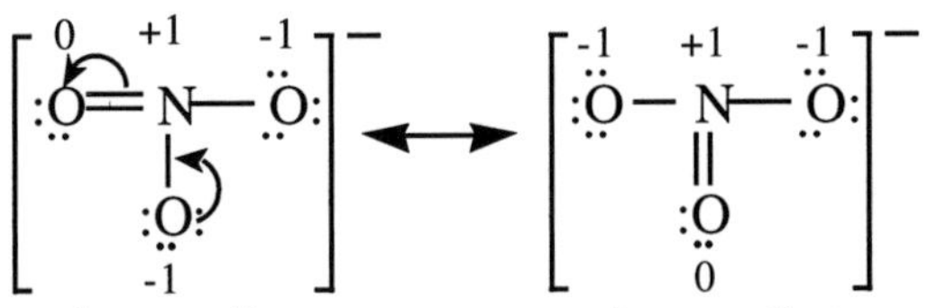

A lone pair is converted to a bonding pair and an adjacent bonding pair (from a multiple bond) is then converted to a lone pair.

A Minor Contributor to the real structure is one in which one or more of the following apply:

a)   one of the elements has less than an octet (excluding exceptions given above). Elements from row 2 cannot have more than an octet -- more than an octet for row 2 elements is not permissible.

b)   the most electronegative element does not have the most negative formal charge. *A structure with less than an octet and one in which the most electronegative element (especially oxygen) has the most positive formal charge is not considered a minor resonance contributor.*

c)   elements have high formal charges.

Minor contributors to the real structure are basically "unimportant" contributors; however, sometimes compounds exhibit reactivity that is best explained by writing a minor resonance contributor.

Minor resonance contributors can be obtained by converting one of the bonds in a multiple bond (of a major contributor) into a lone pair (see example below); by performing this operation, one of the elements will have less than an octet.

Example,

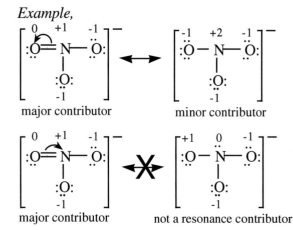

major contributor   minor contributor

The second structure is a minor contributor because N does not have an octet. Also, N has a high formal charge.

major contributor   not a resonance contributor

The second structure is not considered a resonance contributor because O (the one with a FC = +1) does not have an octet and has the most positive formal charge (see reason b in minor resonance contributors)

Although including all resonance structures provides a more accurate description of a molecule, often only one Lewis structure (the major contributor) is used to represent a molecule.

Example Problems:

1. Which of the following pairs are resonance structures of each other? If they are resonance structures, are they equivalent resonance structures or are they major/minor contributors.

a) H-C-Ö-H   H-C-Ö-H
      ‖ |
     :O   :O:

      A   B

A & B are not equivalent resonance structures. Structure A is the major contributor and structure B is a minor contributor because C does not have an octet.

b) H-C-Ö-H   H-C-Ö-H
      ‖   ⫴
     :O   :O

      A   B

These are not resonance structures, structure B is not a permissible Lewis structure because C has more than an octet.

c) $\left[\begin{array}{c} \text{H-C-Ö:} \\ \text{‖} \\ \text{:O} \end{array} \right]^{-}$ $\left[\begin{array}{c} \text{H-C=Ö:} \\ \text{|} \\ \text{:O:} \end{array} \right]^{-}$

      A   B

These are equivalent resonance structures.

d) $\left[\text{:C≡N-Ö:} \right]^{-}$ $\left[\text{:C̈=N=Ö:} \right]^{-}$

        A   B

These are not equivalent resonance structures. Structure A is the major contributor based on formal charges: Structure A (FC on C = -1, N = +1, O = -1) Structure B (FC on C = -2, N = +1, and O = 0). In structure B, C has a high formal charge and O, which is the most electronegative atom, does not have the most negative formal charge.

2. Indicate whether or not the each of the following have equivalent major resonance contributors. If equivalent major resonance contributors are present, then how many equivalent resonance structures are there.

a) CO_3^{2-} b) SO_2 c) H_2O d) ClO_2^{-}

a) yes, 3   b) yes, 2   c) no   d) no

EXERCISES

Lewis Structures

1. Write the Lewis dot structure for the ions produced by:

    a) Cs   b) Sr   c) C   d) As   e) Te   f) I

2. Write the Lewis Structure for the following compounds (assume that all are ionic) :

    a) LiF   b) K_2S c) AlN   d) Al_4C_3 e) $GaCl_3$

3. Write the Lewis Structure for the following:

    a) ClO_2^- b) ClO_3^- c) SO_3^{2-} d) AsH_3 e) BF_3 f) NO_3^- g) CH_2O h) SiH_4

    i) BrF_3 j) SeO_3 k) BrO_4^- l) $SeCl_6$ m) AsF_5 n) IF_5 o) IF_4^- p) XeF_2

    q) IF_4^+ r) $XeOF_4$ s) N_2H_4 t) C_2H_2 u) H_3PO_4

4. How many total bonding pair(s) and lone pair(s) are present in each of the following.

    a) CO   b) BF_3 c) NOCl   d) H_3O^+ e) NH_2^- f) PCl_5 g) SF_4 h) ICl_2^-

Formal Charge

5. Assign formal charges to each atom in the following:

    a) $\left[:N\equiv N\text{-}\ddot{N}:\right]^-$ b) $\left[:\ddot{O}=N=\ddot{O}:\right]^+$ c) $:\ddot{O}=C=\ddot{O}:$ d) $:\ddot{O}\text{-}\ddot{S}=\ddot{O}:$

Resonance

6. Which of the following pairs are resonance structures of each other?

    a) $\left[:N\equiv N\text{-}\ddot{N}:\right]^-$ $\left[:\ddot{N}=N=\ddot{N}:\right]^-$ b) $\left[:\ddot{N}\text{-}N\equiv N:\right]^-$ $\left[:N\equiv N\text{-}\ddot{N}:\right]^-$

    Yes   Yes

    c) $:\ddot{O}=C=\ddot{O}:$

    Yes
    w Some stru

    :O:
    ‖
    C
    ‖
    :O:

    d) $\left[:\ddot{O}=N=\ddot{O}:\right]^+$ $\left[:\ddot{O}\equiv N\text{-}\ddot{O}:\right]^+$

    No

    e) $:\ddot{O}=C=\ddot{O}:$ $:\ddot{O}\equiv C\text{-}\ddot{O}:$

    Yes   minor

    f) $:C\equiv O:$ $:C=\ddot{O}:$

    Yes   minor

    g) H-C≡C-H   H-$\ddot{C}$=C-H

    No   minor

    h) $:\ddot{Cl}\text{-}Be\text{-}\ddot{Cl}:$ $:\ddot{Cl}=Be\text{-}\ddot{Cl}:$

    No

7. Of those structures in question 6 that are resonance structures, which are equivalent resonance structures?   b

8. Of those structures in question 6 that are non-equivalent resonance structures, which is the major and which is a minor contributor?

9. Indicate whether or not each of the following have equivalent major resonance contributors. If equivalent major resonance contributors are present, then how many equivalent resonance structures are there?

    a) SeO_3 b) PO_4^{3-} c) I_3^- d) PO_3^{3-} e) SO_3^{2-}

MULTIPLE CHOICE PRACTICE EXAM FOR MODULE 11

1. The Lewis structure for MgF_2 is:

    1) $:\ddot{F}\text{-}Mg\text{-}\ddot{F}:$ 2) $:\ddot{F}\text{-}\ddot{M}g\text{-}\ddot{F}:$ 3) $(Mg^{2+})(:\ddot{F}:^-)_2$ 4) $(\cdot Mg\cdot^{2+})(:\ddot{F}:^-)_2$ 5) $(:\ddot{M}g:^{2+})(:\ddot{F}:^-)_2$

2. Which of the following compounds contain both ionic and covalent bonds?
    1) PBr_3 2) Fe_2O_3 3) H_2O 4) $MgSO_4$ 5) CH_3OH

3. The Lewis structure for HPO_3^{2-} is:

    1) $\left[H\text{-}\ddot{O}\text{-}P\text{-}\ddot{O}: \atop \|\ \ \ :\ddot{O}: \right]^{2-}$ 2) $\left[H\text{-}\ddot{O}\text{-}P\text{-}\ddot{O}: \atop |\ \ \ :\ddot{O}: \right]^{2-}$ 3) $\left[{H \atop |} \atop :\ddot{O}\text{-}P\text{-}\ddot{O}: \atop {| \atop :\ddot{O}:} \right]^{2-}$

    4) $\left[H\text{-}\ddot{O}\text{-}\ddot{P}\text{-}\ddot{O}: \atop \|\ \ \ :\ddot{O}: \right]^{2-}$ 5) $\left[H\text{-}\ddot{O}\text{-}P\text{-}\ddot{O}\text{-}\ddot{O}: \right]^{2-}$

4. The Lewis structure for As_2H_4 is:

    1) $\begin{matrix} H\text{-}As\text{=}As\text{-}H \\ |\ \ \ \ \ | \\ H\ \ \ H \end{matrix}$ 2) $\begin{matrix} H \\ | \\ H\text{-}\ddot{A}s\text{-}\ddot{A}s\text{-}H \\ | \\ H \end{matrix}$ 3) $\begin{matrix} H\text{-}As\text{-}As\text{-}H \\ |\ \ \ \ \ | \\ H\ \ \ H \end{matrix}$

    4) $H\text{-}\ddot{A}s\text{-}H\text{-}H\text{-}\ddot{A}s\text{-}H$ 5) $\begin{matrix} H\text{-}\ddot{A}s\text{-}\ddot{A}s\text{-}H \\ |\ \ \ \ \ | \\ H\ \ \ H \end{matrix}$

5. The Lewis structure for $TeCl_4$ is:

    1) $\begin{matrix} :\ddot{C}l \\ \ \ \ \ \diagdown \\ :\ddot{C}l\text{/}\ Te\text{=}\ddot{C}l: \\ | \\ :\ddot{C}l: \end{matrix}$ 2) $\begin{matrix} :\ddot{C}l: \\ | \\ :\ddot{C}l\text{—}Te\text{—}\ddot{C}l: \\ | \\ :\ddot{C}l: \end{matrix}$ 3) $\begin{matrix} :\ddot{C}l \\ \ \ \ \ \diagdown \\ :\ddot{C}l\text{/}\ Te\text{—}\ddot{C}l: \\ | \\ :\ddot{C}l: \end{matrix}$

    4) $\begin{matrix} :\ddot{C}l: \\ | \\ :\ddot{C}l\text{=}Te\text{=}\ddot{C}l: \\ | \\ :\ddot{C}l: \end{matrix}$ 5) $\begin{matrix} :\ddot{C}l\diagdown\ \ \ \diagup\ddot{C}l: \\ Te \\ :\ddot{C}l\diagup\ \ \ \diagdown\ddot{C}l: \end{matrix}$

6. The Lewis structure for SiH_2Cl_2 is:

    1) $\begin{matrix} H\text{-}\ddot{S}i\text{—}\ddot{C}l\text{—}\ddot{C}l: \\ | \\ H \end{matrix}$ 2) $\begin{matrix} :\ddot{C}l \\ \ \ \ \ \diagdown \\ :\ddot{C}l\text{/}\ \ddot{S}i\text{—}H \\ | \\ H \end{matrix}$ 3) $\begin{matrix} H \\ | \\ :\ddot{C}l\text{=}Si\text{=}\ddot{C}l: \\ | \\ H \end{matrix}$

    4) $\begin{matrix} H \\ | \\ :\ddot{C}l\text{—}Si\text{—}\ddot{C}l: \\ | \\ H \end{matrix}$ 5) $H\text{—}\ddot{C}l\text{—}Si\text{—}\ddot{C}l\text{—}H$

7. In the molecule XeF_2, how many lone pairs are around the central element?
    1) 0   2) 1   3) 2   4) 3   5) 4

8. In the molecule SO_2, how many lone pairs are around the central element?
    1) 0   2) 1   3) 2   4) 3   5) 4

9. How many <u>total</u> bonding electron pairs (BP) and lone electron pairs (LP) are in NOCl?
    1) BP = 2, LP = 1   2) BP = 2, LP = 5   3) BP = 3, LP = 6
    4) BP = 4, LP = 4   5) BP = 5, LP = 4

10. Which of the following molecules violate the octet rule?
                    a. OF_2 b. PBr_5 c. BeI_2

    1) only b   2) only c   3) only a & c   4) only b & c   5) a, b, & c

11. Which of the following molecules contain three bonding electron pairs and no lone pairs around the central element?
                    a. H_3O^+ b. BF_3 c. CH_2O

    1) only a   2) only b   3) only b & c   4) only a & b   5) a, b, & c

12. Which of the following molecules contain at least one multiple bond?
                    a. CO   b. C_2H_6 c. CCl_4

    1) only a   2) only b   3) only b & c   4) only a & b   5) a, b, & c

13. Which of the following molecules contain only one lone electron pair around the central element?
                    a. SO_2 b. NH_3 c. ICl_4^+

    1) only a   2) only b   3) only b & c   4) only a & b   5) a, b, & c

Draw the Lewis Structure for H_2CO_3, then anwer questions 14 - 17
14. How many <u>total</u> bonding electron pairs are in H_2CO_3?
    1) 2   2) 3   3) 4   4) 5   5) 6

15. How many <u>total</u> nonbonding (lone) electron pairs are in H_2CO_3?
    1) 2   2) 3   3) 4   4) 5   5) 6

16. How many <u>total</u> nonbonding (lone) electrons are in H_2CO_3?
    1) 4   2) 6   3) 8   4) 10   5) 12

17. What is the formal charge on C in H_2CO_3?
    1) 0   2) +1   3) +2   4) -2   5) +4

18. What is the formal charge on N in NH_2^{1-} ?
    1) 0   2) +1   3) +2   4) -1   5) +5

19. Which of the following have three equivalent major resonance contributors?
                    a. SO_3 b. PBr_3 c. CO_3^{2-}

    1) only b   2) only c   3) only b & c   4) only a & c   5) a, b, & c

20. Which of the following choices constitute resonance structures (including minor contributors)?

    1) a ⟷ b   2) a ⟷ c   3) b ⟷ c
    4) none of the above   5) all of the above

MODULE 11 - ANSWERS

1. a) Cs^+ b) Sr^{2+} c) $:\ddot{C}:^{4-}$ d) $:\ddot{As}:^{3-}$ e) $:\ddot{Te}:^{2-}$ f) $:\ddot{I}:^-$

2. a) $(Li^+)\ (:\ddot{F}:^-)$ b) $(K^+)_2\ (:\ddot{S}:^{2-})$ c) $(Al^{3+})\ (:\ddot{N}:^{3-})$ d) $(Al^{3+})_4(:\ddot{C}:^{4-})_3$ e) $(Ga^{3+})\ (:\ddot{Cl}:^-)_3$

3. a) $\left[:\ddot{O}-\ddot{Cl}\rightarrow\ddot{O}:\right]^-$

    b) $\left[\begin{array}{c}:\ddot{O}-\ddot{Cl}\rightarrow\ddot{O}:\\ \downarrow\\ :\ddot{O}:\end{array}\right]^-$

    c) $\left[\begin{array}{c}:\ddot{O}-\ddot{S}-\ddot{O}:\\ \downarrow\\ :\ddot{O}:\end{array}\right]^{2-}$

    d) $H-\ddot{As}-H$ with H below

    e) $:\ddot{F}-B-\ddot{F}:$ with $:\ddot{F}:$ below

    f) $\left[\begin{array}{c}:\ddot{O}-N=\ddot{O}:\\ \downarrow\\ :\ddot{O}:\end{array}\right]^-$

    g) $H-\underset{\overset{\|}{:\ddot{O}:}}{C}-H$

    h) $H-\overset{H}{\underset{H}{Si}}-H$

    i) $:\ddot{F}-\ddot{Br}\big\langle\begin{array}{c}:\ddot{F}:\\ :\ddot{F}:\end{array}$

    j) $:\ddot{O}\leftarrow Se=\ddot{O}:$ with $:\ddot{O}:$ below

    k) $\left[:\ddot{O}\leftarrow\overset{\overset{:\ddot{O}:}{|}}{Br}\rightarrow\ddot{O}:\right]^-$ with $:\ddot{O}:$ below

    l) Se surrounded by six $:\ddot{Cl}:$

    m) $:\ddot{F}-As\big\langle$ with F's around

    n) I surrounded by six $:\ddot{F}:$

    o) $\left[\overset{:\ddot{F}:}{\underset{:\ddot{F}:}{I}}\big\langle\begin{array}{c}:\ddot{F}:\\ :\ddot{F}:\end{array}\right]^-$

    p) $:\ddot{F}-\overset{..}{Xe}-\ddot{F}:$

    q) $\left[\overset{:\ddot{F}:}{\underset{:\ddot{F}:}{I}}\big\langle\begin{array}{c}:\ddot{F}:\\ :\ddot{F}:\end{array}\right]^+$

    r) Xe with $:\ddot{O}:$ above (↑) and four $:\ddot{F}:$ around

    s) $H-\overset{..}{\underset{H}{N}}-\overset{..}{\underset{H}{N}}-H$

    t) $H-C\equiv C-H$

    u) $H-\ddot{O}-\overset{\overset{:\ddot{O}:}{\uparrow}}{\underset{:\ddot{O}-H}{P}}-\ddot{O}-H$

4. a) LP = 2, BP = 3   b) LP = 9, BP = 3   c) LP = 6, BP = 3   d) LP = 1, BP = 3
    e) LP = 2, BP = 2   f) LP = 15, BP = 5   g) LP = 13, BP = 4   h) LP = 9, BP = 2

5. a) $\left[:N\overset{0}{\equiv}\overset{+1}{N}-\overset{-2}{\ddot{N}}:\right]^-$

    b) $\left[:\overset{0}{\ddot{O}}=\overset{+1}{N}=\overset{0}{\ddot{O}}:\right]^+$

    c) $:\overset{0}{\ddot{O}}=\overset{0}{C}=\overset{0}{\ddot{O}}:$

    d) $:\overset{-1}{\ddot{O}}-\overset{+1}{\ddot{S}}=\overset{0}{\ddot{O}}:$

6. a) yes   b) yes   c) no, same structure   d) no, octet violated by 2nd structure
    e) yes   f) yes   g) yes   h) no, Be can't have more than 4 e⁻

7. b

8. a) 1st structure-minor, 2nd structure-major [FC's are lower]
    e) 1st structure-major, 2nd structure-minor [C does not have an octet]
    f) 1st structure-major, 2nd structure-minor [C does not have an octet; O doesn't have the most negative FC (FC on C = 0 and FC on O = 0)--one can argue that this is really not a viable resonance contributor]
    g) 1st structure-major, 2nd structure-minor [2nd C does not have an octet]

9. a) yes, 3   b) no   c) no   d) no   e) no

MODULE 12.   *Valence Shell Electron Pair Repulsion Theory and Valence Bond Theory*

I.   **Valence Shell Electron Pair Repulsion Theory (VSEPR Theory)**

Useful in determining molecular geometries.

Assumptions:

      a) Each valence shell electron pair around the central atom is significant.

      b) Repulsions among valence shell electron pairs determine the shape of the molecule.

It thus follows that valence shell electron pairs around the central atom are arranged so that repulsions among them are as small as possible. (Order of Repulsion: LP/LP >> LP/BP > BP/BP)

Guidelines to Predicting Molecular Geometries & Bond Angles:

1. Write the Lewis Structure.
2. Count the number of bonding pairs and lone pairs around the central atom. Treat a double/triple bond as one bonding pair .
3. Use Table 1 to predict geometry.
4. When lone pairs are present, bond angles are slightly less than those given (except, linear = 180° & square planar = 90°).   When only 2 atoms are present, it is inappropriate to speak of bond angles.

Example Problem: Predict the Shape & Bond Angles for the following compounds:

          a) CO_2 b) AlH_3 c) HCl d) NH_2^- e) IF_4^+ f) IF_4^-

a)   :Ö=C=Ö: Shape: Linear - because around the central element the total number of BP + LP = 2 (2 BP & 0 LP).

Bond angle ($\angle$ OCO): 180°

b) 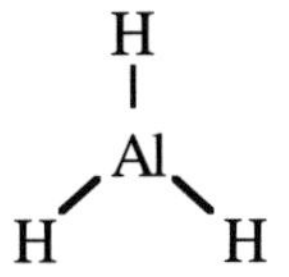   Shape: Trigonal Planar - because around the central element the total number of BP + LP = 3 (3 BP & 0 LP).

Bond Angle ($\angle$ HAlH): 120°

c)   H-C̈l: Shape: Linear - any time there are just two atoms the shape is always linear.

Since there are only 2 atoms, one can not really speak of a bond angle.

d) 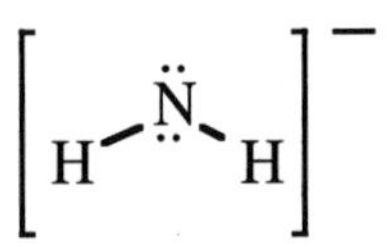   Shape: V-shaped - because around the central element the total number of BP + LP = 4 (2 BP & 2 LP).

Bond Angle ($\angle$ HNH): less than 109.5° due to the presence of lone pairs of electrons.

e) 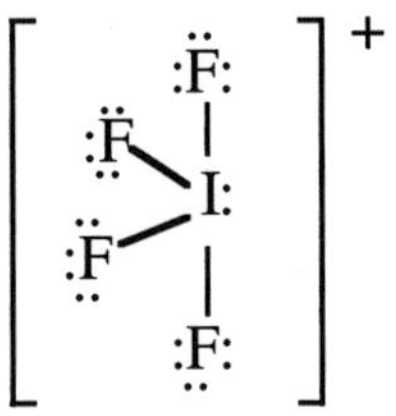   Shape: see-saw - because around the central element the total number of BP + LP = 5 (4 BP & 1 LP).

Bond Angle ($\angle$ FIF): less than 90° (axial to equatorial), less than 120° (equatorial to equatorial), & less than 180° (axial to axial) due to the presence of the lone pair of electrons.

f) 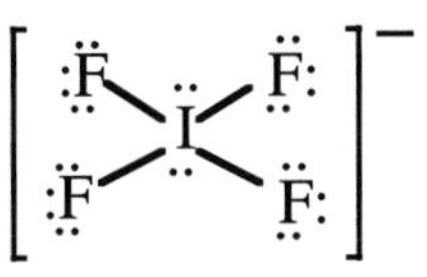   Shape: Square planar - because around the central element the total number of BP + LP = 6 (4 BP & 2 LP).

Bond Angle ($\angle$ FIF): 90° & 180° (effect of lone pairs, which are opposite each other, cancel out.)

Table 1 - VSEPR & VB Theory - Molecular Geometries

BP + LP	0 LP's	1 LP	2 LP's	3 LP's	VB Theory Hybrid Orbitals
2	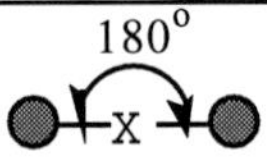 $180°$ linear CO_2, $BeCl_2$				 sp linear
3	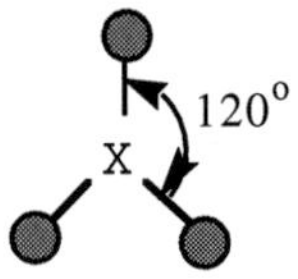 $120°$ trigonal planar BF_3, CO_3^{2-}	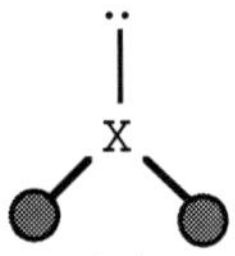 V-shaped or bent SO_2, NOCl			 sp^2 trigonal planar
4	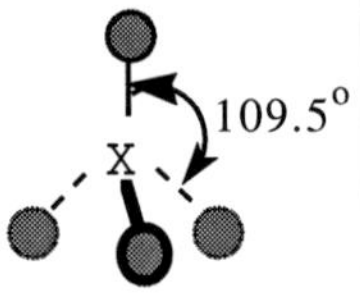 $109.5°$ tetrahedral CH_4, NH_4^+	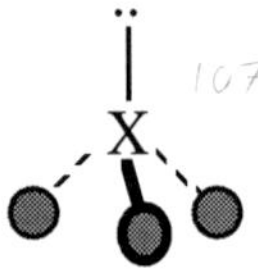 trigonal pyramidal NH_3, H_3O^+	 V-shaped or bent H_2O, NH_2^-		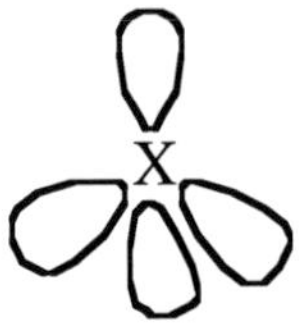 sp^3 tetrahedral
5	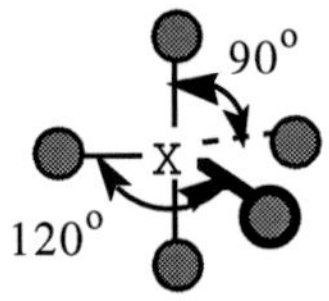 $90°$ $120°$ trigonal bipyramid PCl_5, AsF_5	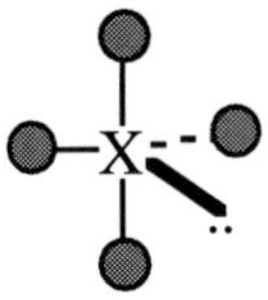 see-saw or distorted tetrahedron SF_4, IF_4^+	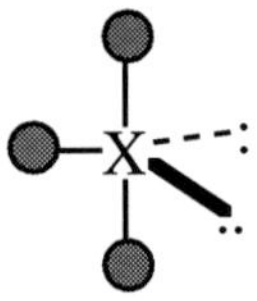 T-shaped ICl_3, BrF_3	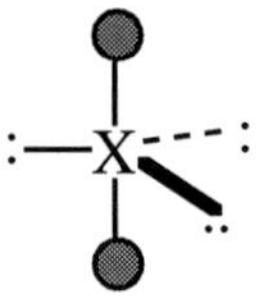 linear XeF_2, ICl_2^-	 sp^3d (or dsp^3) trigonal bipyramid
6	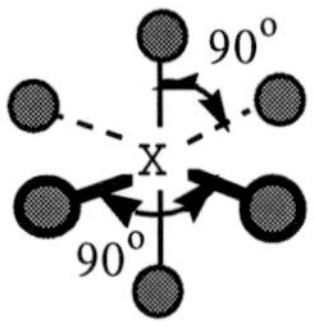 $90°$ $90°$ octahedral SF_6, PCl_6^-	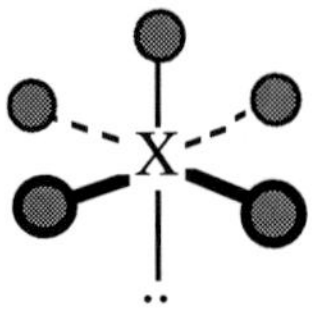 square pyramidal $XeOF_4$, ICl_5	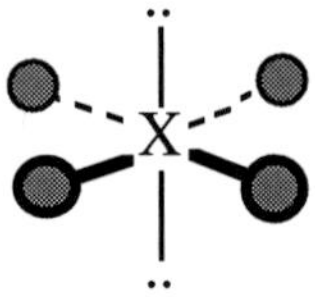 square planar XeF_4, ICl_4^-		 sp^3d^2 (or d^2sp^3) octahedral

LP = lone pair, BP = bonding pair

tetrahedral = tetrahedron

octahedral = octadehdron

For BP + LP = 5 --->   positions in triangular plane are called *equatorial*; those above and below the triangular plane are called *axial*

II. **Valence Bond Theory (VB Theory)**

Assumptions:

Covalent bonds are formed when atomic orbitals on different atoms overlap and electrons are shared.

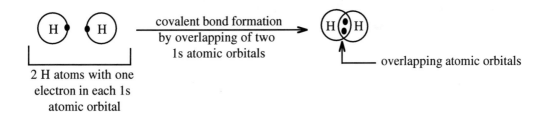

2 H atoms with one
electron in each 1s
atomic orbital

covalent bond formation
by overlapping of two
1s atomic orbitals

overlapping atomic orbitals

Each lone pair occupies a separate orbital.

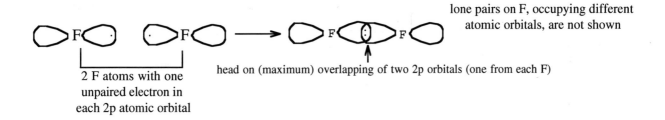

2 F atoms with one
unpaired electron in
each 2p atomic orbital

head on (maximum) overlapping of two 2p orbitals (one from each F)

lone pairs on F, occupying different
atomic orbitals, are not shown

To provide the necessary atomic orbitals to explain the experimentally observed geometry, it is usually necessary to invoke the concept of hybridization.

✳ *Hybridization -*   Mixing of a set of valence atomic orbitals to form a new set of atomic orbitals with the same total number of electron capacity and with properties and energies intermediate between those of the original unhybridized orbitals. Hybridization allows the central element to have orbitals that can overlap more effectively (and thus form a stronger bond) with its surronding atoms.

A. *Valence Bond Picture of AB₂ Molecules with no unshared electrons on A*
    Linear Molecules

Example: $BeCl_2$

Electronic Configuration - Be: [He] $\underset{2s}{\uparrow\downarrow}$ $\underset{2p}{-\ -\ -}$

Electronic Configuration - Cl: [Ne] $\underset{3s}{\uparrow\downarrow}$ $\underset{3p}{\uparrow\downarrow\ \uparrow\downarrow\ \uparrow}$

The Be atom must make available two orbitals (with one e⁻ in each orbital) one for each bonding Cl electron (the unpaired e⁻ in the 3p orbital). The Be atom must then promote one of the paired e⁻ in the 2s orbital to one of the 2p orbitals (the next highest energy orbital).

Electronic Configuration - Be: [He] $\underset{2s}{\uparrow\downarrow}$ $\underset{2p}{-\ -\ -}$ $\xrightarrow{\text{promotion}}$ [He] $\underset{2s}{\uparrow}$ $\underset{2p}{\uparrow\ \ -}$

As a result there would be two Be orbitals available for bonding. However, the 2s and 2p orbitals cannot effectively and equally overlap with the 3p orbital of Cl.

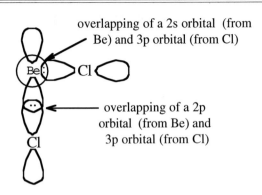

overlapping of a 2s orbital (from Be) and 3p orbital (from Cl)

Ineffective and unequal
overlapping of atomic orbitals

overlapping of a 2p
orbital (from Be) and
3p orbital (from Cl)

Experimental observations show that both Be-Cl bonds are equivalent in bond length and bond strength. Therefore simple promotion of an electron is not the only explanation. *Hybridization* of the 2s & one of the 2p orbitals on Be must occur. This hybridization forms *two* new orbitals called an *sp hybrid* - one electron is occupying each hybrid orbital (Hund's Rule).

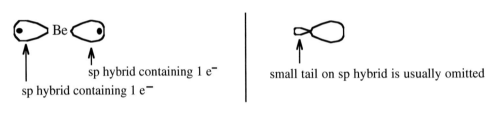

Now each Cl atom having a 3p orbital with one electron in it, can overlap with each of the sp hybrid orbitals of Be. As in VSEPR theory, hybrid orbitals are arranged so that repulsions among them are as small as possible. The Be and two Cl nuclei lie on a straight line - this is consistent with the experimental observations that the molecule is linear.

lone pairs on Cl are not shown

overlapping of an sp hybrid orbital (on Be) with a 3p atomic orbital (on Cl)

B. *Valence Bond Picture of AB₃ Molecules with no unshared electrons on A*
Trigonal Planar Molecules

Example: AlH_3

Electronic Configuration -   Al: [Ne] $\underset{3s}{\uparrow\downarrow}$ $\underset{3p}{\uparrow}$ $-$ 3 H: $\underset{1s}{\uparrow}$

3 hybrid orbitals (one e⁻ in each orbital) on Al are needed to be able to overlap with each of the three 1s atomic orbitals on H (one e⁻ in each orbital).

$$[Ne] \underset{3s}{\uparrow\downarrow} \quad \underset{3p}{\uparrow} \quad - \quad \xrightarrow[\text{\& hybridization}]{\text{promotion}} \quad [Ne] \underset{sp^2}{\uparrow \;\; \uparrow \;\; \uparrow} \quad \underset{3p}{\quad}$$

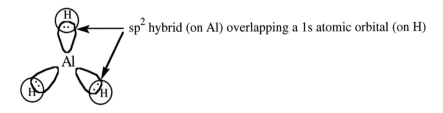

sp² hybrid (on Al) overlapping a 1s atomic orbital (on H)

C. *Valence Bond Picture of AB₄ Molecules with no unshared electrons on A*
Tetrahedral Molecules

Example: CH₄

Electronic Configuration - C: [He] $\underset{2s}{↑↓}$ $\underset{2p}{↑ \quad ↑}$ —   4 H: $\underset{1s}{↑}$

4 hybrid orbitals (one e⁻ in each orbital) on C are needed to be able to overlap with each of the four 1s atomic orbitals on H (one e⁻ in each orbital).

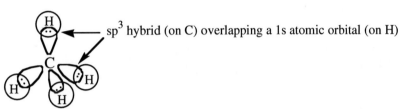

[He] $\underset{2s}{↑↓}$ $\underset{2p}{↑ \quad ↑}$ — $\xrightarrow[\text{& hybridization}]{\text{promotion}}$ [He] $\underset{sp^3}{↑ \ ↑ \ ↑ \ ↑}$

sp³ hybrid (on C) overlapping a 1s atomic orbital (on H)

D. *Valence Bond Picture of AB₃ Molecules with one unshared pair of electrons on A*
Trigonal Pyramidal Molecules

Example: NH₃

Electronic Configuration - N: [He] $\underset{2s}{↑↓}$ $\underset{2p}{↑ \ ↑ \ ↑}$ 3 H: $\underset{1s}{↑}$

Three orbitals with one e⁻ in each is already available, so only hybridization of the one-2s and the three-2p orbitals (to form four-sp³ hybrids) is necessary. Hybridization is necessary in order to account for experimental observations. Note that all valence orbitals (on the central element), whether they have one or two electrons, must be hybridized.

[He] $\underset{2s}{↑↓}$ $\underset{2p}{↑ \ ↑ \ ↑}$ $\xrightarrow{\text{hybridization}}$ [He] $\underset{sp^3}{↑↓ \ ↑ \ ↑ \ ↑}$

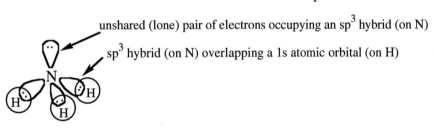

unshared (lone) pair of electrons occupying an sp³ hybrid (on N)

sp³ hybrid (on N) overlapping a 1s atomic orbital (on H)

E. *Valence Bond Picture of AB₅ Molecules with no unshared pair of electrons on A*
Trigonal Bipyramidal Molecules

Example: PH₅

Electronic Configuration - P: [Ne] $\underset{3s}{↑↓}$ $\underset{3p}{↑ \ ↑ \ ↑}$ $\underset{3d}{— \ — \ — \ — \ —}$ 5 H: $\underset{1s}{↑}$

5 hybrid orbitals (one e⁻ in each orbital) on P are needed to be able to overlap with each of the five 1s atomic orbital on H (one e⁻ in each orbital).

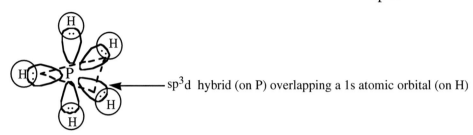

[Ne] $\underset{3s}{\uparrow\downarrow}$ $\underset{}{\uparrow}$ $\underset{}{\uparrow}$ $\underset{3p}{\uparrow}$ $— —$ $\underset{3d}{—}$ $— —$ $\xrightarrow[\text{hybridization}]{\text{promotion \&}}$ [Ne] $\underset{}{\uparrow}$ $\underset{}{\uparrow}$ $\underset{}{\uparrow}$ $\underset{sp^3d}{\uparrow\uparrow}$ $— \underset{}{—} \underset{3d}{—} —$

sp^3d hybrid (on P) overlapping a 1s atomic orbital (on H)

F. *Valence Bond Picture of AB_6 Molecules with no unshared pair of electrons on A*
Octahedral Molecules

Example: SH_6

Electronic Configuration - S: [Ne] $\underset{3s}{\uparrow\downarrow}$ $\underset{}{\uparrow\downarrow}$ $\underset{}{\uparrow}$ $\underset{3p}{\uparrow}$ $— —$ $\underset{3d}{—}$ $— —$ 6 H: $\underset{1s}{\uparrow}$

6 hybrid orbitals (one e⁻ in each orbital) on S are needed to be able to overlap with each of the six-1s atomic orbital on H (one e⁻ in each orbital).

[Ne] $\underset{3s}{\uparrow\downarrow}$ $\underset{}{\uparrow\downarrow}$ $\underset{}{\uparrow}$ $\underset{3p}{\uparrow}$ $— —$ $\underset{3d}{—}$ $— —$ $\xrightarrow[\text{hybridization}]{\text{promotion \&}}$ [Ne] $\underset{}{\uparrow}$ $\underset{}{\uparrow}$ $\underset{}{\uparrow}$ $\underset{}{\uparrow}$ $\underset{sp^3d^2}{\uparrow\uparrow}$ $— \underset{}{—} \underset{3d}{—} —$

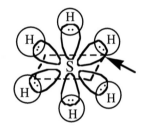

sp^3d^2 hybrid (on S) overlapping a 1s atomic orbital (on H

G. *Valence Bond Picture of Compounds Containing Double Bonds*

Example: C_2H_4

Electronic Configuration - C: [He] $\underset{2s}{\uparrow\downarrow}$ $\underset{}{\uparrow}$ $\underset{2p}{\uparrow}$ $—$ H: $\underset{1s}{\uparrow}$

Incomplete (Skeletal) Structure

H⟍   ⟋H
  ⟍C₁—C₂⟍
H⟋   ⟍H

What is needed, are 3 hybrid orbitals (on each C) with one electron in each orbital to be able to overlap with: a) each of the two-1s atomic orbitals on H (one e⁻ in each orbital), and b) one-hybrid (containing one e⁻) on the other carbon.

C_1 [He] $\underset{2s}{\uparrow\downarrow}$ $\underset{}{\uparrow}$ $\underset{2p}{\uparrow}$ $—$ $\xrightarrow[\text{\& hybridization}]{\text{promotion}}$ [He] $\underset{}{\uparrow}$ $\underset{}{\uparrow}$ $\underset{sp^2}{\uparrow}$ $\underset{2p_z}{\uparrow}$

C_2 [He] $\underset{2s}{\uparrow\downarrow}$ $\underset{}{\uparrow}$ $\underset{2p}{\uparrow}$ $—$ $\xrightarrow[\text{\& hybridization}]{\text{promotion}}$ [He] $\underset{}{\uparrow}$ $\underset{}{\uparrow}$ $\underset{sp^2}{\uparrow}$ $\underset{2p_z}{\uparrow}$

The two unhybridized $2p_z$ orbitals (one on each C) form another bond by overlapping sideways, this type of bond is called a pi-bond.

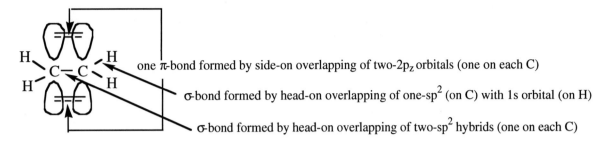

one π-bond formed by side-on overlapping of two-$2p_z$ orbitals (one on each C)

σ-bond formed by head-on overlapping of one-sp^2 (on C) with 1s orbital (on H)

σ-bond formed by head-on overlapping of two-sp^2 hybrids (one on each C)

Double bonds are made up of: one sigma (σ) & one pi (π) bond. The π-bond is ⊥ to the σ-bond.

sigma (σ) bond - A bond resulting from the head-on overlap of atomic orbitals, in which the region of electron sharing is along a cylindrically symmetrical imaginary line connecting the bonded atoms.

pi (π) bond - A bond resulting from the side-on overlap of atomic orbitals, in which the region of electron sharing are on opposite sides of the imaginary line connecting the bonded atoms and parallel to this line. *π–bonds are weaker than σ–bonds.*

H. *Valence Bond Picture of Compounds Containing Triple Bonds*

Example: C_2H_2

Electronic Configuration -   C: [He] $\underset{2s}{\uparrow\downarrow}$ $\underset{2p}{\uparrow\ \ \uparrow\ \ -}$ H: $\underset{1s}{\uparrow}$

Incomplete (Skeletal) Structure

H— C₁—C₂—H   What is needed, are 2 hybrid orbitals (on each C) with one electron in each orbital to be able to overlap with: a) the 1s atomic orbitals on H (one e⁻ in the orbital), and b) one-hybrid (containing one e⁻) on the other carbon.

C_1 [He] $\underset{2s}{\uparrow\downarrow}$ $\underset{2p}{\uparrow\ \ \uparrow\ \ -}$ $\xrightarrow[\text{\& hybridization}]{\text{promotion}}$ [He] $\underset{sp}{\uparrow\ \ \uparrow}$ $\underset{2p_y\ \ 2p_z}{\uparrow\ \ \ \ \uparrow}$

C_2 [He] $\underset{2s}{\uparrow\downarrow}$ $\underset{2p}{\uparrow\ \ \uparrow\ \ -}$ $\xrightarrow[\text{\& hybridization}]{\text{promotion}}$ [He] $\underset{sp}{\uparrow\ \ \uparrow}$ $\underset{2p_y\ \ 2p_z}{\uparrow\ \ \ \ \uparrow}$

The two unhybridized $2p_z$ orbitals (one on each C) form a pi-bond by overlapping sideways and the two unhybridized $2p_y$ orbitals (one on each C) form another pi-bond by overlapping sideways.

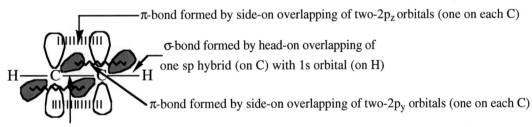

π-bond formed by side-on overlapping of two-$2p_z$ orbitals (one on each C)

σ-bond formed by head-on overlapping of one sp hybrid (on C) with 1s orbital (on H)

π-bond formed by side-on overlapping of two-$2p_y$ orbitals (one on each C)

σ-bond formed by head-on overlapping of two-sp hybrid orbitals (one on each C)

Triple bonds are made up of: two π-bonds and one σ-bond. The two π-bonds are perpendicular to each other and also perpendicular to the σ-bond.

Bond strength: triple > double > single

III. Hybridization on Carbon

There are more than three million known organic compounds (compounds containing carbon) vs. about 300,000 inorganic compounds (compounds containing atoms other than carbon).   Organic compounds are so special because carbon atoms form stable bonds with other carbon atoms as well as bonds to hydrogen, oxygen, nitrogen, and halogens.   Depending on the number of bonding pairs (under normal circumstances, carbon has no lone pairs) the hybridization and molecular geometry around carbon is as follows:

BP around C	Hybridization	Geometry (Shape)
4	sp^3	tetrahedral
3	sp^2	trigonal planar
2	sp	linear

The hybridization on each of the following carbons is as follows (subscripts are used strictly for the purpose of identification).

$$H_2C_1=C_2=C_3H-C_4H_2-C_5\equiv C_6-H \qquad \text{Molecule X}$$

C_1 (3 BP) -> sp^2; C_2 (2 BP) -> sp; C_3 (3 BP) -> sp^2;

C_4 (4 BP) -> sp^3; C_5 (2 BP) -> sp; C_6 (2 BP) -> sp

Example Problems: (Refer to Molecule X above):

1. What two carbon atoms have the strongest bond?

    Triple bonds are the strongest --> The bond between C_5 & C_6 is the strongest.

2. Which carbon atoms are linear?

    Those carbons having only 2 BP are linear --> C_2, C_5 & C_6 are linear.

3. How many sigma and pi bonds are there in Molecule X?

    All single bonds are sigma bonds. Double bonds are made up of 1 sigma and 1 pi bond. Triple bonds are made up of 1 sigma and two pi bonds ---> Molecule X has 4 pi bonds and 11 sigma bonds.

4. What is the molecular geometry of each carbon?

    C_2, C_5, and C_6 are linear (2 BP + 0 LP)

    C_1 and C_3 are trigonal planar (3 BP + 0 LP)

    C_4 is tetrahedral (4 BP + 0 LP)

5. What is the bond angle $\angle C_2C_3C_4$?

    Since C_3 has 3 BP + 0 LP the $C_2C_3C_4$ bond angle is ~120°

6. The bond between C_4 and C_5, is made up by the overlapping of what kind of orbitals?

    The hybrid orbitals on C_4 are sp^3 hybrids while those on C_5 are sp hybrids. Therefore, the bond between C_4 & C_5 is made up by the head-on overlapping of an sp^3 hybrid on C_4 with an sp hybrid on C_5.

7. The bond between C_1 and H, is made up by the overlapping of what kind of orbitals?

    The hybrid orbitals on C_1 are sp^2 hybrids while H has a 1s atomic orbital. Therefore, the bond between C_1 & H is made up by the head-on overlapping of an sp^2 hybrid on C_1 with 1s atomic orbital on H.

IV. Molecular Polarity

Even though a bond may be polar, the molecule as a whole can be non-polar (have no permanent dipole moment) if it is symmetrical. Draw the Lewis structure of the molecule and see if it is symmetrical.

The following will be considered as symmetrical:

a) molecules having the same atoms bonded to the central element without any lone pairs being present around the central element,

b) molecules in which the central element contains 2 identical BP and 3 LP (sp^3d - linear), or

c) molecules in which the central element contains 4 identical BP and 2 LP (sp^3d^2 - square planar).

[Other molecules are symmetrical but you will not be held accountable for them.]

Example Problems:

1. Indicate whether each of the following molecules - $BeCl_2$, $BeClF$, BF_3, NH_3, and XeF_4 - are polar or non- polar.

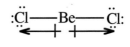

The two bond dipoles are identical in magnitude and opposite in direction; therefore, they cancel each other out and the result is a non-polar molecule having no permanent dipole moment.

Even though Be has no lone pairs, the surrounding atoms are not the same; therefore, this molecule is polar.

The three bond dipoles are identical in magnitude and opposite in direction; therefore, they cancel each other out and the result is a non-polar molecule having no permanent dipole moment.

The molecule is polar because of the presence of a lone pair of electrons on the central element.

Even though this molecule contains lone pairs of electrons they are opposite each other and their effect cancels out, the 4 bond dipoles (Xe-F) are identical in magnitude but opposite in direction their effect also cancels out. This square planar molecule with 4 identical bonding pairs is therefore non-polar and has no permanent dipole moment.

2. Indicate whether the following: XeF_4, ICl_3, $SiCl_4$, SeO_2, $SiBr_4$, SF_4, $CHCl_3$, ICl_2^-, have a permanent dipole moment or not.

XeF_4 (square planar), $SiCl_4$ (tetrahedral), $SiBr_4$ (tetrahedral), and ICl_2^- (sp^3d - linear) have no permanent dipole moments

ICl_3 (T-shaped), SeO_2 (sp^2 - V-shaped), SF_4 (see saw), $CHCl_3$ (tetrahedral) have permanent dipole moments

3. Which of the following: S=C=O, S=C=S, Se=C=O, or S=C=Se, has the largest dipole moment? [Lone pairs on the surrounding atoms have been omitted.]

For these linear molecules, the molecule with the largest dipole moment is Se=C=O, on one side there is the more electronegative atom (O) and on the other side there is the less electronegative atom (Se).

EXERCISES

VSEPR Theory

1. Predict the Shape (Molecular/Ionic Geometry) and Bond Angles for each of the following:
    a) $SiSe_2$ b) $AlCl_3$ c) $AsSeBr$ d) $CHCl_3$ e) PCl_3 f) ClO_2^- g) IBr_5
    h) $SeBr_6$ i) $TeCl_4$ j) ICl_4^- k) $AsCl_4^+$ l) BrO_3^- m) XeO_3

2. Which of the following species are V-shaped?   a) $SiSe_2$ b) H_2Se c) $AsSeBr$ d) SeS_2

3. Which of the molecules in question 2 have only one lone pair around the central element ?

4. Are any compounds in which oxygen is the central element capable of having trigonal bipyramidal or octahedral electronic geometries (i.e., geometries that take into account both LP & BP)? EXPLAIN.

5. Which of the following geometries is preferred when the central element has 4 BP + 1LP? EXPLAIN.

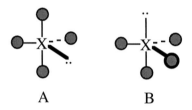

A   B

VB Theory

6. When one-s orbital and two-p orbitals are hybridized, a) what is that hybrid called, b) how many hybrid orbitals form, c) what is the shape of the hybrid orbitals, and d) what is the bond angle between the hybrids?

7. Show the promotion (if needed) and hybridization process occuring at the central element for each of the following: a) H_2Se b) ICl_3 c) XeF_4 d) SF_4 e) AsF_5 f) XeF_2

8. What is the hybridization around the central element in each of the species in question 1?

9. Which of the molecules in question 2 are sp^2 hybridized?

10. For each of the following compounds that contain only P-halogen bonds, what orbitals are overlapping in the formation of one of the covalent bonds?   a) PCl_3 b) PF_5 c) PI_6^-

Hybridization on Carbon

11. Refer to Molecule Y when answering this question:

$$H-\overset{\overset{\textstyle H}{|}}{\underset{\underset{\textstyle H}{|}}{C_1}}-\overset{\overset{\textstyle H}{|}}{C_2}=\overset{\overset{\textstyle :O:}{||}}{\underset{\underset{\textstyle H}{|}}{C_3}}-C_4-\overset{\overset{\textstyle H}{|}}{\underset{\underset{\textstyle H}{|}}{C_5}}-H \qquad \text{Molecule Y}$$

    a) How many sigma and pi bonds are there in Molecule Y?
    b) Which carbon(s) is/are trigonal planar?
    c) Which carbon(s) is/are tetrahedral?
    d) Which carbons are sp hybridized?
    e) Which bond is stronger, the C_1-C_2 bond or the C_2=C_3 bond?
    f) The sigma bond between C_2 & C_3, is made up by the overlapping of what kind of orbitals?
    g) What is the bond angle $\angle C_4C_5H$?

Molecular Polarity

12. Which of the molecules/ions in question 1 have no dipole moments?

13. Which of the molecules/ions in question 1 are polar?

MULTIPLE CHOICE PRACTICE EXAM FOR MODULE 12

1. Which of the following molecules are V-shaped (bent)?
   a. H_2O b. CH_4 c. SO_2
   1) only a   2) only c   3) only a and b   4) only a and c   5) none

2. What is the molecular geometry of BrF_5?
   1) trigonal bipyramidal   2) square planar   3) see-saw
   4) T-shaped   5) square pyramidal

3. The $\angle$ H-N-H in NH_3 is:
   1) 109.5°   2) less than 109.5°   3) 120°
   4) less than 120°   5) less than 90°, 120°, and 180°

4. The $\angle$ Cl-I-Cl in ICl_3 is:
   1) 109.5°   2) less than 109.5°   3) 120°
   4) less than 90° and 180°   5) less than 90°, 120°, and 180°

Consider the following molecule when answering questions 5 - 7 ----> $AlBr_3$

5. What is the shape of $AlBr_3$?
   1) trigonal planar   2) tetrahedral   3) trigonal pyramidal
   4) T-shaped   5) V-shaped

6. The hybridization around the central element in the compound $AlBr_3$ is:
   1) sp   2) sp^2 3) sp^3 4) sp^3d 5) sp^3d^2

7. The $\angle$ Br-Al-Br in $AlBr_3$ is:
   1) 109.5°   2) less than 109.5°   3) 120°
   4) less than 120°   5) less than 90°, 120°, and 180°

Consider the following molecule when answering questions 8 - 13 ----> $SeBr_4$

8. What is the molecular geometry of $SeBr_4$?
   1) tetrahedral   2) square planar   3) see-saw   4) rectangular   5) trigonal pyramidal

9. The hybridization around the central element in the compound $SeBr_4$ is:
   1) sp   2) sp^2 3) sp^3 4) sp^3d 5) sp^3d^2

10. The $\angle$ Br-Se-Br in $SeBr_4$ is:
    1) 109.5°   2) less than 109.5°   3) 120°
    4) less than 120°   5) less than 90°, 120°, and 180°

11. According to VB theory, one of the Se-Br bonds in $SeBr_4$ is formed by the overlap of what orbitals:
    1) an sp^3 hybrid on Se with a 4p atomic orbital on Br
    2) a sp^3d hybrid on Se with a 4p atomic orbital on Br
    3) an sp^3 hybrid on Se with a 4s atomic orbital on Br
    4) an sp^3 hybrid on Se with a 4p hybrid orbital on Br
    5) a sp^3d hybrid on Se with a 3p atomic orbital on Br

12. According to VB theory, how many valence atomic orbitals on selenium (in the compound $SeBr_4$) are left unhybridized (after bonding)?
    1) 1   2) 2   3) 3   4) 4   5) 5

13. Which of the following correctly depicts the promotion & hybridization process occuring in selenium in order to form the molecule $SeBr_4$? [Only the valence shell is be shown.]

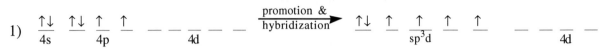

Consider the following molecule when answering questions 14 - 16 (each carbon is subscripted with a number, strictly for the purpose of identification):

$$H_{\diagdown}C_1=C_2=\overset{\overset{\textstyle H}{|}}{C_3}-C_4\equiv C_5-\overset{\overset{\textstyle H}{|}}{\underset{\underset{\textstyle H}{|}}{C_6}}-\overset{\overset{\textstyle H}{|}}{\underset{\underset{\textstyle H}{|}}{C_7}}-H \qquad \text{Molecule X}$$

14. In Molecule X, which of the following have bond angles of 120°?
   1) ∠ H-C_1-H   2) ∠ C_1-C_2-C_3 3) ∠ C_2-C_3-C_4
   4) Two of the above   5) All of the above

15. Which of the following carbons in Molecule X is sp^2 hybridized?
   1) C_1 2) C_2 3) C_3
   4) Two of the above   5) All of the above

16. The geometry around which of the following carbons in Molecule X is linear?
   1) C_1 2) C_2 3) C_3
   4) Two of the above   5) All of the above

17. Which of the following bonds (in Molecule X) is the strongest?
   1) C_1=C_2 2) C_1=C_2 3) C_3-C_4
   4) C_4≡C_5 5) C_7-H

18. Which of the following statements is correct about the formation of π-bonds?
   1) π-bonds are formed by the side ways overlapping of two-s orbitals.
   2) π-bonds are formed by the head on overlapping of two-hybrid orbitals.
   3) π-bonds are formed by the head on overlapping of two-s orbitals.
   4) π-bonds are formed by the head on overlapping of three-p orbitals.
   5) π-bonds are formed by the side ways overlapping of two-p orbitals.

19. Which of the following molecules is polar?
   1) CH_4 2) NH_3 3) CO_2
   4) Two of the above   5) None of the above

20. Which of the following molecules have no permanent dipole moment?
    1) CH_4 2) NH_3 3) CO_2
    4) Two of the above   5) None of the above

MODULE 12 - ANSWERS

1. a) linear, $\angle$ SeSiSe = 180°   b) trigonal planar, $\angle$ ClAlCl = 120°
    c) V-shaped, $\angle$ AsSeBr = <120°   d) tetrahedral, $\angle$ HCCl = 109.5°
    e) trigonal pyramidal, $\angle$ ClPCl = < 109.5°   f) V-shaped, $\angle$ OClO = <109.5°
    g) square pyramid, $\angle$ BrIBr = <90° & <180°   h) octahedral, $\angle$ BrSeBr = 90° & 180°
    i) see-saw, $\angle$ ClTeCl = <90°, <120°, & <180°   j) square planar, $\angle$ ClICl = 90° & 180°
    k) tetrahedral, $\angle$ ClAsCl = 109.5°   l) trigonal pyramidal, $\angle$ OBrO = <109.5°
    m) trigonal pyramidal, $\angle$ OXeO = <109.5°

2. b, c, & d

3. c & d

4. No because central elements having trigonal bipyramidal or octahedral electronic geometries break the octet rule. Oxygen can't break the octet rule (elements in row 2 only have s & p orbitals available --> can accomodate only 8 e⁻). Only elements in periods 3, 4, 5, 6, & 7 can have more than an octet.

5. Taking the order of repulsion into account, LP/LP >> LP/BP > BP/BP, the geometry with the fewest number of close respulsive LP/BP interactions is the preferred one. Structure A has 2 - 90° LP/BP interactions & 2 - 90° LP/BP interactions. Structure B has 3 - 90° LP/BP interactions & 1 - 180° LP/BP interactions. Structure A is preferred because it has the fewest number of close repulsive LP/BP (2 - 90° LP/BP interactions vs. 3 - 90° LP/BP interactions).

6. a) sp^2 b) 3   c) trigonal planar   d) 120°

7. a) [Ar] (4s: ↑↓)(4p: ↑↓ ↑ ↑) $\xrightarrow{\text{hybridization}}$ [Ar] (↑↓ ↑↓ ↑ ↑) sp^3

    b) [Kr] (5s: ↑↓)(5p: ↑↓ ↑↓ ↑)(5d: — — — — —) $\xrightarrow{\text{promotion \& hybridization}}$ [Kr] (↑↓ ↑↓ ↑ ↑↑) sp^3d (5d: — — — —)

    c) [Kr] (5s: ↑↓)(5p: ↑↓ ↑↓ ↑↓)(5d: — — — — —) $\xrightarrow{\text{promotion \& hybridization}}$ [Kr] (↑↓ ↑↓ ↑ ↑↑ ↑) sp^3d^2 (5d: — — —)

    d) [Ne] (3s: ↑↓)(3p: ↑↓ ↑↓ ↑)(3d: — — — — —) $\xrightarrow{\text{promotion \& hybridization}}$ [Ne] (↑↓ ↑ ↑ ↑↑) sp^3d (3d: — — — —)

    e) [Ar] (4s: ↑↓)(4p: ↑ ↑ ↑)(4d: — — — — —) $\xrightarrow{\text{promotion \& hybridization}}$ [Ar] (↑ ↑ ↑ ↑↑) sp^3d (4d: — — — —)

    f) [Kr] (5s: ↑↓)(5p: ↑↓ ↑↓ ↑↓)(5d: — — — — —) $\xrightarrow{\text{promotion \& hybridization}}$ [Kr] (↑↓ ↑↓ ↑↓ ↑ ↑) sp^3d (5d: — — —)

8. a) sp   b) sp^2 c) sp^2 d) sp^3 e) sp^3 f) sp^3 g) sp^3d^2 h) sp^3d^2 i) sp^3d j) sp^3d^2
    k) sp^3 l) sp^3 m) sp^3

9. c & d

10. a) sp^3 on P (with 1 e⁻) overlapping with one of one of the 3p orbitals on Cl (with 1 e⁻)
    b) sp^3d on P (with 1 e⁻) overlapping with one of one of the 2p orbitals on F (with 1 e⁻)
    c) sp^3d^2 on P (with 1 e⁻) overlapping with one of one of the 5p orbitals on I (with 1 e⁻)

11. a) 13 sigma bonds and 2 pi bonds   b) C_2, C_3, & C_4 c) C_1 & C_5 d) none   e) $C_2=C_3$
    f) sp^2 on C_2 (with 1 e⁻) overlapping with an sp^2 on C_3 (with 1 e⁻)   g) 109.5°

12. a, b, h, j, k

13. c, d, e, f, g, i, m, l

MODULE 13. *Molecular Orbital Theory*

I. **Molecular Orbital Theory (MO Theory)**

Postulate:

When atomic orbitals on different atoms combine molecular orbitals form, so that electrons in them belong to the molecule as a whole.

MO theory gives better descriptions of electron cloud distributions, bond energies, and magnetic properties, but it is not very easy to visualize as VB theory. MO theory does not invoke the usage of hybrid orbitals. MO theory is very mathematical and requires the use of advanced calculus.

Paramagnetism vs Diamagnetism - Predictions from VB & MO Theories

Example ----> O_2 - experiments show that O_2 is paramagnetic.

VB Theory predicts that O_2 is diamagnetic having a double bond and no unpaired electrons. It predicts sp^2 hybridization at oxygen.

Electronic Configuration - O: [He] $\frac{\uparrow\downarrow}{2s}$ $\frac{\uparrow\downarrow}{}\frac{\uparrow}{}\frac{\uparrow}{2p}$

[He] $\frac{\uparrow\downarrow}{2s}$ $\frac{\uparrow\downarrow}{}\frac{\uparrow}{}\frac{\uparrow}{2p}$ $\xrightarrow{\text{hybridization}}$ [He] $\frac{\uparrow\downarrow}{}\frac{\uparrow\downarrow}{}\frac{\uparrow}{sp^2}$ $\frac{\uparrow}{2p \text{ (used in } \pi\text{-bond)}}$

However, MO Theory predicts that O_2 is paramagnetic (with 2 unpaired electrons) - see Example Problem 3b on page 4 of this module.

Therefore, as seen in the above example and for other reasons, MO theory was developed.

When two atomic orbitals overlap they can be in phase or out of phase. Overlapping of two AO's (atomic orbitals), produces two MO's - one bonding and one antibonding.

In phase overlapping produces a *bonding molecular orbital* whose energy is lower and as a consequence more stable than the combining atomic orbitals.

Out of phase overlapping produces an *antibonding molecular orbital* whose energy is higher and as a consequence is less stable than the combining atomic orbitals. The antibonding MO's contain a nodal plane which is a region in which the probability of finding an electron is zero.

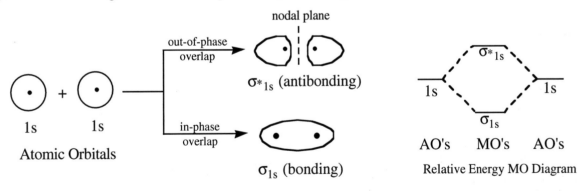

- Both MO's are designated as sigma (σ) orbitals - indicating that they are cylinderically symmetrical about the internuclear axis. All sigma orbitals have nodal planes bisecting the internuclear axis.
- Subscripts indicate the AO's that have been combined.
- The asterisk denotes an antibonding orbital.
- When filling MO's with electrons, Hund's Rule & Pauli's Exclusion Principle apply.
- Electrons in bonding MO's are more stable (lower energy) than in the individual atoms.
- Electrons in antibonding MO's are less stable (higher energy) than in the individual atoms.

- Head-on overlap of two-2p$_x$ orbitals produces two MO's -- σ_{2p_x} and $\sigma*_{2p_x}$

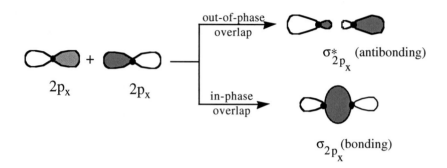

- Depending on whether all p-orbitals overlap, there can be as many as two π_p & $\pi*_p$ MO's.
- Side-on overlap of two-2p$_z$ orbitals produces two MO's -- π_{2p_z} and $\pi*_{2p_z}$
- Side-on overlap of two-2p$_y$ orbitals produces two MO's -- π_{2p_y} and $\pi*_{2p_y}$
- The two π_{2p} & $\pi*_{2p}$ MO's are perpendicular to each other.
- There is a nodal plane along the internuclear axis for all π- MO's.

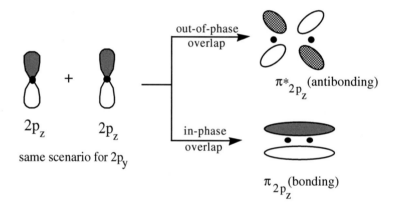

A. Bond Order (bo) and Bond Stability

$$bo = \frac{\text{bonding electrons - antibonding electrons}}{2}$$

- Usually bond order corresponds to the number of bonds described by VB theory.
  bo = 1 (single bond), bo = 2 (double bond), bo = 3 (triple bond)
- Species having an odd number of electrons have fractional bo's.
- The greater the bo, the more stable we predict the molecule to be (i.e., for stable molecules the number of electrons in bonding MO's is always greater than that in antibonding MO's).
- The greater the bo, the stronger and shorter the bond will be.

B. Homonuclear Diatomic Molecules (first & second row)

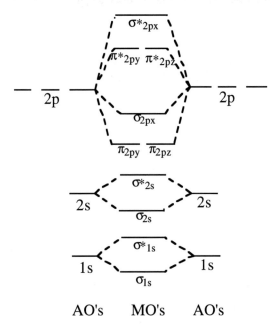

AO's   MO's   AO's

Energy Diagram H_2 - Ne_2

The diagram to your left shows the energy of MO's from H_2 to Ne_2. [NOTE: Your text may have a different energy diagram than this; however, this is the one we are going to use.]

The number of electrons in a molecular orbital is equal to the sum of all the electrons present in each individual atom in the molecule. For example, the # of electrons in the MO for B_2 is equal to 10 (each B has 5 electrons; 2 B x 5 e⁻ = 10 e⁻).

Rules for filling molecular orbitals are basically the same as those rules for filling AO's:

- An MO can hold a maximum of 2 electrons, and these electrons must have opposite spins (Pauli Exclusion Principle)

- All degenerate (i.e., same energy) MO's must be occupied by a single electron, having the same spin, before being paired (Hund's Rule).

Shorthand Energy Level Diagram Notation

σ_{1s}, $\sigma*_{1s}$, σ_{2s}, $\sigma*_{2s}$, π_{2py}, π_{2pz}, σ_{2px}, $\pi*_{2py}$, $\pi*_{2pz}$, $\sigma*_{2px}$

Example Problems:

1. Write the MO energy diagram for H_2, He_2, and He_2^+. Also, calculate the bond order for each and predict whether each is paramagnetic or diamagnetic.

a) H_2

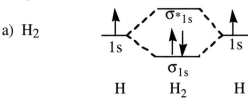

$$bo = \frac{2-0}{2} = 1$$

Diamagnetic

b) He_2

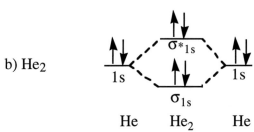

$$bo = \frac{2-2}{2} = 0$$

"Diamagnetic?" -- since He_2 is an unknown molecule (bo = 0) it is rather inappropriate to predict its magnetic properties.

c) He_2^+

$$bo = \frac{2-1}{2} = 0.5$$

Paramagnetic

2. Of H_2, He_2, and He_2^+ which: a) has the shortest bond, b) is predicted to be the least stable, c) has the weakest bond?

    a) H_2 (bo is the largest)

    b) He_2 (bo is the smallest)

    c) He_2 (bo is the smallest; actually a bo of zero implies that there is no bond at all between two He atoms).

3. Write the electronic configuration (filled shorthand notation energy diagram) for B_2, O_2, F_2^{1-} and B_2^+. Also, calculate the bond order for each specie and predict whether the specie is diamagnetic or paramagnetic.

    a) B_2 - 10 e⁻ total (5e⁻ from each B ----> 2 x 5e⁻ = 10e⁻)

$$\sigma_{1s}^2 \ \sigma^*_{1s}^2 \ \sigma_{2s}^2 \ \sigma^*_{2s}^2 \ \pi_{2p_y}^1 \ \pi_{2p_z}^1$$

Paramagnetic, $bo = \dfrac{6-4}{2} = 1$

    b) O_2 - 16 e⁻ total (8e⁻ from each O ---> 2 x 8e⁻ = 16e⁻)

$$\sigma_{1s}^2 \ \sigma^*_{1s}^2 \ \sigma_{2s}^2 \ \sigma^*_{2s}^2 \ \pi_{2p_y}^2 \ \pi_{2p_z}^2 \ \sigma_{2p_x}^2 \ \pi^*_{2p_y}^1 \ \pi^*_{2p_z}^1$$

Paramagnetic, $bo = \dfrac{10-6}{2} = 2$

    c) F_2^{1-} - 19 e⁻ total (9e⁻ from each F + 1e⁻ from the -1 charge ---> (2 x 8e⁻) + 1e⁻ = 19e⁻)

$$\sigma_{1s}^2 \ \sigma^*_{1s}^2 \ \sigma_{2s}^2 \ \sigma^*_{2s}^2 \ \pi_{2p_y}^2 \ \pi_{2p_z}^2 \ \sigma_{2p_x}^2 \ \pi^*_{2p_y}^2 \ \pi^*_{2p_z}^2 \ \sigma^*_{2p_x}^1$$

Paraamagnetic, $bo = \dfrac{10-9}{2} = 0.5$

    d) B_2^+ - 9 e⁻ total (5e⁻ from each B - 1e⁻ from the +1 charge ----> (2 x 5e⁻) - 1e⁻ = 9e⁻)

$$\sigma_{1s}^2 \ \sigma^*_{1s}^2 \ \sigma_{2s}^2 \ \sigma^*_{2s}^2 \ \pi_{2p_y}^1$$

Paramagnetic, $bo = \dfrac{5-4}{2} = 0.5$

C. Heteronuclear Diatomic Molecules (first and second row)

MO energy diagrams as those depicted for homonuclear diatomic molecules are inappropriate for hetereonuclear diatomic molecules. This is because the corresponding AO's of two different elements have different energies due to the differences in nuclear charge. In cases such as these, the AO's of the more electronegative element are lower in energy than the corresponding AO's of the less electronegative element. If the two elements are similar (e.g., CN, CO, NO) the diagram for the homonuclear diatomics can be modified by slightly skewing it.

For heteronuclear diatomics, we will only concern ourselves with the shorthand energy diagram, as well as, determining the bond order and magnetic properties for these diatomic molecules. The shorthand energy level diagram (electronic configuration) is the same for homonuclear and heteronuclear diatomic molecules.

Shorthand Energy Level Diagram Notation

σ_{1s}, σ^*_{1s}, σ_{2s}, σ^*_{2s}, π_{2p_y}, π_{2p_z}, σ_{2p_x}, $\pi^*_{2p_y}$, $\pi^*_{2p_z}$, $\sigma^*_{2p_x}$

Example Problems:

1. What is the electronic configuration (filled shorthand MO energy diagram), the bond order, and how many unpaired electrons do each of the following have: a) NO b) CN⁻ c) NO^{1+}?

a) NO - 15 e⁻ total (7e⁻ from N + 8e⁻ from O)

$$\sigma_{1s}^2 \quad \sigma*_{1s}^2 \quad \sigma_{2s}^2 \quad \sigma*_{2s}^2 \quad \pi_{2p_y}^2 \quad \pi_{2p_z}^2 \quad \sigma_{2p_x}^2 \quad \pi*_{2p_y}^1$$

$$bo = \frac{10-5}{2} = 2.5$$

one unpaired e⁻

b) CN^{1-} - 14 e⁻ total (6e⁻ from C + 7e⁻ from N + 1e⁻ from -1charge)

$$\sigma_{1s}^2 \quad \sigma*_{1s}^2 \quad \sigma_{2s}^2 \quad \sigma*_{2s}^2 \quad \pi_{2p_y}^2 \quad \pi_{2p_z}^2 \quad \sigma_{2p_x}^2$$

$$bo = \frac{10-4}{2} = 3$$

no unpaired e⁻

c) NO^{1+} - 14 e⁻ total (7e⁻ from N + 8e⁻ from O - 1e⁻ from +1 charge)

$$\sigma_{1s}^2 \quad \sigma*_{1s}^2 \quad \sigma_{2s}^2 \quad \sigma*_{2s}^2 \quad \pi_{2p_y}^2 \quad \pi_{2p_z}^2 \quad \sigma_{2p_x}^2$$

$$bo = \frac{10-4}{2} = 3$$

no unpaired e⁻

2. Is CN^- isoelectronic with NO^{1+}?

Refereing to the previous problem, we see that both CN^- and NO^+ have the same "electronic configuration"; therefore, they are isoelectronic.

EXERCISES

Molecular Orbital Theory

1. Write the electronic configuration (filled shorthand energy level diagram) for each of the following species. Calculate the bond order for each, give the number of unpaired electrons for each, and predict whether each is paramagnetic or diamagnetic.

    a) H_2^{1+} b) He_2^{1-} c) Li_2^{1+} d) C_2 e) Be_2

    f) CO   g) OF^{1-} h) NO^{1-} i) BC^{1+} j) HHe^{1+}

2. Which of the species in question 14:
    a) is predicted to be the most stable?
    b) have bond orders of zero?
    c) is predicted to have the shortest bond?
    d) is predicted to have the longest bond?
    e) is predicted to have the strongest bond?
    f) is predicted to have the weakest bond?
    g) have fractional bond orders (without performing the calculations how would you predict that the bond order was going to be a fraction)?

3. Fill in the blanks:
    a) C_2^{2+} has _____ electron(s) in the π_{2py} MO and _____ electron(s) in the π_{2pz} MO.
    b) N_2^{1-} has _____ electron(s) in the π_{2py} MO and _____ electron(s) in the π_{2pz} MO.

4. Consider the following species when answering this question: Li_2^{2+}, Li_2, Li_2^{1-}
    a) Arrange the species in order of increasing predicted stability.
    b) Arrange the species in order of predicted increasing bond strength.
    c) Arrange the species in order of increasing bond order.

5. Which homonuclear diatomic species have the following electronic configurations?

    a) X_2^{1+} $\sigma_{1s}^2\ \sigma*_{1s}^2\ \sigma_{2s}^2\ \sigma*_{2s}^2\ \pi_{2py}^2\ \pi_{2pz}^1$

    b) X_2 $\sigma_{1s}^2\ \sigma*_{1s}^2\ \sigma_{2s}^2\ \sigma*_{2s}^2\ \pi_{2py}^2\ \pi_{2pz}^2\ \sigma_{2px}^2\ \pi*_{2py}^2\ \pi*_{2pz}^2$

    c) X_2^{1-} $\sigma_{1s}^2\ \sigma*_{1s}^2\ \sigma_{2s}^2\ \sigma*_{2s}^2\ \pi_{2py}^2\ \pi_{2pz}^2\ \sigma_{2px}^2\ \pi*_{2py}^2\ \pi*_{2pz}^1$

6. Which of the following species would be "isoelectronic" with N_2?
    a) CN^{1-} b) C_2^{2-} c) NO^{1+} d) O_2^{1+}

7. What happens to the internuclear distance (in MO terms) as H_2 is ionized to H_2^{1+} and then to H_2^{2+}?

8. For the specie N_2^{1-} arrange the following MO's in order of increasing energy -- σ_{2px} π_{2py} π_{2pz}.

MULTIPLE CHOICE PRACTICE EXAM FOR MODULE 13

1. According to MO theory, which of the following is paramagnetic?
   1) Be_2
   2) Li_2^+
   3) H_2
   4) He_2
   5) None of the above

2. According to MO theory, which of the following has the shortest bond?
   1) Be_2
   2) Li_2^+
   3) H_2
   4) He_2
   5) All have the same bond length

3. According to MO theory, which of the following is the most stable?
   1) Be_2
   2) Li_2^+
   3) H_2
   4) He_2
   5) All have the same stability

4. According to MO theory, which of the following has the strongest bond?
   1) Be_2
   2) Li_2^+
   3) H_2
   4) He_2
   5) All have the same strength

5. According to MO theory, what is the bond order for Li_2^+?
   1) 0
   2) 0.5
   3) 1.0
   4) 1.5
   5) 2.0

6. What is the shorthand energy diagram (electronic configuration) for Be_2?
   1) $\sigma_{1s}^2\ \sigma*_{1s}^2$
   2) $\sigma_{1s}^2\ \sigma*_{1s}^2\ \sigma_{2s}^1\ \sigma*_{2s}^1\ \pi_{2p_y}^1\ \pi_{2p_z}^1$
   3) $\sigma_{1s}^2\ \sigma*_{1s}^2\ \pi_{2s}^2\ \pi*_{2s}^2$
   4) $\sigma_{1s}^2\ \sigma*_{1s}^2\ \sigma_{2s}^2\ \sigma*_{2s}^2$
   5) $\sigma_{1s}^2\ \pi*_{1s}^2\ \sigma_{2s}^2\ \pi*_{2s}^2$

7. Which of the following species is isoelectronic with CN^-?
   1) NO
   2) CO
   3) N_2
   4) Two of the above
   5) None of the above

8. Which of the following statements is correct about the $\sigma*_{1s}$ molecular orbital (MO)?
   a. This particular MO is more stable than the combining 1s orbitals used in its formation.
   b. This particular MO is lower in energy than the combining 1s orbitals used in its formation.
   c. This particular MO is formed by the out of phase overlapping of two-1s atomic orbitals.
   1) only a
   2) only b
   3) only c
   4) only b & c
   5) only a & b

9. When three-2p orbitals are combined with three-2p orbitals _____.
   a. Six molecular orbitals are formed.
   b. Three bonding and three antibonding molecular orbitals are formed.
   c. Two π-antibonding molecular orbitals are formed.
   1) only a
   2) only b
   3) only c
   4) only a & b
   5) a, b, and c

MODULE 13 - ANSWERS

1.   a) $\sigma 1s^1$ bo = 0.5   1 unpaired e⁻   paramagnetic

   b) $\sigma 1s^2$ $\sigma*1s^2$ $\sigma 2s^1$ bo = 0.5   1 unpaired e⁻   paramagnetic

   c) $\sigma 1s^2$ $\sigma*1s^2$ $\sigma 2s^1$ bo = 0.5   1 unpaired e⁻   paramagnetic

   d) $\sigma 1s^2$ $\sigma*1s^2$ $\sigma 2s^2$ $\sigma*2s^2$ $\pi 2p_y^2$ $\pi 2p_z^2$ bo = 2.0   0 unpaired e⁻   diamagnetic

   e) $\sigma 1s^2$ $\sigma*1s^2$ $\sigma 2s^2$ $\sigma*2s^2$ bo = 0.0   0 unpaired e⁻   diamagnetic

   f) $\sigma 1s^2$ $\sigma*1s^2$ $\sigma 2s^2$ $\sigma*2s^2$ $\pi 2p_y^2$ $\pi 2p_z^2$ $\sigma 2p_x^2$ bo = 3.0   0 unpaired e⁻   diamagnetic

   g) $\sigma 1s^2$ $\sigma*1s^2$ $\sigma 2s^2$ $\sigma*2s^2$ $\pi 2p_y^2$ $\pi 2p_z^2$ $\sigma 2p_x^2$ $\pi*2p_y^2$ $\pi*2p_z^2$ bo = 1.0   0 unpaired e⁻   diamagnetic

   h) $\sigma 1s^2$ $\sigma*1s^2$ $\sigma 2s^2$ $\sigma*2s^2$ $\pi 2p_y^2$ $\pi 2p_z^2$ $\sigma 2p_x^2$ $\pi*2p_y^1$ $\pi*2p_z^1$ bo = 2.0   2 unpaired e⁻   paramagnetic

   i) $\sigma 1s^2$ $\sigma*1s^2$ $\sigma 2s^2$ $\sigma*2s^2$ $\pi 2p_y^1$ $\pi 2p_z^1$ bo = 1.0   2 unpaired e⁻   paramagnetic

   j) $\sigma 1s^2$ bo = 1.0   0 unparired e⁻   diamagnetic

2.   a) f

   b) e

   c) f

   d) e (loosely speaking, those species having bo = 0 have the "longest bond")

   e) f

   f) e (loosely speaking, those species having bo = 0 have the "weakest bond")

   g) a, b, & c (species having an odd number of electrons will have fractional bond orders)

3.   a) 1 & 1

   b) 2 & 2

4.   a) $Li_2^{2+} < Li_2^{1-} < Li_2$

   b) $Li_2^{2+} < Li_2^{1-} < Li_2$

   c) $Li_2^{2+} < Li_2^{1-} < Li_2$

5.   a) C_2^{1+}

   b) F_2

   c) O_2^{1-}

6.   a, b, & c (Since N_2 has 14e⁻, those species having 14 e⁻ would be isoelectronic with N_2).

7.   The internuclear distance increases (H_2, bo = 1.0; H_2^{1+}, bo = 0.5; H_2^{2+}, bo = 0.0)

8. $\pi 2p_y = \pi 2p_z < \sigma 2p_x$

MODULE 14. *Acids and Bases: Properties, Theories, and Strengths*

I. Properties of Aqueous Solutions of Acids and Bases

Acids	Bases
a) Have a sour taste. b) Turn blue litmus paper (an acid-base indicator) red. c) Are electrolytes. d) React with bases.	a) Taste bitter. b) Turn red litmus paper (an acid-base indicator) blue. c) Are electrolytes. d) React with acids. e) Feel slippery or soapy.

II. Acid-Base Theories

There are three common theories that define acids and bases.

A. Arrhenius Theory

The most specific and least inclusive definition of acids and bases was presented by S. Arrhenius. This is the working definition of acids and bases that most people are familiar with.

Acids - Substances that ionize in water to produce H^+. [NOTE: $H^+_{(aq)}$ really exists as H_3O^+ (hydrated hydrogen ion).] Recall that strong acids ionize completely in water (i.e., are strong electrolytes) while weak acids do not ionize completely in water (i.e., are weak electrolytes).

$$HClO_4 \xrightarrow{H_2O} H^+ + ClO_4^- \qquad \text{(strong acid -- ionizes totally in water)}$$

$$HF \xrightleftharpoons{H_2O} H^+ + F^- \qquad \text{(weak acid -- does not totally ionize in water)}$$

Bases - Substances that ionize in water to produce OH^-. Recall that strong bases ionize completely in water (i.e., are strong electrolytes) while weak bases do not ionize completely in water (i.e., are weak electrolytes).

$$NaOH \xrightarrow{H_2O} Na^+ + OH^- \qquad \text{(strong base -- ionizes totally in water)}$$

$$NH_4OH \xrightleftharpoons{H_2O} NH_4^+ + OH^- \qquad \text{(weak base -- does not totally ionize in water)}$$

Neutralization - Combination of $H^+_{(aq)}$ with $OH^-_{(aq)}$ to produce $H_2O_{(l)}$

B. Brønsted-Lowry Theory

J. N. Brønsted and T.M. Lowry independently presented logical extensions of the Arrhenius theory of acids and bases.

> Acids - Proton (H^+) donor
>
> Bases - Proton (H^+) acceptor

Usually, a Brønsted-Lowry acid can be recognized by looking for an Arrhenius acid (compound with an H at the beginning of its formula except for H_2O or H_2O_2) or a cation that has at least one hydrogen ion. Water and acidic salts, as you will soon see, can behave as both a Brønsted-Lowry acid or base depending on what they are reacted with.

Usually, a Brønsted-Lowry base can be recognized by looking for an Arrhenius base (ionic compound with an OH at end of its formula), an anion, or a specie in which the central element has a lone pair of electrons.

The complete ionization of HCl (a strong acid) in water is an acid-base reaction in which water acts as a base (i.e., accepts a proton from HCl).

The incomplete ionization of HF (a weak acid) is similar to that of HCl; however, HF does not ionize completely in water. The double arrow indicates that this is a reversible reaction.

When ammonia is placed in water, it does not ionize completely. The N in NH_3 accepts a proton (i.e., acts as a base) from water, which acts as the acid.

Amines, hydrocarbon derivatives of ammonia, are weak bases in water. Amines are made by replacing one, two or all three H's in ammonia with a hydrocarbon. Since amines are weak bases, when placed in water, they do not completely ionize. The N from the amine accepts a proton from water.

As can be seen from the above examples, water can act as both an acid and a base depending on what it is reacted with. Water is thus said to be amphiprotic (i.e., can act as both a proton donor or proton acceptor).

Brønsted-Lowry acid-base reactions are described in terms of *conjugate acid-base pairs*, which are species that differ from each other by a proton.

$$H\text{-}\ddot{C}l: \quad + \quad H\text{-}\overset{\cdot\cdot}{\underset{\cdot\cdot}{O}}\text{-}H \quad \longrightarrow \quad \left[\begin{array}{c} H \\ | \\ H\text{-}\overset{}{\underset{\cdot\cdot}{O}}\text{-}H \end{array} \right]^{+} \quad + \quad :\ddot{\underset{\cdot\cdot}{C}}l:^{-}$$

acid   base   conjugate   conjugate
acid   base
derived from   derived from
base   acid

The stronger an acid is, the weaker its conjugate base. Likewise, the stronger the base is, the weaker its conjugate acid. This statement leads us to the following conclusion:

Since HCl is a stronger acid than HF; then, Cl^- is a weaker base than F^-.

Water undergoes self-ionization (auto-ionization) to a very small extent to produce equal amounts of hydrated hydrogen ions and hydroxide ions. This auto-ionization can thus be considered an acid-base reaction.

$$H\text{-}\overset{\cdot\cdot}{\underset{\cdot\cdot}{O}}\text{-}H \quad + \quad H\text{-}\overset{\cdot\cdot}{\underset{\cdot\cdot}{O}}\text{-}H \quad \rightleftharpoons \quad \left[\begin{array}{c} H \\ | \\ H\text{-}\overset{}{\underset{\cdot\cdot}{O}}\text{-}H \end{array} \right]^{+} \quad + \quad :\overset{\cdot\cdot}{\underset{\cdot\cdot}{O}}\text{-}H^{-}$$

acid   base   conjugate   conjugate
acid   base

Example Problems

1. Write an equation that illustrates how HCN and NH_4^+ are considered Brønsted-Lowry acids in water. Also, identify (c)onjugate acid-base pairs.

    a) $HCN \ + \ H_2O \ \rightleftharpoons \ H_3O^+ \ + \ CN^-$

         acid   base   c. acid   c. base

    b) $NH_4^+ \ + \ H_2O \ \rightleftharpoons \ NH_3 \ + \ H_3O^+$

         acid   base   c. base   c. acid

2. Write an equation that illustrates how S^{2-} and NCl_3 are considered Brønsted-Lowry bases in water. Also, identify (c)onjugate acid-base pairs.

    a) $S^{2-} \ + \ H_2O \ \rightleftharpoons \ HS^- \ + \ OH^-$

         base   acid   c. acid   c. base

    b) $NCl_3 \ + \ H_2O \ \rightleftharpoons \ NHCl_3^+ \ + \ OH^-$

         base   acid   c. acid   c. base

3. Give the conjugate acid for H_2O, Cl^-, CN^-, NH_3.

    H_3O^+, HCl, HCN, NH_4^+

4. Give the conjugate base for H_2O, PH_4^+, HS^-, NH_3

    OH^-, PH_3, S^{2-}, NH_2^-

5. Identify the Brønsted-Lowry acids and bases and conjugate acids and bases in the following reactions.

a) HS⁻ + HI →   b) NH₄⁺ + ClO⁻ →

$$\text{a) } \underset{\text{base}}{\text{HS}^-} \ + \ \underset{\text{acid}}{\text{HI}} \ \rightarrow \ \underset{\text{c. acid}}{\text{H}_2\text{S}} \ + \ \underset{\text{c. base}}{\text{I}^-}$$

$$\text{b) } \underset{\text{acid}}{\text{NH}_4^+} \ + \ \underset{\text{base}}{\text{ClO}^-} \ \rightarrow \ \underset{\text{c. base}}{\text{NH}_3} \ + \ \underset{\text{c. acid}}{\text{HClO}}$$

6. Which is the stronger base OH⁻ or Br⁻?

The strongest base is the one that is derived from the weakest acid. OH⁻ is derived from H_2O and Br⁻ is derived from HBr. Since H_2O is the weaker acid, OH⁻ is the stronger base.

C. Lewis Theory

The most comprehensive and inclusive definition of acids and bases has been the one presented by G.N. Lewis.

> Acids - Electron pair acceptor
>
> Bases - Electron pair donor

The following are examples of a Lewis acid-base reaction.

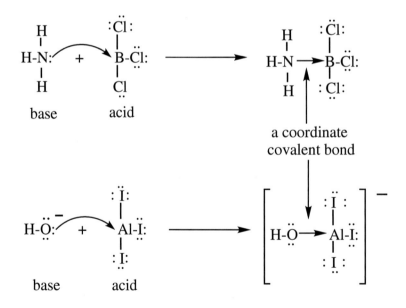

Many Lewis acids come from compounds in which the central element is a member of Group IIIA, mainly B and Al. Remember that these atoms have less than an octet (i.e, a sextet). Compounds containing these elements can react with an electron pair donor to form a complex in which this IIIA element attains an octet as a consequence of the acid-base reaction.

III. Strengths of Acids

A. Binary Acids

The tendency for a binary acid, in the same family, to ionize depends mainly on the strength of the H-X bond. The bond strength increases on going up a family:

$$\text{(strongest H-X bond)} \quad \longrightarrow \quad HF \gg HCl > HBr > HI \quad \longrightarrow \quad \text{(weakest H-X bond)}$$

The stronger the bond, the weaker the acid. In comparison of acids derived from atoms in the same group, *the acid becomes stronger as you go down a family.* Acid strength increases in the following manner for VIA and VIIA elements:

$$HF \ll HCl < HBr < HI$$

$$H_2O \ll H_2S < H_2Se < H_2Te$$

In water, as you may recall, HCl, HBr, and HI are all strong acids. Water is sufficiently basic that it does not distinguish between these acids and is referred to as a *leveling solvent.* If a less basic solvent, such as acetic acid, is used the above acid strengths can be verified for HCl, HBr, and HI.

As a result of water's leveling effect, H_3O^+ is the strongest acid that can exist in an aqueous solution.

Similar observations have been made for aqueous solutions of strong soluble metal hydroxide bases such as NaOH and LiOH. Thus, *OH⁻ is the strongest base that can exist in an aqueous solution.* Bases stronger than OH⁻, such as metal amides (e.g., $NaNH_2$) and metal hydrides (e.g., NaH) react completely in water and are thus leveled.

$$NH_2^- + H_2O \rightarrow NH_3 + OH^-$$

$$H^- + H_2O \rightarrow H_2 + OH^-$$

Going across a period, the dominant factor in determining acid strength is the polarity of the H-X bond. Going across a period (from left to right), the electronegativity of "X" increases, the H-X bond is more polar, and the acid strength increases. The following acid strengths are observed for elements in the second period:

$$CH_4 < NH_3 < H_2O < HF$$

B. Ternary Acids

Most ternary acids (i.e., acids containing 3 elements) are oxyacids. These acids are labelled either as monoprotic or polyprotic depending on the number of "acidic" hydrogens that they contain.

$$HNO_3 \text{ and } HClO \quad \text{monoprotic} \qquad\qquad H_2SO_4 \text{ and } H_3PO_3 \quad \text{polyprotic}$$

The only strong polyprotic acid (in water) H_2SO_4, ionizes in two steps. The first ionization step is complete and the second step is not complete. For polyprotic acids, the first ionization step occurs to a greater extent than the second step.

$$\text{Step 1:} \quad H_2SO_4 \text{ (aq)} \rightarrow H^+ \text{ (aq)} + HSO_4^- \text{ (aq)}$$

$$\text{Step 2:} \quad HSO_4^- \text{ (aq)} \xrightleftharpoons{\quad\quad} H^+ \text{ (aq)} + SO_4^{2-}$$

Among oxyacids having the same central element, acid strength increases with increasing number of oxygens.

$$H_2SO_3 < H_2SO_4 \qquad HNO_2 < HNO_3 \qquad HClO < HClO_2 < HClO_3 < HClO_4$$

*For **most** oxyacids containing different elements in the same oxidation state from the same family, acid strength increases with increasing central element electronegativity.*

$$H_2SeO_4 < H_2SO_4 \qquad H_3PO_4 < HNO_3 \qquad HBrO_4 < HClO_4$$

Table 1. Relative acid-base strengths of several conjugate pairs.

	acid	base	

increasing acid strength →

100% ionized in dilute aqueous solutions:

acid	base
$HClO_4$	ClO_4^-
H_2SO_4	HSO_4^-
HI	I^-
HBr	Br^-
HCl	Cl^-
HNO_3	NO_3^-

Negligible base strength in water

Equilibrium mixture of unionized acid, conjugate base and H^+:

acid	base
H_3O^+	H_2O
HSO_4^-	SO_4^{2-}
H_3PO_4	$H_2PO_4^-$
HF	F^-
$HC_2H_3O_2$	$C_2H_3O_2^-$
H_2S	HS^-
HCN	CN^-
H_2O_2	HO_2^-
H_2O	OH^-

increasing base strength →

You can use Table 1 to predict the direction of an acid-base reaction. The direction for an acid-base reaction always favors the weaker acid and base (i.e., the normal direction of reaction is for the stronger acid to donate a proton to the stronger base to form the weaker acid and base). Consider the following acid-base reaction,

$$HCN + Br^- \rightleftharpoons CN^- + HBr$$

Comparing the acids on both sides of the equation -- HCN and HBr -- since HCN is a weaker acid than HBr, the reaction to form HCN is favored. You could have focused your attention on the bases instead, whichever you choose the answer would be the same. Thus, since Br^- is a weaker base than CN^- the reaction to form Br^- is favored. Hence, the preferred direction for the reaction is from right to left. How this "favoritism" in direction is indicated, is by having the arrow in the direction in which the reaction is favored be longer.

$$HCN + Br^- \overset{\longleftarrow}{\longrightarrow} CN^- + HBr$$

Example Problems

1. Write all steps in the complete ionization of H_3PO_4.

   Recall that phosphoric acid is a weak acid. Therefore, the first ionization step is incomplete; however, it occurs to a greater extent than the second or third step.

   Step 1: $H_3PO_4 \text{ (aq)} \rightleftharpoons H^+ \text{ (aq)} + H_2PO_4^- \text{ (aq)}$

   Step 2: $H_2PO_4^- \text{ (aq)} \rightleftharpoons H^+ \text{ (aq)} + HPO_4^{2-}$

   Step 3: $HPO_4^{2-} \text{ (aq)} \rightleftharpoons H^+ \text{ (aq)} + PO_4^{3-}$

2. In each of the following which is the stronger acid:

   a) H_3PO_3 or H_3PO_4 ----> H_3PO_4 since it has more oxygens

   b) HClO or HBrO -----> HClO since Cl is more electronegative than Br.

Leveling effect

3. The following fictitious elements -- Bu, Bz, Bm, By -- form the following hydrogen containing binary compounds (all of which are water soluble). When making these compounds, these elements have enough lone electron pairs to form an octet. These compounds have the following acid strengths relative to that of the hydronium ion and water.

$$HBu > H_2Bz > H_3O^+ > H_3Bm > H_2O > ByH_3$$

a) Which acid(s) get levelled in water?

HBu and H_2Bz -- water levels (i.e., completely ionizes) any acid that is stronger than its conjugate acid H_3O^+.

b) What is the conjugate base of H_2Bz?

HBz^-

c) What is the conjugate acid of ByH_3?

ByH_4^+

d) Complete the following acid-base reactions. Label the acid, base, (c)onjugate acid, and (c)onjugate base.

   A. $HBu + H_2O \rightarrow$ B. $ByH_3 + H_2O \rightarrow$

   A. HBu + H_2O $\rightarrow$ Bu^- + H_3O^+
         acid   base   c. base   c. acid

   B. ByH_3 + H_2O $\rightarrow$ ByH_4^+ + OH^-
         base   acid   c. acid   c. base

4. Determine the direction of the following reaction from the relative strengths of acids and bases.

$$H_2S + C_2H_3O_2^- \rightleftharpoons HS^- + HC_2H_3O_2$$

Since H_2S is a weaker acid than $HC_2H_3O_2$ its formation is favored. You could have compared base strengths as well. Since $C_2H_3O_2^-$ is a weaker base than HS^-, its formation is favored. Hence, the reaction from right to left is favored.

$$H_2S + C_2H_3O_2^- \overset{\longleftarrow}{\longrightarrow} HS^- + HC_2H_3O_2$$

IV. Acidic and Basic Salts

A. Acidic Salts

If less than a stoichiometric amount of base is reacted with a polyprotic acid, the resulting salt is known as an acidic salt because it is capable of neutralizing a base.

$H_3PO_4 \text{ (aq)} + KOH \text{ (aq)} \rightarrow KH_2PO_4 \text{ (aq)} + H_2O \text{ (l)}$
                                          an acidic salt

$H_3PO_4 \text{ (aq)} + 2 KOH \text{ (aq)} \rightarrow K_2HPO_4 \text{ (aq)} + 2 H_2O \text{ (l)}$
                                          an acidic salt

$H_3PO_4 \text{ (aq)} + 3 KOH \text{ (aq)} \rightarrow K_3PO_4 \text{ (aq)} + 3 H_2O \text{ (l)}$
                                         a "normal" salt

$KH_2PO_4 \text{ (aq)} + KOH \text{ (aq)} \rightarrow K_2HPO_4 \text{ (aq)} + H_2O \text{ (l)}$
                                          an acidic salt

Interestingly enough, aqueous solutions of acidic salts are not necessarily acidic, but they do neutralize bases. You will learn more about this in future chemistry courses.

B. Basic Salts

If less than a stoichiometric amount of acid is reacted with a polyhydroxy base, the resulting salt is known as a basic salt because it is capable of neutralizing an acid.

$$Al(OH)_3 \text{ (s)} \quad + \quad HBr \text{ (aq)} \quad \rightarrow \quad Al(OH)_2Br \text{ (s)} \quad + \quad H_2O \text{ (l)}$$
aluminum dihydroxide bromide
a basic salt

$$Al(OH)_3 \text{ (s)} \quad + \quad 2 \; HBr \text{ (aq)} \quad \rightarrow \quad Al(OH)Br_2 \text{ (s)} \quad + \quad 2 \; H_2O \text{ (l)}$$
aluminum hydroxide dibromide
a basic salt

$$Al(OH)_3 \text{ (s)} \quad + \quad 3 \; HBr \text{ (aq)} \quad \rightarrow \quad AlBr_3 \text{ (s)} \quad + \quad 3 \; H_2O \text{ (l)}$$
aluminum bromide
a "normal" salt

$$Al(OH)_2Br \text{ (s)} \quad + \quad HBr \text{ (aq)} \quad \rightarrow \quad Al(OH)Br_2 \text{ (s)} \quad + \quad H_2O \text{ (l)}$$

Interestingly enough, aqueous solutions of basic salts are not necessarily basic, but they do neutralize acids. Most basic hydroxides are water insoluble. You will learn more about this in future chemistry courses.

V. Amphiprotism and Amphoterism

As has been demonstrated above, whether a particular substance behaves as an acid or a base depends on its "environment". A substance is said to be amphiprotic if it can both accept and donate a proton. A substance is said to be amphoteric if it can both act as an acid and a base.

Acidic salts are good examples of substances that are both amphiprotic and amphoteric.

$$KH_2PO_4 \text{ (aq)} \quad + \quad KOH \text{ (aq)} \quad \rightarrow \quad K_2HPO_4 \text{ (aq)} \quad + \quad H_2O \text{ (l)}$$
acting as an acid
(donating proton to OH^- in KOH)

$$KH_2PO_4 \text{ (aq)} \quad + \quad HCl \text{ (aq)} \quad \rightarrow \quad H_3PO_4 \text{ (aq)} \quad + \quad KCl \text{ (aq)}$$
acting as a base
(accepting proton from H^+ in HCl)

Good examples of substances that are amphoteric, but not amphiprotic are the insoluble metal hydroxides.

$$Al(OH)_3 \text{ (s)} \quad + \quad HBr \text{ (aq)} \quad \rightarrow \quad Al(OH)_2Br \text{ (s)} + \quad H_2O \text{ (l)}$$
acting as a base

$$Al(OH)_3 \text{ (s)} \quad + \quad NaOH \text{ (aq)} \quad \rightarrow \quad Na^+[Al(OH)_4]^- \text{ (aq)}$$
acting as an acid

Insoluble metal hydroxides when reacted with excess strong soluble hydroxides, form soluble complexes as seen in the above example.

EXERCISES

Acid-Base Theory

1. Write an equation showing how the following behave as Arrhenius acid.
   a) $HBrO_4$ $HBrO_4 \xrightarrow{H_2O} H^+ + BrO_4^-$
   b) $HC_2H_3O_2$ $HC_2H_3O_2 \xrightarrow{H_2O} H^+ + C_2H_3O_2^-$

2. Write an equation showing how the following behave as an Arrhenius base.
   a) $CuOH$ $CuOH \rightleftharpoons Cu^+ + OH^-$
   b) $CsOH$ $CsOH \rightleftharpoons Cs^+ - OH^-$

3. Identify the Brønsted-Lowry acids and bases and conjugate acids and bases in the following reactions.

   a) HBr + $C_2H_3O_2^-$ $\rightleftharpoons$ Br^- + $HC_2H_3O_2$
   acid   base   c.base   c.acid
   b) HO_2^- + $HC_2H_3O_2$ $\rightleftharpoons$ H_2O_2 + $C_2H_3O_2^-$
   base   acid   c.acid   c.base
   c) HBr + S^{2-} $\rightleftharpoons$ Br^- + HS^-
   acid   base   c.base   c.acid
   d) HCN + H_2O $\rightleftharpoons$ H_3O^+ + CN^-
   acid   base   c.acid   c.base
   e) $H_2PO_4^-$ + H_2SO_4 $\rightleftharpoons$ H_3PO_4 + HSO_4^-
   base   acid   c.acid   c.base
   f) HSO_4^- + HCN $\rightleftharpoons$ CN^- + H_2SO_4
   base   acid   c.base   c.acid

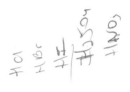

4. Without the help of Table 1, for each of the reactions in question 3, indicate the preferred direction of the reaction.

5. Give the conjugate acid for each of the following species.
   a) O^{2-} b) NH_3 c) $(CH_3)_2NH$ (an amine)

6. Give the conjugate base for each of the following species.
   a) OH^- b) NH_3 c) $(CH_3)_2NH$ (an amine)

7. Which of the following acids get levelled in water?
   a) HF b) HBr c) HNO_3

8. In each of the following which is the stronger acid.
   a) HBr or HI b) H_2S or HS^- c) HNO_3 or HNO_2
   d) H_3AsO_4 or H_3PO_4 e) CH_4 or NH_3 f) H_2Te or H_2Se

9. In each of the following which is the stronger base.
   a) Br^- or I^- b) S^{2-} or HS^- c) NO_3^- or NO_2^-
   d) $H_2AsO_4^-$ or $H_2PO_4^-$ e) CH_3^- or NH_2^- f) HTe^- or HSe^-

10. Complete the following Lewis acid-base reactions and identify the Lewis acid and base.
    a) $:PH_3$ + BF_3 $\rightarrow$
    b) $AlCl_3$ + Cl^- $\rightarrow$

11. Complete the following acid-base reactions.
    a) H_3AsO_4 + $2\,LiOH$ $\rightarrow$
    b) NaH_2PO_4 + $2\,NaOH$ $\rightarrow$
    c) $Sn(OH)_2$ + HBr $\rightarrow$

12. Given the acid strengths for the following acids derived from the fictitious elements -- Bu, Bz, Bm, By -- which would be strong electrolytes in water?

    $$HBu > H_2Bz > H_3O^+ > H_3Bm > H_2O > ByH_3$$

MULTIPLE CHOICE PRACTICE EXAM FOR MODULE 14

1. Which of the following is an Arrhenius acid?
    1) CH_4 2) H_2S 3) HI
    4) two of the above   5) all of the above

2. In which of the following reactions is the first reactant written acting as an acid?

    a. NH_3 + HS^- $\rightleftharpoons$ NH_4^+ + S^{2-}

    b. H_2O + HS^- $\rightleftharpoons$ H_2S + OH^-

    c. H_3O^+ + NH_3 $\rightleftharpoons$ NH_4^+ + H_2O

    1) only a   2) only b   3) only c
    4) two of the above   5) none of the above

3. Which is the weakest acid?
    1) $HClO_4$ 2) H_2S 3) HBr   4) H_2Te 5) HCl

4. Which is the weakest base?

    1) ClO_4^- 2) HS^- 3) F^- 4) ClO_3^- 5) HSO_3^-

5. Given the acid strengths for the following acids derived from the fictitious elements -- Bu, Bz, Bm, By -- which would be a weak electrolyte or non-electrolyte in water?

    $$HBu > H_3O^+ > H_3Bm > H_2O > H_2Bz > ByH_3$$

    1) H_3Bm 2) ByH_3 3) H_2Bz
    4) two of the above   5) all of the above

6. Given the acid strengths for the following acids derived from the fictitious elements -- Bu, Bz, Bm, By -- which would be levelled in water?

    $$HBu > H_2Bz > H_3O^+ > HBuO > H_3Bm > H_2O > ByH_3$$

    1) HBu   2) H_3Bm 3) HBuO
    4) two of the above   5) all of the above

7. In which of the following reactions is the first reactant written acting as a Lewis acid?
    a. $NH(CH_3)_2$ + BCl_3 $\rightarrow$
    b. $AlCl_3$ + Cl^- $\rightarrow$
    c. NH_3 + H^+ $\rightarrow$

    1) only a   2) only b   3) only c
    4) two of the above   5) none of the above

8. In which of the following reactions is the left to right direction favored?

    a. NH_2^- + HSO_4^- $\rightleftharpoons$ NH_3 + SO_4^{2-}

    b. H_2O + HBr $\rightleftharpoons$ H_3O^+ + Br^-

    c. H_3O^+ + NH_3 $\rightleftharpoons$ NH_4^+ + H_2O

    1) only a   2) only b   3) only c
    4) two of the above   5) all of the above

9. Which is/are amphiprotic?

    1) Cl^- 2) NH_3 3) $AlCl_3$
    4) two of the above   5) all of the above

10. Which of the following is (are) a correct statement about bases?
     1) they are proton acceptors
     2) they are electron pair acceptors
     3) they turn blue litmus paper red
     4) two of the above
     5) none of the above

11. The equation that shows the auto-ionization of ammonia is:

     1) $NH_3 + H_2O \rightleftharpoons NH_4^+ + OH^-$

     2) $NH_3 + H_2O \rightleftharpoons NH_3 + H^+ + OH^-$

     3) $NH_3 + NH_3 \rightleftharpoons NH_4^+ + NH_2^-$

     4) $2 NH_3 + H_2O \rightleftharpoons H_3N\text{-}NH_3 + H^+ + OH^-$

     5) $NH_3 + H_3O^+ \rightleftharpoons NH_4^+ + H_2O$

12. Which of the following is (are) a conjugate acid/base pair in this order (i.e., the acid is written first and then the base -- acid / base)?

     1) H_2O / OH^- 2) NH_3 / NH_4^+ 3) $NH_2(CH_3)_2^+$ / $NH(CH_3)_2$
     4) two of the above   5) all of the above

MODULE 14 - ANSWERS

1. a) $HBrO_4 \xrightarrow{H_2O} H^+ + BrO_4^-$ b) $HC_2H_3O_2 \xrightleftharpoons{H_2O} H^+ + C_2H_3O_2^-$

2. a) $CuOH \xrightleftharpoons{H_2O} Cu^+ + OH^-$ b) $CsOH \xrightarrow{H_2O} Cs^+ + OH^-$

3. a) $HBr + C_2H_3O_2^- \rightleftharpoons Br^- + HC_2H_3O_2$
   acid   base   c.base   c.acid

   b) $HO_2^- + HC_2H_3O_2 \rightleftharpoons H_2O_2 + C_2H_3O_2^-$
   base   acid   c.acid   c.base

   c) $HBr + S^{2-} \rightleftharpoons Br^- + HS^-$
   acid   base   c.base   c.acid

   d) $HCN + H_2O \rightleftharpoons H_3O^+ + CN^-$
   acid   base   c.acid   c.base

   e) $H_2PO_4^- + H_2SO_4 \rightleftharpoons H_3PO_4 + HSO_4^-$
   base   acid   c.acid   c.base

   f) $HSO_4^- + HCN \rightleftharpoons CN^- + H_2SO_4$
   base   acid   c.base   c.acid

4. left to right: a, b, c, e   right to left: d, f

5. a) HO^- b) NH_4^+ c) $(CH_3)_2NH_2^+$

6. a) O^{2-} b) NH_2^- c) $(CH_3)_2N^-$

7. b and c

8. a) HI b) H_2S c) HNO_3 d) H_3PO_4 e) NH_3 f) H_2Te

9. a) Br^- b) S^{2-} c) NO_2^- d) $H_2AsO_4^-$ e) CH_3^- f) HSe^-

10. a) $:PH_3 + BF_3 \rightarrow H_3P{\rightarrow}BF_3$
    base   acid

    b) $AlCl_3 + Cl^- \rightarrow Cl{\rightarrow}AlCl_3$
    acid   base

11. a) $H_3AsO_4 + 2\,LiOH \rightarrow Li_2HAsO_4 + 2\,H_2O$
    b) $NaH_2PO_4 + 2\,NaOH \rightarrow Na_3PO_4 + 2\,H_2O$
    c) $Sn(OH)_2 + HBr \rightarrow Sn(OH)Br + H_2O$

12. HBu and H_2Bz

APPENDIX 1
Answers to Multiple Choice Practice Exams

MODULE

Question Number	1	2	3	4	5	6	7	8	9	10	11	12	13	14
1	4	1	5	5	3	1	3	5	5	2	3	4	2	4
2	1	1	5	4	4	1	5	2	3	3	4	5	3	4
3	4	2	2	3	2	3	4	3	4	4	2	2	3	2
4	3	3	4	5	1	2	2	4	3	2	5	4	3	1
5	5	4	3	3	3	4	5	2	2	3	3	1	2	5
6	2	4	2	3	1	1	1	3	4	5	4	2	4	1
7	4	1	2	2	3	3	2	4	3	5	4	3	4	2
8	2	2	4	1	2	1	3	5	4	1	2	3	3	5
9	5	5	5	2	4	2	5	5	1	1	3	4	5	2
10	2	5	5	4	5	4	2	3	2	2	4	5		1
11	3	2	4	3	5	2	5	3	3	4	2	2		3
12	5	3	1	1	1	3	2	2	1	3	1	4		4
13	1	2	2	1	2	2	4	1	2	4	5	1		
14	4	3	5	1	4	4	4	4	3	1	5	4		
15	2	4	3	2	4	2	3	2	4	4	5	4		
16	1		4	4	3	5	1	2	5	4	5	2		
17	4		3	2	5	3	4	5	4	4	1	4		
18	3		4	3	2	4		4	2	4	4	5		
19	1		5	5	3	4		3	5	5	4	2		
20	1		2	4	3	3		5	4	1	1	4		
21	3		4	5	1	4		4		3				
22	4		4	3	2	2		2		3				
23			2	2		1				2				
24			1	4		4								
25			2	3		3								
26				5										
27				4										
28				4										

APPENDIX 2

Conversion Factors, Prefixes, and Physical Constants

Conversion Factors

English-English

volume	mass	length	time
1 pt = 16 fl oz	1 lb = 16 oz	1 ft = 12 in	1 min = 60 sec
1 qt = 2 pt	1 ton = 2000 lb	1 yd = 3 ft	1 hr = 60 min
1 gal = 4 qt		1 mi = 5280 ft	1 day = 24 hr

Metric-English

1 L = 1.06 qt	1 lb = 454. g	1 in = 2.54 cm

Others

$1 \text{ Å} = 10^{-10} \text{ m} = 10^{-8} \text{ cm}$

$1 \text{ cal} = 4.184 \text{ J} = 4.129 \times 10^{-2} \text{ L·atm}$

$1 \text{ atm} = 760 \text{ torr} = 760 \text{ mm Hg} = 1.013 \times 10^5 \text{ Pa} = 14.70 \frac{\text{lb}}{\text{in}^2}$

Prefixes

Prefix	Abbreviation	Meaning
giga	G	10^9 (1,000,000,000)
mega	M	10^6 (1,000,000)
kilo	k	10^3 (1,000)
hecto	h	10^2 (100)
deka	da	10^1 (10)
deci	d	10^{-1} (0.1)
centi	c	10^{-2} (0.01)
milli	m	10^{-3} (0.001)
micro	μ	10^{-6} (0.000001)
nano	n	10^{-9} (0.000000001)
pico	p	10^{-12} (0.000000000001)

Physical Constants

Atomic Mass Unit $1 \text{ amu} = 1.66 \times 10^{-24} \text{ g}$

Avogadro's Number $N = 6.02 \times 10^{23}$

Gas Constant $R = 0.0821 \frac{\text{L·atm}}{\text{mol · K}} = 62.4 \frac{\text{L·torr}}{\text{mol · K}} = 1.987 \frac{\text{cal}}{\text{mol · K}} = 8.314 \frac{\text{J}}{\text{mol · K}}$

Molar Volume (STP) $V_m = 22.4 \frac{\text{L}}{\text{mol}}$

Planck's Constant $h = 6.63 \times 10^{-34} \text{ J·sec} = 6.63 \times 10^{-27} \text{ erg·sec}$

Rydberg Constant $R = 1.097 \times 10^7 \text{ m}^- = 1.097 \times 10^5 \text{ cm}^-$

Speed of Light $c = 3.00 \times 10^8 \frac{\text{m}}{\text{sec}} = 3.00 \times 10^{10} \frac{\text{cm}}{\text{sec}}$

Appendix 3 – Nomeclature Concept Maps

Nomeclature Concept Map For Binary Compounds

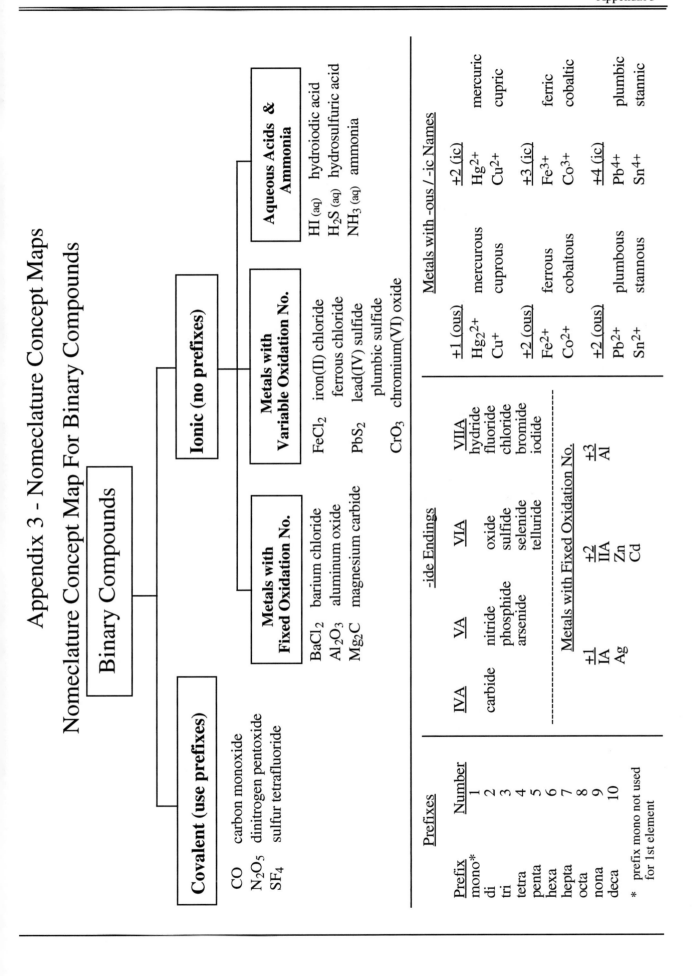

Binary Compounds

Covalent (use prefixes)

CO   carbon monoxide
N_2O_5 dinitrogen pentoxide
SF_4 sulfur tetrafluoride

Ionic (no prefixes)

Metals with Fixed Oxidation No.

$BaCl_2$ barium chloride
Al_2O_3 aluminum oxide
Mg_2C magnesium carbide

Metals with Variable Oxidation No.

$FeCl_2$ iron(II) chloride
      ferrous chloride
PbS_2 lead(IV) sulfide
      plumbic sulfide
CrO_3 chromium(VI) oxide

Aqueous Acids & Ammonia

$HI_{(aq)}$ hydroiodic acid
$H_2S_{(aq)}$ hydrosulfuric acid
$NH_{3\,(aq)}$ ammonia

Prefixes

Prefix	Number
mono*	1
di	2
tri	3
tetra	4
penta	5
hexa	6
hepta	7
octa	8
nona	9
deca	10

* prefix mono not used for 1st element

-ide Endings

IVA	VA	VIA	VIIA
carbide	nitride	oxide	hydride
	phosphide	sulfide	fluoride
	arsenide	selenide	chloride
		telluride	bromide
			iodide

Metals with Fixed Oxidation No.

+1	+2	+3
IA	IIA	Al
Ag	Zn	
	Cd	

Metals with -ous / -ic Names

+1 (ous)		+2 (ic)	
Hg_2^{2+}	mercurous	Hg^{2+}	mercuric
Cu^+	cuprous	Cu^{2+}	cupric

+2 (ous)		+3 (ic)	
Fe^{2+}	ferrous	Fe^{3+}	ferric
Co^{2+}	cobaltous	Co^{3+}	cobaltic

+2 (ous)		+4 (ic)	
Pb^{2+}	plumbous	Pb^{4+}	plumbic
Sn^{2+}	stannous	Sn^{4+}	stannic

Nomenclature Concept Map For Compounds Containing Polyatomic Ions

Oxyacids

HClO	hypochlorous acid
HClO$_2$	chlorous acid
HClO$_3$	chloric acid
HClO$_4$	perchloric acid

Compounds with Ammonium Ion

NH$_4$Cl	ammonium chloride
(NH$_4$)$_2$TeO$_3$	ammonium tellurite

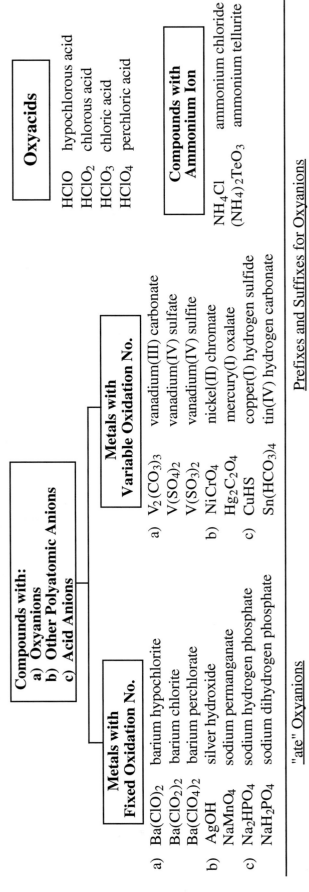

Compounds with:
a) Oxyanions
b) Other Polyatomic Anions
c) Acid Anions

Metals with Variable Oxidation No.

a) V$_2$(CO$_3$)$_3$ — vanadium(III) carbonate
   V(SO$_4$)$_2$ — vanadium(IV) sulfate
   V(SO$_3$)$_2$ — vanadium(IV) sulfite
b) NiCrO$_4$ — nickel(II) chromate
   Hg$_2$C$_2$O$_4$ — mercury(I) oxalate
c) CuHS — copper(I) hydrogen sulfide
   Sn(HCO$_3$)$_4$ — tin(IV) hydrogen carbonate

Metals with Fixed Oxidation No.

a) Ba(ClO)$_2$ — barium hypochlorite
   Ba(ClO$_2$)$_2$ — barium chlorite
   Ba(ClO$_4$)$_2$ — barium perchlorate
b) AgOH — silver hydroxide
   NaMnO$_4$ — sodium permanganate
c) Na$_2$HPO$_4$ — sodium hydrogen phosphate
   NaH$_2$PO$_4$ — sodium dihydrogen phosphate

Prefixes and Suffixes for Oxyanions

2 O's less than "ate" hypo____ite	1 O less than "ate" ____ite	"ate" ____ate	1 O more than "ate" per____ate

Prefixes and Suffixes for Oxyacids

2 O's less than "ic" hypo____ous acid	1 O less than "ic" ____ous acid	"ic" acid ____ic acid	1 O more than "ic" per____ic acid

Other Polyatomic Ions

NH$_4^+$ ammonium	OH$^-$ hydroxide	CN$^-$ cyanide	SCN$^-$ thiocyanate	C$_2$H$_3$O$_2^-$ acetate	MnO$_4^-$ permanganate
	CrO$_4^{2-}$ chromate	Cr$_2$O$_7^{2-}$ dichromate	C$_2$O$_4^{2-}$ oxalate	O$_2^{2-}$ peroxide	

"ate" Oxyanions

IIIA	IVA	VA	VIA	VIIA
BO$_3^{3-}$ borate	CO$_3^{2-}$ carbonate	NO$_3^-$ nitrate	—	—
	SiO$_3^{2-}$ silicate	PO$_4^{3-}$ phosphate	SO$_4^{2-}$ sulfate	ClO$_3^-$ chlorate
		AsO$_4^{3-}$ arsenate	SeO$_4^{2-}$ selenate	BrO$_3^-$ bromate
			TeO$_4^{2-}$ tellurate	IO$_3^-$ iodate

Acid Anions --> Add 1 H to -2 anion (anion becomes -1, add hydrogen in front of anion name)
Add 1 H to -3 anion (anion becomes -2, add hydrogen in front of anion name)
Add 2 H to -3 anion (anion becomes -1, add dihydrogen in front of anion name)

APPENDIX 4
SOULIBILITY RULES AND ELECTROMOTIVE SERIES

SOLUBILITY RULES

1. All salts of alkali metals (IA) are *soluble*.

2. All NH_4^+ salts are *soluble*.

3. All salts containing the anions: NO_3^-, ClO_3^-, ClO_4^-, $C_2H_3O_2^-$ are *soluble*.

4. All Cl^-, Br^-, and I^- are *soluble* except for Ag^+, Pb^{2+}, and Hg_2^{2+} salts.

5. All SO_4^{2-} are *soluble* except for Pb^{2+}, Sr^{2+}, and Ba^{2+} salts.

6. All O^{2-} are *insoluble* except for IA metals, Ca^{2+}, Sr^{2+}, and Ba^{2+}. [Soluble metal oxides, form hydroxides; for example: $CaO \xrightarrow{H_2O} Ca^{2+} + 2\ OH^-$]

7. All OH^- are *insoluble* except for IA metals, NH_4^+, Ba^{2+} and Sr^{2+}.

8. All salts containing the anions: CO_3^{2-}, PO_4^{3-}, AsO_4^{3-}, S^{2-} and SO_3^{2-} are *insoluble* except for IA metals and NH_4^+ salts.

9. For salts containing the anions not mentioned above (e.g., $Cr_2O_7^{2-}$, P^{3-}, CrO_4^{2-}, $C_2O_4^{2-}$, etc.) assume that they are *insoluble* except for IA metals and NH_4^+ salts, unless otherwise informed.

Electromotive (Activity) Series*
for metals

Li>K>Ba>Sr>Ca>Na>*Mg>Al>Zn>Cr>Fe* >Cd>Co>Ni>Sn>Pb>(H)>Sb>Bi>Cu>Hg>Ag>Pd>Pt>Au

for halogens

F>Cl>Br>I

---

* with metals having variable oxidation numbers, one of its lower oxidation states is often formed:

Cr^{3+}, Fe^{2+}, Co^{2+}, Ni^{2+}, Sn^{2+}, Pb^{2+}, Sb^{3+}, Cu^+, Hg_2^{2+}, Pd^{3+}, Pt^{3+}

* Bold Print: Reacts with H_2O (l) ; Bold-Italics Print: Reacts with steam (i.e., $H_2O_{(g)}$)

APPENDIX 5
CHM 1045 PRACTICE FINAL EXAM

The following is a list of topics from the first 12 chapters of General Chemistry by Whitten, Davis, Peck, and Stanley (7th Edition) which will be included on the departmental final exam. Unless otherwise stated this exam will have 30 multiple choice questions. Under each topic there are practice question(s) that are intended to help you prepare for the final examination.

Chapter 1

- *Measurements and Conversions (English-Metric, temperature, density)*

1. 25.7 L = _____ gal
   - 1) 2.57 10^4 2) 6.42   3) 6.79   4) 27.2   5) 6.06

2. A car travelling at 30.0 mph is travelling at how many cm/sec?
   - 1) 6.71×1^{-1} 2) 2.69×10^9 3) 1.44   4) 2.08×10^2 5) 1.34×10^3

3. How many cm^2 are in 5.02×10^2 in^2?
   - 1) 3.24×10^3 2) 778×10^{-1} 3) 7.78×10^1 4) 1.28×10^3 5) 8.23×10^4

4. What is the density of a substance (in g/mL) that weighs 52.2 dg and occupies a volume of 2.78 cubic centimeters?
   - 1) 14.5   2) 0.33   3) 18.8   4) 1.88   5) 0.533

5. If the temperature of a piece of metal was 190°F, what would its temperature in °C be?
   - 1) 374   2) 2.4   3) 87.8   4) 463   5) -83

- *Heat Transfer and Specific Heat*

6. If 1.05×10^4 Joules of energy are absorbed 100. g of water (s_{water} = 4.184 J/g · °C) at 35.0°C, then what will its final temperature be?
   - 1) 60.1   2) 25.1   3) 9.9   4) 439.   5) 474.

$$q = m \times s \times \Delta T$$

$$1.05 \times 10^4 = 100 \times 4.184 \times \Delta T$$

$$\frac{1.05 \times 10^4}{100 \times 4.184} = \Delta T$$

$$25.10 = \Delta T$$

$$+ 35.0$$

$$60.1$$

Chapter 2

- ## Composition Stoichiometry (g <--> mol <--> atoms, etc.)

  1. How many molecules of O_2 are in 3.21 g of O_2?
      1) 3.02×10^{22} 2) 1.93×10^{24} 3) 0.100   4) 6.04×10^{22} 5) 6.02×10^{23}

  2. How many oxygen atoms are there in 0.139 g of K_3PO_4 (FW = 212)?
      1) 3.94×10^{20} 2) 1.58×10^{21} 3) 9.72×10^{20} 4) 2.61×10^{21} 5) 6.55×10^{-4}

  3. What is the average mass of one formula unit of K_3PO_4 (FW = 212) in grams?
      1) 212   2) 1.28×10^{-20} 3) 3.52×10^{-22} 4) 7.84×10^{-27} 5) 1.66×10^{-22}

- ## Empirical and Molecular Formula

  4. If a compound were found to contain 26.95% sulfur, 13.43% oxygen, and 59.61% chlorine, then calculate its empirical formula? (AW ---> S = 32.06, O = 16.00, Cl = 35.45)
      1) SO_2Cl_2 2) S_2OCl_2 3) S_2O_2Cl 4) SOCl   5) $SOCl_2$
  5. If a 1.520 g sample of a compound containing only N and O was found to contain 0.960 g of O, then calculate its empirical formula? (AW ---> N = 14.0, O = 16.0)
      1) NO   2) NO_2 3) N_2O_3 4) N_2O 5) N_3O_2

  6. 5.275 g of H_2O were produced when 3.712 g of a compound containing C and H were completely burned. Given this information, what is the empirical formula of this compound?
      1) C_3H_7 2) C_4H_9 3) C_5H_{11} 4) C_6H_{13} 5) C_4H_5

  7. If the molecular weight of an unknown compound is 90.0 g/mol, then what is its molecular formula given that its empirical formula is CH_3?
      1) CH_3 2) C_3H_9 3) C_6H_{18} 4) C_7H_{21} 5) C_9H_{27}

- ## % Composition

  8. Calculate the % N in $(NH_4)_2SO_4$ (FW = 132). $\frac{28}{132} \times 100$
      1) 5.30   2) 7.58   3) 10.6   4) 21.2   5) 37.9

  9. When a 4.78 g sample of a compound containing chlorine reacted with excess silver nitrate $(AgNO_3)$, 7.11 g of AgCl (FW = 143) were produced. Given this information, what is the percent composition of chlorine in the 4.78 g sample?
      1) 37.0   2) 67.2   3) 24.8   4) 47.3   5) 52.4

Chapter 3

- ### Balancing Equations

  1. When the following equation is balanced, the coefficient in front of O_2 is:
     $$C_{12}H_{24}O_{12} \; + \; 12\,O_2 \; \rightarrow \; 12\,CO_2 \; + \; 12\,H_2O$$

     1) 6   2) 7   3) 9   4) 13   5) 12

  2. When the following equation is balanced, the sum of all the coefficients is (remember to add coefficients of 1):
     $$3\,Ce(NO_3)_4 \; + \; 4\,Na_3PO_4 \; \rightarrow \; Ce_3(PO_4)_4 \; + \; 12\,NaNO_3$$

     1) 4   2) 8   3) 16   4) 20   5) 24

- ### Reaction Stoichiometry

  Consider the following balanced reaction when answering questions 18 - 19
  $$S_8 \; + \; 12\,O_2 \; \rightarrow \; 8\,SO_3$$

  3. How many grams of oxygen are needed to completely react with 2.78 g of sulfur?
     1) 26.8   2) 2.71   3) 2.03   4) 32.4   5) 4.15

  4. How many grams of SO_3 would be produced when 0.825 mol of O_2 is reacted with excess S_8?
     1) 99.1   2) 529   3) 44.1   4) 66.1   5) 0.550

- ### Limiting Reagent Problems

  5. How many mol of $FeBr_3$ will be produced when 0.326 mol of Fe are mixed with 65.8 g of Br_2 according to the following balanced equation?
     $$2\,Fe \; + \; 3\,Br_2 \; \rightarrow \; 2\,FeBr_3$$

     1) 0.326   2) 0.163   3) 0.412   4) 0.275   5) 0.618

- ### % Yield

  6. Calculate the % yield if 74.0 g of $FeBr_3$ (FW = 296) were isolated from the reaction of 0.412 mol of Br_2 with excess Fe according to the following balanced equation?
     $$2\,Fe \; + \; 3\,Br_2 \; \rightarrow \; 2\,FeBr_3$$

     1) 90.9%   2) 79.1%   3) 76.7%   4) 60.1%   5) 126%

- ### Molarity Problems

  7. What is the molarity of a NaOH solution prepared by dissolving 22.0 g of NaOH (FW = 40.0) in 500. mL of solution?
     1) 0.044   2) 1.10×10^{-3} 3) 1.10   4) 1.76   5) 3.78

  8. How many grams of $CaBr_2$ (FW = 200) are needed to prepare 800. mL of a 1.50 M solution of $CaBr_2$?
     1) 375.   2) 240.   3) 2.40×10^5 4) 107.   5) 178.

- ### Interconversion between Molarity and % by weight

  9. What is the weight percent of a 12.0 M HCl solution ($d_{(12.0\,M\,HCl)}$ = 1.18 g/mL)?
     1) 27.9   2) 38.8   3) 49.6   4) 51.7   5) 37.1

10. Commercial sulfuric acid is 96.4% H_2SO_4 (FW = 98.1) by weight, and its specific gravity is 1.84. Calculate the molarity of commerical sulfuric acid.

   1) 18.1   2) 8.18   3) 1.91   4) 1.77   5) 52.4

- *Dilution Problems*

   11. How many mL of water do you need to add to 6.00 M HCl in order to prepare 500. mL of   1.25 M HCl?   [Assume that all the volumes are additive.]

   1) 396.   2) 3.75×10^3 3) 2.40   4) 104.   5) 2.40×10^3

   12. You could prepare a 0.650 M NaOH solution by diluting _____ mL of 6.60 M NaOH to a total volume of _____mL.

   1) 39.6, 442   2) 39.6, 402   3) 57.4, 362   4) 57.4, 402   5) 57.4, 459

- *Solution Stoichiometry*

   Consider the following balanced reactionwhen answering questions 28 - 30

   $$3\,NaOH \ + \ H_3PO_4 \rightarrow Na_3PO_4 \ + \ 3\,H_2O$$

   13. How many liters of 0.200 M NaOH would be needed to produce 2.75 g of Na_3PO_4 (FW = 164)?

   1) 27.9   2) 0.252   3) 83.8   4) 4.12×10^4 5) 1.01×10^{-2}

   14. How many mL of 0.500 M H_3PO_4 are needed to react with 25.0 mL of 0.200 M NaOH?

   1) 7.50   2) 3.33   3) 20.8   4) 10.0   5) 50.0

   15. What is the molarity of an NaOH solution that requires 31.2 mL of it to completely react with 23.5 mL of a 0.72 M H_3PO_4 solution?

   1) 0.542   2) 0.617   3) 1.62   4) 1.84   5) 0.956

Chapter 4

- ## *Group Name of Elements*

    1. Which of the following elements is a noble gas?
        1) H   2) Xe   3) O   4) F   5) N

    2. Which of the following is a halogen?
        1) F   2) S   3) At
        4) Two of the above choices.
        5) All of the above choices.

    3. Which of the following elements are in the second transition series?
        1) Ag   2) Be   3) La
        4) Two of the above choices.
        5) None of the above choices.

- ## *Categorize Substances as Weak or Strong Electrolytes*

    4. Which of the following is a weak electrolyte?

            a. $Ba(OH)_2$ b. NH_4OH c. $Ni(OH)_2$
        1) only a   2) only b and c   3) only c
        4) only a and c   5) a, b, and c

    5. Which of the following is a strong electrolyte?

            a. $PbSO_4$ b. $HgCl_2$ c. $(NH_4)_2S$
        1) only a   2) only b and c   3) only a and b
        4) only c   5) a, b, and c

    6. Which of the following is a non-electrolyte?
        1) $C_6H_{12}O_6$ 2) H_3PO_4 3) KOH
        4) Two of the above choices.
        5) None of the above choices.

- ## *Classify Reaction Type*

    7. The following can be classified as what type of reaction: $P_4O_{10} + 6\,Na_2O \rightarrow 4\,Na_3PO_4$

        1) combination   2) decomposition   3) combustion
        4) single replacement   5) double replacement

    8. The following can be classified as what type of reaction: $CH_4 + 2\,O_2 \rightarrow CO_2 + 2\,H_2O$

        1) combination   2) decomposition   3) combustion
        4) single replacement   5) double replacement

- ## *Complete and Balance Single Replacement Reactions*

    9. When the following reaction is completed and balanced, what is the sum of the coefficients (don't forget to include coefficients of 1)?

        $$Zn_{(s)} + Fe_2(SO_4)_{3\,(aq)} \rightarrow$$

        1) 5   2) 9   3) 8   4) 7   5) 10

10. When the following reaction is completed and balanced, the products (including coefficients and physical state) are:

$$Al_{(s)} + HC_2H_3O_{2 (aq)} \rightarrow$$

1) $AlC_2H_3O_{2 (aq)} + H_{(g)}$ 2) $Al(C_2H_3O_2)_{3 (aq)} + 3 H_{(g)}$ 3) $2 AlC_2H_3O_{2 (aq)} + H_2$ (g)

4) $2 Al(C_2H_3O_2)_{3 (aq)} + 3 H_{2 (g)}$ 5) no reaction takes place

11. When $Br_{2 (l)}$ is added to a solution of CoI_3,
   1) $CoBr_{2 (aq)}$ and $I_{2 (s)}$ are formed.
   2) $CoBr_{3 (aq)}$ and $I_{2 (s)}$ are formed.
   3) $CoBr_{3 (s)}$ and $I_{2 (g)}$ are formed.
   4) $Co_3Br_{2 (aq)}$ and $I_{(s)}$ are formed.
   5) There is no reaction.

- **_Complete and Balance Double Replacement Reactions_**

12. When the following reaction is completed and balanced, what is the sum of the coefficients (don't forget to include coefficients of 1)?

$$H_2CO_{3 (aq)} + Ni(OH)_{4 (s)} \rightarrow$$

1) 5   2) 8   3) 7   4) 6   5) 10

13. If aqueous $Ba(OH)_2$ is mixed with aqueous $FeCl_3$, _____ precipitates out of the solution.

1) $BaCl_2$ 2) $Fe(OH)_2$ 3) $BaCl_3$ 4) Fe   5) $Fe(OH)_3$

14. When the following reaction is completed and balanced, the products (including coefficients and physical state) are:

$$Na_2SeO_{3 (aq)} + H_3PO_{4 (aq)} \rightarrow$$

1) $Na_2PO_{4 (aq)} + H_3SeO_{3 (aq)}$ 2) $2 Na_3PO_{4 (aq)} + 3 H_2SeO_{3 (aq)}$
3) $NaPO_{4 (aq)} + H_3SeO_{3 (aq)}$ 4) $2 Na_2PO_{4 (aq)} + 3 H_2SeO_{3 (g)}$
5) no reaction takes place(g)

- **_Oxidation Numbers_**

15. What is the oxidation number of P in P_2O_5?
   1) -10   2) +10   3) -5   4) +5   5) +2

16. What is the oxidation number of each atom in $(NH_4)_2S$?
   1) N = -3, H = +1, S = -2   2) N = -5, H = +1, S = -1
   3) N = -2, H = +6, S = -2   4) N = -5, H = +1, S = -2
   5) N = +5, H = +1, S = -2

- **_Identify Oxidizing and Reducing Agent in Redox Reactions_**

17. In which of the following _unbalanced_ reactions is bold-faced species acting as a reducing agent?

   a. **Cu** + NO_3^- → Cu^{2+} + NO

   b. ClO_3^- + **N$_2$H$_4$** → Cl^- + 6 NO

   c. $S_2O_3^{2-}$ + **I$_2$** → SO_4^{2-} + I^-

   1) only a   2) only b   3) only c
   4) only a and b   5) a, b, and c

- *Nomenclature*

18. The formula for carbonous acid is:
    1) H_2CO_3 2) H_3CO_3 3) H_3CO_2 4) HCO_2 5) H_2CO_2

19. The formula for silver hydrogen arsenite is:
    1) $SiHAsO_3$ 2) Ag_2HAsO_3 3) $Ag(HAsO_3)_2$ 4) $AgHAsO_3$ 5) $AgHAsO_4$

20. The formula for iron(II) cyanide is:
    1) $FeCN$ 2) $Fe(CN)_3$ 3) $Fe(CN)_2$ 4) $Fe_2(CN)_3$ 5) $Fe_3(CN)_2$

21. Which formula goes with what name?
    1) $Na_2Cr_2O_7$: sodium chromate
    3) $H_2C_2O_4$: oxalic acid
    5) $FePO_4$: ferrous phosphate

    2) K_2MnO_4 : potassium permanganate
    4) $HI_{(aq)}$: hydrogen iodic acid

22. Which formula goes with what name?
    1) $Hg_2Cr_2O_7$: mercury(I) dichromate
    3) H_2SO_3 : sulfous acid
    5) $CdSO_4$: cadmium(II) sulfate

    2) BO_3^{3-} : borite ion
    4) KS_2 : potassium sulfide

23. Which formula goes with what name?
    1) $HgSO_4$: mercurous sulfate
    3) $Sn(OH)_3$: stannous hydroxide
    5) $AlBr$: aluminum bromide

    2) KH_2BO_3 : potassium dihydrogen borate
    4) ZnH_2S : zinc dihydrogen sulfide

Chapter 5

- ### *Average Atomic Weights and Isotopes*

    1. Fictitious element X (average atomic mass = 254.9 amu) has only two common isotopes. If one isotope has an abundance of 72.00% and a mass of 250.9 amu, what is the average atomic mass of the other isotope?

        1) 265.2   2) 20.80   3) 245.9   4) 250.9

        5) There is not enough information to answer this question.

- ### *Electromagnetic Radiation*

    2. What is the wavelength (in m) of an x-ray whose frequency is 6.21×10^{18} Hz?

        1) 5.37×10^{-28} 2) 4.83×10^{-9} 3) 2.07×10^{10} 4) 1.86×10^{27} 5) 4.83×10^{-11}

    3. If the wavelength of a photon of ultraviolet light is 500 Å, then what is its energy (in erg)?

        1) 9.95×10^{-26} 2) 1.10×10^{-30} 3) 3.98×10^{-11} 4) 3.98×10^{-21} 5) 1.10×10^{-32}

- ### *Spectroscopic Electronic Configuration*

    4. The electronic configuration for Zn^{2+} is:

        1) $1s^2 2s^2 2p^6 3s^2 3p^6 4s^0 3d^{10}$ 2) $1s^2 2s^2 2p^6 3s^2 3p^6 4s^2 3d^8$

        3) $1s^2 2s^2 2p^6 3s^2 3p^6 4s^2 3d^{10}$ 4) $1s^2 2s^2 2p^6 3s^2 3p^6 4s^0 4d^{10}$

        5) $1s^2 2s^2 2p^6 3s^2 3p^6 4s^2 3d^{10} 4p^2$

    5. Which orbital starts getting filled after the 4d orbital has been completely filled ?

        1) 5f   2) 4f   3) 5p   4) 5s   5) 5d

- ### *Orbital Diagrams*

    6. The orbital diagram for N^- is:

        1) ↑↓   ↑↓   ↑↑ ↑ ↑   2) ↑↓   ↑↓   ↑↓ ↑ ↑
            1s   2s   2p   1s   2s   2p

        3) ↑↓   ↑↓   ↑ ↑ ↑   4) ↑↑   ↑↑   ↑↑ ↑ ↑
            1s   2s   2p   1s   2s   2p

        5) ↑↓   ↑↓   ↑↓ ↑↓ ↑
            1s   2s   2p

    7. How many unpaired electron(s) does Ge^{4+} have?

        1) 2   2) 3   3) 4   4) 1   5) 0

- ### *Exceptional Electronic Configuration*

    8. What is the shorthand electronic configuration for Au^+?

        1) $[Xe] 6s^0 4f^{14} 5d^{10}$ 2) $[Xe] 6s^2 4f^{14} 5d^{10}$ 3) $[Xe] 6s^1 4f^{14} 5d^{10}$

        4) $[Xe] 6s^1 4f^{14} 5d^9$ 5) $[Xe] 6s^1 4f^{14} 6d^9$

    9. Which elements in the first transition series are an exception to the Aufbau Principle?

        1) V and Ni   2) Ni and Ag   3) Cr and Cu   4) Fe and Cu   5) Mn and Zn

    10. How many unpaired electron(s) does Cr have?

        1) 2   2) 3   3) 4   4) 5   5) 6

Chapter 6

- ## *Trends in Atomic Radii*

    1. Which of the following atoms has the smallest atomic radius?
        1) Na   2) Al   3) Cl   4) Kr   5) Ga

    2. Which of the following has the largest radius?
        1) K^+ 2) Ca^{2+} 3) Cl^- 4) Ar   5) S^{2-}

- ## *Trends in Ionization Energy, Electron Affinity, and Electronegativity*

    3. Which of the following atoms has the largest first ionization energy?
        1) K   2) Ca   3) Ga   4) Si   5) Al

    4. Which of the following atoms forms a +1 ion most readiliy?
        1) K   2) Ca   3) Ga   4) Si   5) Al

    5. Which of the following atoms will gain an electron the most readily?
        1) K   2) Ca   3) Ga   4) Si   5) Al

    6. Which of the following ions will form the most readily?
        1) K^{1-} 2) Ca^{1-} 3) Ga^{1-} 4) Si^{1-} 5) Al^{1-}

    7. Which of the following atoms is most electronegative?
        1) K   2) Ca   3) Ga   4) Si   5) Al
    8. Which of the following statements are true?
        1) The second ionization energy is always smaller than the first ionization energy.
        2) The ionization energy of P is greater than that S because P has a half-filled 3p orbital.
        3) The ionization energy for metals is greater than that for non-metals.
        4) Electronegativity tends to increase on going from top to bottom in a family of elements.
        5) Two or more of the above statements are true.

Chapter 7

- **Ionic Bonding**
    1. The bond formed between which of the following has the most ionic character?
        1) Rb-I   2) Li-F   3) Fr-I   4) K-F   5) Cs-F

    2. How many of the following compounds have ionic bonding?
                    CCl_4 KNO_3 NH_4Cl AlF_3
        1) 0   2) 2   3) 3   4) 1   5) 4

- **Covalent Bonding**
    3. The bond formed between which of the following has the most covalent character?
        1) F-F   2) Cl-F   3) I-F   4) O-F   5) N-F

    4. The bond formed between which of the following has the least covalent character?
        1) F-F   2) H-Cl   3) H-Br   4) H-F   5) H-I

    5. Which of the following compounds contain both ionic and covalent bonds?
        1) PBr_3 2) Fe_2O_3 3) H_2O 4) $MgSO_4$ 5) CH_3OH

- **Bond Polarity**
    6. The bond formed between which of the following is most polar?
        1) F-F   2) Cl-F   3) I-F   4) O-F   5) N-F

    7. Which of the following bonds has the largest dipole?
        1) F-F   2) Cl-F   3) I-F   4) O-F   5) N-F

- **Lewis Structure of Molecules and Polyatomic Ions**
    8. The Lewis structure for As_2H_4 is:

        1)   H-As=As-H
                       | |
                       H   H

        2)   H
                        | ..
                   H-As-As-H
                        |
                        H

        3)   H-As-As-H
                     | |
                     H   H

        4)   H-Äs-H-H-Äs-H

        5)   H-Äs-Äs-H
                     | |
                     H   H

    9. In the molecule XeF_2, how many lone pairs are around the central element?
        1) 0   2) 1   3) 2   4) 3   5) 4

    10. How many <u>total</u> nonbonding (lone) electron pairs are in H_2CO_3?
        1) 2   2) 3   3) 4   4) 5   5) 6

    11. How many total sigma and pi bonds are present in NOCl?
        1) 1   2) 2   3) 3   4) 4   5) 5

- **Resonance**
    12. Which of the following have three equivalent major resonance contributors?
                a. SO_3 b. PBr_3 c. CO_3^{2-}
        1) only b   2) only c   3) only b & c   4) only a & c   5) a, b, & c

- **Formal Charge**
    13. What is the formal charge on C in H_2CO_3?
        1) 0   2) +1   3) +2   4) -2   5) +4

Chapter 8

- ## *Valence Shell Electron Pair Repulsion Theory / Shapes and Valence Bond Theory*

    1. What is the shape of $AlBr_3$?
        1) trigonal planar   2) tetrahedral   3) trigonal pyramidal
        4) T-shaped   5) V-shaped

    2. The $\angle Br-Al-Br$ in $AlBr_3$ is:
        1) 109.5°   2) less than 109.5°   3) 120°
        4) less than 120°   5) less than 90°, 120°, and 180°

    3. The hybridization around the central element in the compound $AlBr_3$ is:
        1) sp   2) sp^2 3) sp^3 4) dsp^3 5) d^2sp^3

    4. What is the molecular geometry of $SeBr_4$?
        1) tetrahedral   2) square planar   3) see-saw
        4) rectangular   5) trigonal pyramidal

    5. The hybridization around the central element in the compound $SeBr_4$ is:
        1) sp   2) sp^2 3) sp^3 4) dsp^3 5) d^2sp^3

    6. The $\angle Br-Se-Br$ in $SeBr_4$ is:
        1) 109.5°   2) less than 109.5°   3) 120°
        4) less than 120°   5) less than 90°, 120°, and 180°

    7. According to VB theory, how many valence atomic orbitals on selenium (in the compound $SeBr_4$) are left unhybridized (after bonding)?
        1) 1   2) 2   3) 3   4) 4   5) 5

- ## *Polarity of Molecules*

    8. Which of the following molecules is (are) polar?
        1) CH_4 2) NH_3 3) CO_2
        4) Two of the above   5) None of the above

    9. Which of the following molecules have no permanent dipole moment?
        1) XeF_2 2) XeF_4 3) PCl_5
        4) Two of the above   5) All of the above

Chapter 9

No topics

Chapter 10

- ## *Arrhenius, Brønsted, Lewis Acid-Base Theory (definitions)*

    1   Which of the following is (are) a correct statement about bases?
    1) they are proton acceptors
    2) they are electron pair acceptors
    3) when placed in water they produce OH⁻
    4) two of the above
    5) none of the above

- ## *Relative Strength of Acids/Bases Based on Comparative Structure*

    2.   Which is the weakest acid?
    1) $HClO_4$ 2) H_2S 3) HBr   4) H_2Te 5) HCl

    3.   Which is the weakest base?
    1) ClO_4^- 2) HS^- 3) F^- 4) ClO_3^- 5) HSO_3^-

Chapter 11

- ***Equivalent Weight and Normality***

    1. What is the equivalent weight (in g/eq) of H_3PO_4?
        1) 98.0   2) 294.   3) 49.0   4) 196.   5) 32.7

    2. What is the equivalent weight (in g/eq) of NiO_2 as it undergoes the following redox half-reaction? (This half-reaction is not *balanced*.)
        $$NiO_2 \rightarrow Ni(OH)_2$$
        1) 90.7   2) 181.   3) 45.4   4) 22.7   5) 363.

    3. What is the normality of a solution prepared by mixing 76.8 g of H_3AsO_4 (FW = 142) in enough water to prepare 800. mL of solution?
        1) 0.676   2) 0.493   3) 0.225   4) 4.44   5) 2.03

- ***Balance Redox Equation in Acid Media***

    4. What is the coefficient in front of the boldfaced substance in the balanced form of the following redox reaction carried out under *acidic* conditions?
        $$Mn^{2+} + \mathbf{H_2O_2} \rightarrow MnO_2$$
        1) 1   2) 5   3) 4   4) 2   5) 3

- ***Balance Redox Equation in Basic Media***

    5. How many electrons are transferred in the following *unbalanced* redox half-reaction when it is carried out under *basic* conditions?
        $$NiO_2 \rightarrow Ni(OH)_2$$
        1) 1   2) 2   3) 3   4) 4   5) 5

    6. What is the coefficient in front of the boldfaced substance in the balanced form of the following redox reaction carried out under *basic* conditions?
        $$S_2O_3^{2-} + \mathbf{I_2} \rightarrow SO_4^{2-} + I^-$$
        1) 1   2) 2   3) 3   4) 4   5) 5

Chapter 12

- ### Boyle's Law, Charles' Law, Avogadro's/Gay Lussac's and Miscelleaneous Gas Law Problems

  1. Gases tend to behave more ideally under which of the following conditions?
      1) 5°C and 10 torr   2) 500°C and 1 torr   3) 50°C and 100 torr
      4) 5°C and 1 torr   5) 500°C and 10 torr

  2. At STP, which of the following occupies the greatest volume?
      1) 4.0 g of He   2) 44.8 L of H_2 3) 32.0 g of CH_4 4) 2.5 mol of Ar
      5) All occupy the same volume at STP.

  3. What would happen to the volume of a gas if: its pressure is doubled and its temperature is decreased from -173°C to -223°C?
      1) double   2) quadruple   3) cut by one-fourth
      4) cut in half   5) increase by a factor of 8

- ### Combined Gas Law Problems

  4. If the volume of a gas at 30.0°C and 10.0 L is reduced to 9.0 L under a constant pressure, then what is the resulting temperature (in °C)?
      1) 30   2) 0   3) 24   4) 27   5) 36

  5. A helium balloon has a volume of 1.50×10^3 L at 0.901 atm and 25°C. When this ballon is taken to an altitude of 20 km, the temperature is -50°C and the atmospheric pressure is 76.0 mm Hg. What is the volume (in L) of this balloon at 20 km?
      1) 2.20×10^2 2) 1.25×10^2 3) 1.01×10^4 4) 1.80×10^2 5) 1.33×10^2

- ### Ideal Gas Equation, Density of Gases, and Molar Mass of Gases

  6. Calculate the pressure (in atm) of 0.652 moles of oxygen gas occupying a 10.0 L cylinder at 30°C.
      1) 1.62   2) 1231   3) 0.617   4) 8.12×10^{-4} 5) 0.161

  7. Calculate the density of Ar (in g/L) at STP.
      1) 1.00   2) 0.561   3) 0.891   4) 1.58   5) 1.78

  8. At STP, which gas has the greatest density?
      1) H_2 2) CH_4 3) Kr   4) N_2 5) Cl_2

  9. If a 1 L sample of a gas at STP is subjected to an increase in pressure and a decrease in temperature, its density will _____.
      1) decrease   2) increase   3) remain the same   4) become zero
      5) increase or decrease depending on the relative increase in P & decrease in T

  10. What is the molar mass of a 0.0564 g sample of an unknown gas inside a 25.0 mL container whose temperature is 100°C and whose pressure is 750 torr?
      1) 85.0   2) 22.2   3) 60.0   4) 18.8   5) 70.0

- ### Stoichiometry Involving Gases

  11. At STP, what volume (in L) of $PH_{3\,(g)}$ should be produced if 100. g of Ca_3P_2 (FW = 182) are reacted with excess H_2O?
      $$Ca_3P_{2\,(s)} + 6\,H_2O_{(l)} \rightarrow 3\,Ca(OH)_{3\,(s)} + 2\,PH_{3\,(g)}$$
      1) 12.3   2) 6.15   3) 24.6   4) 40.8   5) 81.5

12. How many liters of O_2 at 800 torr and 25.0°C would be produced by the decomposition of a 25.0 g sample of 65.0% pure $KMnO_4$ (FW = 158)?
$$8\ KMnO_{4\ (s)}\ \rightarrow\ 4\ K_2MnO_{4\ (s)}\ +\ 2\ Mn_2O_{3\ (s)}\ +\ 5\ O_{2\ (g)}$$

1) 2.39   2) 15.1   3) 3.67   4) 2.29   5) 1.49

13. How many mol of $Al_2(CO_3)_3$ must decompose in order to produce 6.24 L of CO_2 at 298 K and 745 torr according to the following <u>unbalanced</u> chemical equation?
$$Al_2(CO_3)_{3\ (s)}\ \rightarrow\ Al_2O_{3\ (s)}\ +\ CO_{2\ (g)}$$

1) 0.250   2) 0.0833   3) 0.500   4) 4.00   5) 2.00

• *Dalton's Law of Partial Pressures*

14. If a gas sample whose total pressure is 3.00 atm contains 4.00 g of H_2 and 16.0 g of He, then what is the partial pressure (in atm) of H_2 in the sample?

1) 0.600   2) 2.00   3) 18.0   4) 1.00   5) 1.50

15. A mixture containing CO_2, Ar, and CO has a total pressure of 1.82 atm at 25°C. If the partial pressure of CO_2 is 360 torr and that of CO is 664 torr, then what is the partial pressure (in torr) of Ar?

1) 8020   2) 359   3) 0.258   4) 301   5) 5345

16. If 150. mL of Ar at an atmospheric pressure of 758 torr were collected over water at 20.0°C, then what volume (in mL) would this argon sample occupy at STP? (Vapor Pressure of H_2O @ 20.0°C = 17.5 torr)

1) 136   2) 140   3) 157   4) 161   5) 166

17. If a gas sample whose total pressure is 3.00 atm contains 2.00 mol of O_2 and 4.00 mol of N_2, then what is the partial pressure (in atm) of O_2 in the sample?

1) 1.00   2) 0.500   3) 1.50   4) 2.00   5) 0.667

• *Effusion and Diffusion of Gases*

18. If 100. mL of He escapes through an orifice in 36 sec and 100. mL of unknown X takes 72 sec to escape through the same orifice, then what is the molecular weight of unknown X?

1) 1.0   2) 2.0   3) 4.0   4) 8.0   5) 16.0

19. Which of the following gases (under the same conditions) would escape most rapidly from an orifice?

1) Cl_2 2) F_2 3) CO_2 4) N_2 5) O_2

20. If the molecular weight of gas A is nine times less than that of gas B, under the same conditions, an average molecule of gas A is moving at what rate in comparison to that of gas B?
1) 9 times slower   2) 3 times faster   3) 3 times slower
4) 9 times faster   5) At the same rate

ANSWERS TO PRACTICE FINAL EXAM

Chapters

Question Number	1	2	3	4	5	6	7	8	9	10	11	12
1	3	4	5	2	1	3	5	1		4	5	2
2	5	2	4	4	5	5	3	3		2	3	4
3	1	3	5	1	3	4	1	2		1	5	3
4	4	5	3	2	1	1	4	3			1	2
5	3	3	4	2	3	4	4	4			2	3
6	1	2	1	1	2	4	3	5			4	1
7		3	3	1	5	4	3	4				5
8		4	2	3	1	2	5	2				3
9		1	5	2	3		4	5				2
10			1	4	5		5					5
11			1	2			3					3
12			2	2			4					5
13			2	5			1					2
14			2	2								4
15			3	4								2
16				1								1
17				4								1
18				5								5
19				2								4
20				3								2
21				3								
22				1								
23				2								

APPENDIX 6

FORMULAS AND CONVERSIONS THAT SHOULD BE LEARNED FOR FINAL EXAM

NOTE: On the final exam the following constants will be provided

R (gas constant), Avogadro's Number, Planck's Constant, Speed of Light, and Standard Molar Volume

Metric $\Longleftrightarrow$ Metric Conversions

Prefix	Abbreviation	Numerical Value
giga	G	10^9 (1,000,000,000)
mega	M	10^6 (1,000,000)
kilo	k	10^3 (1,000)
deci	d	10^{-1} (0.1)
centi	c	10^{-2} (0.01)
milli	m	10^{-3} (0.001)
micro	μ	10^{-6} (0.000001)

1 mL = 1 cc = 1 cm^3

Metric $\Longleftrightarrow$ English Conversions

volume	mass	length
1 qt = 0.946* L	1 lb = 454.* g	1 in = 2.54 cm

* these numbers have been rounded off to three significant figures

$$density = \frac{mass}{volume} \qquad\qquad Sp.Gr. = \frac{d_{substance}}{1.00 \text{ g/mL}}$$

$$°F = (1.8 \times °C) + 32 \qquad\qquad K = °C + 273$$

$$q = m \times s \times \Delta T \quad \left\{ \begin{array}{l} q = \text{heat transfer} \\ m = \text{mass} \\ s = \text{specific heat} \\ \Delta T = \text{change in temp (final - initial)} \end{array} \right.$$

$$MF = \frac{MW}{EFW} \times EF \quad \left\{ \begin{array}{l} MF = \text{molecular formula} \\ MW = \text{molecuar weight (or formula weight)} \\ EFW = \text{empirical formula weight} \\ EF = \text{empirical formula} \end{array} \right.$$

$$\% \text{ Element} = \frac{\text{g Element in compound}}{FW} \times 100$$

$$\% \text{ Yield} = \frac{\text{actual yield}}{\text{theoretical yield}} \times 100$$

$$\text{Molarity (M)} = \frac{\text{mol solute}}{\text{L soln}} = \frac{\frac{g}{FW}}{\text{L soln}}$$

$$wt\% = \frac{g\ solute}{g\ soln} \times 100$$

$$V_1C_1 = V_2C_2 \qquad \text{(Dilution Formula)}$$

$$AW_{AV} = (f_1 \times AW_1) + (f_2 \times AW_2) + ...$$

$\left\{ \begin{array}{l} f_1 = \text{fraction of isotope \#1} \\ AW_1 = \text{atomic weight of isotope \#1} \\ f_2 = \text{fraction of isotope \#2} \\ AW_2 = \text{atomic weight of isotope \#2} \end{array} \right.$

$$E = h\nu = h\left(\frac{c}{\lambda}\right)$$

$\left\{ \begin{array}{l} E = \text{Energy (Joule = J or erg)} \\ h = \text{Planck's Constant} = 6.63 \times 10^{-34}\ J\cdot sec = 6.63 \times 10^{-27}\ erg\cdot sec \\ c = \text{speed of light} = 3.00 \times 10^8\ m/sec = 3.00 \times 10^{10}\ cm/sec \\ \nu = \text{frequency (sec}^-) \\ \lambda = \text{wavelength (m or cm or Å)} \qquad 1Å = 10^{-8}\ cm = 10^{-10}\ m \end{array} \right.$

$$eq_{acid} = eq_{base}$$
$$eq_{red} = eq_{ox}$$

$$eq = n \times mol = N \times V_{(L)} = (n \times M) \times V_{(L)} = \frac{g}{EW}$$

$\left\{ \begin{array}{l} \text{n for acids} = \#\ H^+ \\ \text{n for bases} = \#\ OH^- \\ \text{n for redox rxns} = \#\ \text{of } e^- \text{ transferred} \\ EW = \frac{FW}{n} \end{array} \right.$

$$\text{Normality (N)} = \frac{eq}{L}$$

STP ---> 0°C (273 K) and 1 atm (760 torr)   @ STP, 1 mol gas = 22.4 L (Standard Molar Volume)

$$\frac{P_1V_1}{T_1} = \frac{P_2V_2}{T_2} \qquad \text{@ constant n} \qquad \textit{T must be in K for all gas law problems}$$

$$PV = nRT \qquad\qquad R \text{ (gas constant)} = 0.0821\ \frac{L\cdot atm}{mole\cdot K} = 62.4\ \frac{L\cdot torr}{mole\cdot K}$$

$$d = \frac{PM}{RT} \qquad\qquad \textit{[d $\propto$ M @ constant T and P]}$$

$$PV = \left(\frac{g}{M}\right)RT \qquad\qquad \text{[NOTE: For gas law problems, M is defined as MW = Molar Mass]}$$

$$P_T = P_A + P_B + ... = n_A\left(\frac{RT}{V}\right) + n_B\left(\frac{RT}{V}\right) + ... = X_AP_T + X_BP_T + ...$$

$\left\{ \begin{array}{l} X_A = \frac{n_A}{n_{total}} \\ X_B = \frac{n_B}{n_{total}} \end{array} \right.$

$$\frac{Rate_A}{Rate_B} = \sqrt{\frac{M_B}{M_A}} \qquad \text{Rate refers to the rate of effusion:}\ \ \frac{V}{t} \Rightarrow \frac{mL}{sec},\ \frac{L}{min},\ \text{etc.}$$

APPENDIX 7

Names and Symbols of Elements that Need to be Learned

Atomic Number	Symbol	Name	Atomic Number	Symbol	Name
1	H	Hydrogen	30	Zn	Zinc
2	He	Helium	31	Ga	Gallium
3	Li	Lithium	32	Ge	Germanium
4	Be	Beryllium	33	As	Arsenic
5	B	Boron	34	Se	Selenium
6	C	Carbon	35	Br	Bromine
7	N	Nitrogen	36	Kr	Krypton
8	O	Oxygen	37	Rb	Rubidium
9	F	Fluorine	38	Sr	Strontium
10	Ne	Neon	46	Pd	Palladium
11	Na	Sodium	47	Ag	Silver
12	Mg	Magnesium	48	Cd	Cadmium
13	Al	Aluminum	49	In	Indium
14	Si	Silicon	50	Sn	Tin
15	P	Phosphorous	51	Sb	Antimony
16	S	Sulfur	52	Te	Tellurium
17	Cl	Chlorine	53	I	Iodine
18	Ar	Argon	54	Xe	Xenon
19	K	Potassium	55	Cs	Cesium
20	Ca	Calcium	56	Ba	Barium
21	Sc	Scandium	78	Pt	Platinum
22	Ti	Titanium	79	Au	Gold
23	V	Vanadium	80	Hg	Mercury
24	Cr	Chromium	81	Tl	Thallium
25	Mn	Manganese	82	Pb	Lead
26	Fe	Iron	83	Bi	Bismuth
27	Co	Cobalt	92	U	Uranium
28	Ni	Nickel	94	Pu	Plutonium
29	Cu	Copper			